Starlight

With the advent of space exploration the science of astronomy enters a new phase—that of practical application significant not only to scientists but also to the public at large. The recent critical developments in astronomy that led up to this new phase are presented in this unique library of astronomy made up of articles that first appeared in the prominent journals *Sky and Telescope, The Sky,* and *The Telescope.*

Starlight

WHAT IT TELLS ABOUT THE STARS

EDITED BY THORNTON PAGE & LOU WILLIAMS PAGE

VOLUME 5 *Sky and Telescope* Library of Astronomy

Illustrated with over 140 photographs, drawings, and diagrams

The Macmillan Company, New York

Collier-Macmillan Limited, London

Library of Congress Catalog Card Number: 67-12798

FIRST PRINTING

The Macmillan Company, New York
Collier-Macmillan Canada Ltd., Toronto, Ontario

Printed in the United States of America

Contents

4. Characteristics of Stars Derived from Spectra

5. Variable Stars and Novae

6. Magnetic Stars and Flare Stars

7. Double Stars and Their Masses

8. Star Counts and Distribution of the Stars

9. Clusters of Stars and the Galaxy

Illustrations

Tables

Preface

Famed in song and story, the stars have become symbols of unchanging constancy, large numbers, and various kinds of guidance. Only during the last hundred years have astronomers learned, by systematic study, the true nature of these distant suns, finding that they are not entirely constant, their number is not infinite, and their "guidance" is limited to the purposes of navigation. As observations with large telescopes increased the power of the human eye, and as the techniques of photography, photoelectric detection, and radio detection were developed, scientists came to recognize wide variety among the stars, to understand the differences, and to use them in reasoning about the nature of the universe.

A great deal of this understanding has developed during the last thirty years. The changing concepts and new discoveries of that interval have been recorded in The Sky, The Telescope, and Sky and Telescope, magazines read by professional astronomers and by many others interested in astronomy.

This volume is a collection of articles arranged in logical sequence, with a few explanatory notes and connecting remarks by the editors. It is intended to show how present ideas developed, and what research is going on now. Each of the articles in this volume is reproduced essentially as it originally appeared in Sky and Telescope or its predecessors, The Sky and The Telescope, with minor modifications for consistency of style. In order to maintain continuity, some tangential material has been cut. When the deletions are short they are not indicated, but omissions of one or more paragraphs are designated by ellipses. Occasional minor changes have been made in the wording to improve clarity or to eliminate repetition. A few explanatory additions have been made, usually within brackets.

Selections for which there is no author credit were prepared by the staff of the applicable magazine. Footnotes supplied by the editors bear the initials T L P, as do the passages of editors' comments interspersed throughout the volume.

The articles reprinted here are only a small fraction of the record; for more detail, the reader is referred to bound volumes of The Sky, The Telescope, and Sky and Telescope, available in most libraries. The Introduction provides a general picture of the stars around us and how astronomers study them by analyzing their light. Chapter 1, on the sun, our nearest star, fills out this picture in more detail, and Chapters 2, 3, and 4 show how starlight can be analyzed to give characteristics of more distant stars, some *very like the sun. Chapter 4 also describes extreme cases, as do Chapters 5 and 6; Chapters 7, 8, and 9 discuss the groups of stars from which so much about stellar masses and evolution has been derived.*

THORNTON PAGE
LOU WILLIAMS PAGE

June 1966

About the Editors

Thornton Page is now Fisk Professor of Astronomy at Wesleyan University, Middletown, Connecticut, and director of the Van Vleck Observatory. After studying at Yale University he went to England as a Rhodes Scholar; he received a Ph.D. from Oxford University in 1938. He then spent two years at the Yerkes Observatory and the University of Chicago. Starting in 1940 he worked for the U.S. Navy on magnetic sea mines, first in the Naval Ordnance Laboratory and then as a junior officer in the Pacific, ending up in Japan studying the effects of atomic-bomb explosions. After the war he returned to the University of Chicago and observed galaxies with the new 82-inch telescope of the McDonald Observatory in western Texas. In 1950 he was called back to military service with the Army's Operations Research Office, spent two years as scientific advisor in the U.S. Army Headquarters, Heidelberg, Germany, and several months in Korea during the war there. Since 1958 he has spent four summers at the Lick and Mount Wilson Observatories in California, taught astronomy courses at the University of Colorado, UCLA, and Yale. During 1965, 1966, and 1967 he has been NAS Research Associate at the Smithsonian and Harvard Observatories.

Mrs. Page received her Ph.D. in geology from the University of Chicago. She is the author of *A Dipper Full of Stars,* and has collaborated with Mr. Page and others in writing a three-volume text, *Introduction to the Physical Sciences.* More recently, she has served as editor of the Connecticut Geological and Natural History Survey, taught a science course at Wesleyan University, and has written a book on geology for young readers called *The Earth and Its Story.* The Pages also collaborated with others in writing the high school text for an earth-science course sponsored by the National Science Foundation and have, individually, produced several research papers in their widely separated fields.

Introduction

How many stars are there? What are they made of? What makes them shine? Are they all the same? How far away are they? How did they get there? How long will they last?

Questions like these have the disarming ring of the kindergarten, yet the answers involve fundamental aspects of modern science; in fact, several of the answers have changed radically in recent years, and none of the questions can be answered briefly. For instance, the number of stars visible to the unaided eye on a clear, dark night is about 2000, and telescopes show many millions more; but individual stars peter out at large distances. Farther away, we see on all sides vast groups of stars called galaxies, and the numbers of galaxies increase with distance, as if they go on forever. Yet the sky is dark at night, and it would be bright all over if there were literally an infinite number of stars.

The makeup of stars, the differences between them, and what makes them shine have all been established by astronomers during the past hundred years and will be discussed in the following chapters. First, it is necessary to clarify just what can be observed, and the broad outlines of the picture that astronomers have pieced together. The first three volumes of this series—1, Wanderers in the Sky; 2, Neighbors of the Earth; and 3, The Origin of the Solar System—were concerned with the earth and relatively nearby objects: satellites, moon, planets, and comets, which are all dominated by the sun. From our spinning earth near the middle of this system, we can see other suns, the "fixed" stars, at vastly greater distances. These distances were first measured only 130 years ago and account for the faintness of the other suns as well as their apparently fixed positions in

1

the sky. Far from being fixed, the stars are now known to be moving with speeds of many miles per second, although the changes we see among them are barely detectable in a lifetime.

These nearly fixed directions as viewed from the earth provide a framework, or coordinate system—a background against which the rotation of the earth and the motions of nearby objects can be recognized and measured (see Wanderers in the Sky). For such purposes astronomers have long used maps of the sky, star charts on which stars, nebulae, and galaxies can be plotted as if the sky were a big black sphere around us.   — T L P

....

Star Charts of
Former Days

GEORGE LOVI

(*Sky and Telescope*, April 1964)

Today's astronomer regards a star chart as a necessary tool of his trade, and he judges it by its usefulness. In earlier centuries, however, a star atlas was as much an artistic expression as a scientific endeavor. Many Renaissance charts, for example, are beautiful products of the engraver's and the printer's art, with handsome woodcuts or metal plates.

In ancient times the heavens were usually mapped on a globe which represented the fictitious outside of the celestial sphere and therefore showed the constellations reversed. Often, as in the case of the famous Farnese globe now in the Naples Museum, only the constellation figures were depicted and not any stars. The tradition of celestial globes lasted until the time of Tycho Brahe (1546–1601), who is said to have constructed a five-foot globe on which he meticulously plotted the positions of stars he observed with his accurate instruments.

The most famous of early printed star atlases is the *Uranometria* of Johann Bayer, published at Augsburg in 1603. This work introduced the system we still use today of designating bright stars by Greek letters and, in some cases, by Roman letters. It is from this source, for instance, that the

FIG. 1. Mythological figures embellish this silver celestial globe, attributed to Tycho Brahe. Constellations appear backwards when viewed on a globe. (American Museum–Hayden Planetarium photograph)

FIG. 2. The constellation Auriga as depicted in the *Uranometria* of Johann Bayer (1603). On the charioteer's back shines brilliant Capella, and above it rides the she-goat. Her kids are in Auriga's right hand, and a whip and bridle are in the other. The stippled band running diagonally across the picture represents the Milky Way, and the dark lower section is part of the zodiac.

FIG. 3. In 1515 Albrecht Dürer engraved this map of the southern heavens, as well as a similar one of the northern sky—the earliest printed star charts. Note that the little-known southern circumpolar stars had not yet been formed into constellations (From *The Complete Woodcuts of Albrecht Dürer* edited by Willi Kurth; W. and G. Foyle, London, 1927; Dover, New York, 1963)

names of Alpha Bootis for Arcturus and Beta Geminorum for Pollux came. The *Uranometria* was printed from fifty-one copper plates engraved by Alexander Mair, and went through five editions up to 1661. Abridged versions have since appeared from time to time.

Bayer constructed his atlas with as much accuracy as pretelescopic measurements of star positions permitted. In far southern constellations such as Centaurus and Lupus, the reliability of his star plotting breaks down badly. And, curiously, Bayer depicts the fourth-magnitude stars Alpha and Beta Sagittarii as first magnitude. Such facts remind us that the portion of the sky invisible from mid-European latitudes was very little known in 1603; almost the only data on far southern stars came from rough observations by Dutch navigators.

During the two centuries following Bayer, a number of similar atlases were produced. No star chart of that era was complete without constellation figures among the stars, as much by necessity as for decoration. Astronomers of the time habitually referred to a sky area by its part in a constellation figure; thus, a newly discovered comet might be announced as "just above Andromeda's left ankle." Every good astronomer had to know his celestial anatomy.

FIG. 4. The constellation Aquarius, the Water Carrier, as drawn for John Flamsteed's *Atlas Coelestis* (1729) by Sir James Thornhill. This map has two grids: one for right ascension and declination, the other for celestial longitude and latitude.

Outstanding among the eighteenth-century representations of the heavens was the *Atlas Coelestis* of John Flamsteed, first Astronomer Royal of England. It was published in 1729 after his death. Flamsteed was the first to prepare an extensive star catalogue using instruments fitted with telescopic sights. For this reason, his star placement is generally more accurate than that in earlier atlases. He introduced a system of numbering the stars of a constellation in the order of their right ascensions. These Flamsteed numbers are in constant use today for the fainter naked-eye stars; 61 Cygni and 70 Ophiuchi are familiar examples. . . .

In the early days of star charts, a star would be said to belong to a particular constellation only if it was part of the figure, or in its proximity. If a star did not seem to belong to any figure, it was labeled *unformed*, that is, not in any constellation. From the days of Ptolemy to Bayer, about a tenth of the stars were so designated. The idea that constellations were areas that together covered the whole celestial sphere is of later origin. During the eighteenth and nineteenth centuries there was much confusion about constellation limits, and it ended only in 1928 when the boundaries we use today were internationally adopted.

In the post-Bayer era, astronomers such as Hevelius and Lacaille took

FIG. 5. Charles Messier, famous for his list of star clusters and nebulae, drew this ornamental chart to show the path of a comet he had discovered in 1764. This is an example of Flamsteed's projection, described in the text. Below the Swan is Vulpecula, the Fox, holding Anser, the Goose, in his mouth and Sagitta, the Arrow, in his forepaw.

FIG. 6. Elaborate constellation figures survived longest in popular atlases such as Elijah H. Burritt's often-reprinted *Geography of the Heavens*. This work greatly stimulated American interest in astronomy in the mid-nineteenth century.

advantage of the unformed stars to create new constellations. This gave rise to faint constellations such as Sextans, Vulpecula, and Lacerta. Some of these star groups originally had longer names: Sextans was first *Sextans Uraniae,* and Vulpecula was *Vulpecula et Anser* (the Fox and Goose). . . .

Toward the middle of the nineteenth century, star charts with constellation figures began to fall out of favor. In his *Outlines of Astronomy,* Sir John Herschel voices the growing sentiment when he says of constellations: "Of course we do not here speak of those uncouth figures and outlines of men and monsters which are usually scribbled over celestial globes and maps, and serve, in a rude and barbarous way, to enable us to talk of groups of stars." One of the last important star atlases with "men and monsters" was Elijah H. Burritt's *Geography of the Heavens*, which appeared in this country in 1835.

The transition from old to new came a few years later with the *Bonner Durchmusterung* charts that F. W. Argelander prepared at Bonn, Germany. Understandably, an atlas containing some 324,000 stars (all those brighter than about tenth magnitude and north of declination −2°) omits the constellation figures, and even constellation boundaries and star designations, in order to avoid crowding.

Today an all-purpose star atlas is no longer possible. When an amateur wants to locate star clusters or galaxies, he chooses an uncluttered and utilitarian map, but there are still times when his preference is for the beautifully drawn mythological figures that go back to the dawn of astronomy.

In order to map so many stars, Argelander needed to measure their positions accurately, so that one star would not be confused with another. As the next article relates, he also recorded each star's brightness on the magnitude scale (see p. 30) ranging from 0 or 1 for the bright stars to 9 or 9.5 for the faint ones.

The position of each star is recorded by two angles (coordinates) similar to longitude and latitude on the earth. Because the sky seems to "turn like a sphere around two celestial poles" (due to the earth's rotation—see Volume 1, Wanderers in the Sky), the east-west coordinate, right ascension, could be measured simply by timing each star's passage across one imaginary line running north and south of the point overhead. The other coordinate, declination, is the angle north or south (positive or negative) from the celestial equator, another imaginary line, halfway between the celestial poles.

Argelander's telescope was mounted so that it could swing along the north-south line, and a scale on the side showed the declination of stars seen in the center of the field of view. His "sidereal clock" was adjusted to run four minutes fast each day, taking account of the eastward drift of the sun among the stars (360° in one year), so that twenty-four hours corresponded to one complete rotation of the sky—or earth. (See Volume 4, Telescopes). — T L P

▪▪▪

Argelander and the BD

ALAN T. MOFFET

(*Sky and Telescope*, May 1965)

At the twelfth general assembly of the International Astronomical Union, held last year in Hamburg, there was an exhibition of instruments and documents connected with the history of astronomy. Delegates with a few minutes to spare could visit the nearby museum and gaze at the notebooks of Bessel and Gauss, ancient astrolabes, reconstructions of Galileo's telescopes, and many other exhibits of interest. Among the instruments was a rather ordinary looking refractor, hardly larger than a spyglass, which stood out only because of a plate on its mounting inscribed "*Bonner Durchmusterung,* 1852–1859."

Normally, this little telescope stands in the entrance hall of the university observatory at Bonn, Germany. When Harvard astronomer E. C. Pickering saw it there at the 1913 meeting of the International Solar Union (forerunner of the IAU), he remarked, "This is the smallest telescope in the world, with which the greatest work has been accomplished!"

For many readers of *Sky and Telescope* the *Bonner Durchmusterung*— or BD as it is usually known—needs no introduction. The working astronomer regards the BD as a fundamental tool of his trade, almost as essential as a clock or a copy of the current *American Ephemeris*. The BD is a star catalogue that contains positions and visual magnitudes of 324,198 stars between declinations $-2°$ and $+90°$. Accompanying the catalogue is a set of charts, on a scale of about three minutes of arc per millimeter, showing the position of each star. These charts are a strong reason for the fame and enduring value of the BD, since they provide a convenient and accurate means of finding one's way around the sky.

Faced with the task of measuring the position of an object on a photographic plate, an astronomer's first move is to pull out the appropriate BD chart and locate the field in which the object lies. The BD catalogue then gives the positions of all nearby stars brighter than ninth magnitude. If a precision of better than about a minute of arc is required, one must consult other catalogues that give much more accurate positions for selected stars. In these works the stars are almost always identified by their BD numbers. . . .

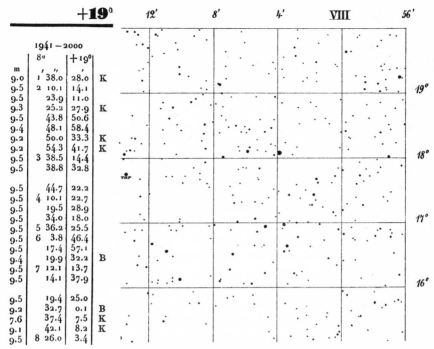

1941−2000			
8ᵘ	+19°		
m	′ ″	′	
9.0	1 38.0	28.0	K
9.5	2 10.1	14.1	
9.5	23.9	11.0	
9.3	25.2	27.9	K
9.5	43.8	50.6	
9.4	48.1	58.4	
9.2	50.0	33.3	K
9.2	54.3	41.7	K
9.5	3 38.5	14.4	
9.5	38.8	32.8	
9.5	44.7	22.2	
9.5	4 10.1	22.7	
9.5	19.5	28.9	
9.5	34.0	18.0	
9.5	5 36.2	25.5	
9.5	6 3.8	46.4	
9.5	17.4	57.1	
9.4	19.9	32.2	B
9.5	7 12.1	13.7	
9.5	14.1	37.9	
9.5	19.4	25.0	
9.2	32.7	0.1	B
7.6	37.4	7.5	K
9.1	42.1	8.2	K
9.5	8 26.0	3.4	

FIG. 7. A section of the BD atlas on the Gemini-Cancer border (right), together with the corresponding part of the catalogue (left). The first line of the latter describes a star BD +19°1941 which is of magnitude 9.0, at right ascension 8ʰ01ᵐ38ˢ.0, declination +19°28′.0. Both chart and catalogue are for the epoch 1855. Stars are listed serially in blocks of ten, so the last line in the first block is for +19°1950, magnitude 9.5. Letters in the last column indicate other catalogues in which a star occurs. On the chart, "var" indicates the variable star V Cancri.

Friedrich Wilhelm August Argelander was born in 1799 in Memel, then a part of Prussia. His mother was Finnish and his father German. . . . Argelander observed from the Alter Zoll, an ancient fortification overlooking the Rhine. . . . There he extended a star catalogue begun by Bessel, recording positions and magnitudes for 22,000 stars between declinations of +45° and +90°. . . .

Argelander was dissatisfied with this catalogue, for it was not uniformly complete to a faint limiting magnitude. He resolved to make a thorough survey of all stars brighter than the ninth magnitude, recording positions with sufficient accuracy to permit the unambiguous identification of each star by other astronomers. For this task Argelander selected a small comet-seeker telescope made by Fraunhofer, having a 3-inch f/8 objective. A

Kellner eyepiece was used to give a magnifying power of 10 and a 6° field of view. A thin half-circle of glass was employed as a reticle. Its edge, aligned along an hour circle, formed the line on which the time of a star's transit was noted. Twenty-one declination marks were placed at intervals of about seven minutes of arc along this line.

The observing routine is best described by Argelander himself in the introduction to the catalogue:

"The observer, whom we may designate as A, sits or lies (according to the altitude of the zone to be observed) on a chair with an adjustable back. The latter is set so that with his body in a comfortable position, the eye of the observer is directly behind the ocular, and he can see a field of somewhat more than two degrees without moving his head. There is no artificial illumination in the room, and the observer's eye is protected from the light of the sky by a shield of black paper at the ocular end of the telescope. . . . Under the wooden floor of the dome sits a second observer, B, who has directly before him a pendulum clock indicating sidereal time. . . .

"As the diurnal motion of the stars brings them one after another past the hour mark, A notes the magnitude and declination of each star passing within 65' or 70' of the center of the field. Without turning his eye from the telescope, A records the declination on a sheet of paper. To prevent writing the numbers on top of one another, the paper is held in a cardboard frame provided with openings which divide the page into five columns. . . . The moment the star disappears behind the hour mark, A calls out the magnitude to B, who notes the sidereal time and writes the time and magnitude in a notebook."

The original notebooks, and even the sheets on which the various A's wrote down the declinations, are carefully preserved at Bonn and have been used from time to time in tracing the few errors in the catalogue. It is interesting to see that the cardboard frames didn't entirely prevent the observers from running the numbers together when they wrote the declinations "blind."

The observations were very strenuous, especially in regions of high star density. Sometimes as many as thirty stars might cross the field per minute. Each observing session lasted no longer than an hour and a quarter, to insure that the observer's senses were not dulled by fatigue. Most of the work of observing was done by two assistants, Eduard Schönfeld and Adalbert Krüger, since Argelander found that "my eyes could not compete with the younger and sharper ones of my colleagues."

Each zone of the survey was observed at least twice, once with the telescope centered on an even degree of declination and the second time on an odd degree. The total number of observations was thus well over 700,000 in seven years. In cases of disagreement between two observations in overlapping zones, checks were made with a larger meridian transit telescope, usually by Argelander.

Although the BD is complete to magnitude 9, a great many stars are included between 9.0 and 9.5. At the faint end the brightness scale was rather uncertain, and stars listed as 9.5 may be as much as a magnitude fainter.

The catalogue was published in three volumes, the last appearing in 1862. The set of forty charts was published in 1863. Argelander and his assistants must have been men of tremendous stamina and energy to carry out this immense task of observation and data reduction in less than eleven years.

After completing the BD, Argelander returned to his work on variable stars. In 1863 he founded the Astronomische Gesellschaft, the first large international organization of astronomers. At a meeting of the AG held in Bonn in 1867, he suggested a program of accurate position measurements to be carried out on all BD stars brighter than magnitude 9. This led to the series of catalogues of the Astronomische Gesellschaft, the AGK, AGK-2, and most recently the AGK-3.

Argelander died in 1875 and was succeeded by Schönfeld. After completing the original BD observations, Schönfeld had left Bonn to go to the observatory in Mannheim. Upon his return he started observations to extend the BD as far to the south as he could observe from Bonn. The fourth volume, with its twenty-five charts, is called the *Südliche Bonner Durchmusterung*, or *Southern* BD, and covers declinations from −2° to −23°. It was published in 1886 and contains 133,659 stars.

The BD charts of the northern hemisphere were reprinted in 1899, on the hundredth anniversary of Argelander's birth, and the associated catalogue volumes were printed in 1903. By popular demand the complete BD was reprinted once again after World War II. This time the catalogue was reproduced as a microbook, with the individual pages photographically reduced by a factor of four. It can still be purchased in this form, for about a hundred dollars. . . .

Although the present-day Bonn astronomers are not inclined to rest on the reputation of their illustrious predecessors, they will have to work very hard to surpass the magnificent achievement of Argelander and the BD.

■■

A New Atlas of
the Heavens

ZDENEK KOPAL

(*Sky and Telescope*, November 1948)

Human efforts to reproduce on charts the apparent distribution of stars in the sky date back to time immemorial. To mention only one less-well-known achievement in this direction: one of the chief titles to fame of the Korean king Li Ch'eng kuei appears to be the completion, under his orders, of a celestial planisphere in Seoul which (judging from the position of Polaris) was probably copied from a much older original, dating perhaps as far back as the early centuries before Christ. We know that the work commanded by the good King Li included 1464 stars and was directed by Ch'uan chin; its computations were supervised by Lin fang tse, with at least nine collaborators on the project. The final copy, completed in 1395, was engraved on stone. The original engraving having been worn out, the work is known to have been engraved on another stone. This is what it meant, in those days, to produce a "new edition" of a star chart. . . .

The advent of telescopic astronomy naturally created an entirely new situation. The number of stars visible through telescopes of increasing power began to grow almost beyond limit, and the search for asteroids, comets, and other faint objects created a demand for much more detailed star charts. The nineteenth century produced the magnificent set of charts based on the famous *Bonner Durchmusterung* and its southern Cordoba continuation—the most extensive charts prepared up to the present. . . .

The new *Atlas of the Heavens*, from the Skalnate Pleso Observatory in Czechoslovakia, stands out among all its predecessors in several respects. It is the first atlas of the sky of its size which covers *both* celestial hemispheres in a homogeneous manner. On its sixteen charts it shows positions of all stars down to 7.75 visual apparent magnitude for the equinox of 1950.0, taken from the Boss *General Catalogue* and the *Henry Draper Catalogue*. A total of 32,571 recorded stars ranks it third in size in the existing literature. . . .

The new atlas—and this is important to emphasize—includes much more than mere positions of the stars. In the nineteenth century, positions were almost all that interested the celestial cartographer. A cluster or a nebular patch, which traversed now and then the field of a transit or meridian circle, evoked but little curiosity on the part of a self-respecting astrometer of bygone days; and an occasional lack of stars in the field was noted, we suspect, primarily as a respite from strenuous work. . . .

Almost one sixth of all stars included in the atlas are known to be double or multiple. Each one of these is marked on the chart in an appropriate manner, which permits its user to discern the number of components in the system and whether the pair is a visual or spectroscopic binary. All known novae, and variable stars attaining at maximum visual magnitude 7.75 or brighter, 443 in number, are likewise marked as such. The atlas shows, furthermore, the positions and relative dimensions of 249 galactic star clusters (from Shapley's catalogue in *Star Clusters*, Cambridge, 1930, Appendix B); all globular clusters and planetary nebulae known up to the present; 1121 extragalactic nebulae of magnitude 13.0 or brighter (according to the Shapley and Ames catalogue, Harvard *Annals*, 88, 1930); as well as 230 galactic gaseous nebulae, the larger of which are indicated by their characteristic shapes as revealed on actual photographs by different observers. The various star clusters and nebulae of apparent brightness greater than 12.0 are denoted on these charts by their respective numbers in the *New General Catalogue* (NGC) or the *Index Catalogue* (IC). Even the dark nebulae and obscuring patches on the sky—Herschel's *Loche im Himmel*—are marked on the charts, with the same attention and care as are the luminous ones. The outlines of the Milky Way are shown according to the work of Pannekoek (*Die Noerdliche Milchstrasse*, Leiden, 1920; *Die Suedliche Milchstrasse*, Lembang, 1929), together with the position of the galactic equator referred to Newcomb's pole, and of the ecliptic. In addition, the limits of the constellations as outlined by Delporte and endorsed in 1930 by the International Astronomical Union are shown.

This wealth of information, which in many previous star charts and atlases was conspicuous by its absence, renders the new atlas unique. It should prove useful to the professional astronomer for his manifold tasks, and still more to the amateurs of both hemispheres—whether for the identification of double or variable stars, for the discovery of new comets among hundreds of known nebulae or unresolved star clusters, or for the choice of interesting objects for celestial photography. . . .

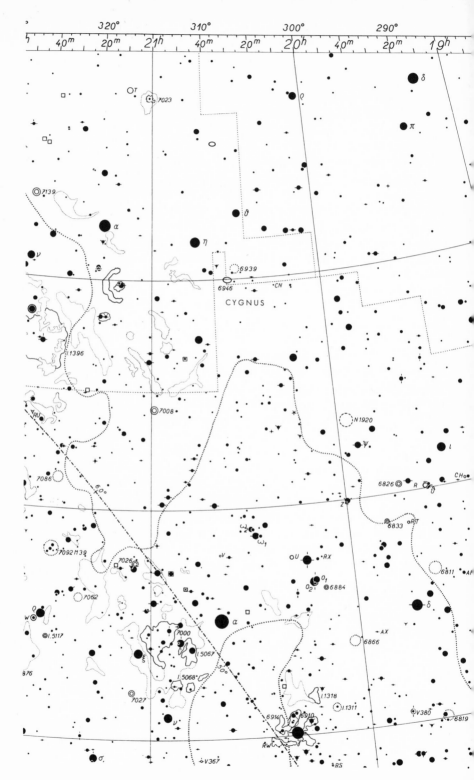

FIG. 8. A chart from the *Atlas of the Heavens* prepared at the Skalnate Pleso Observatory.

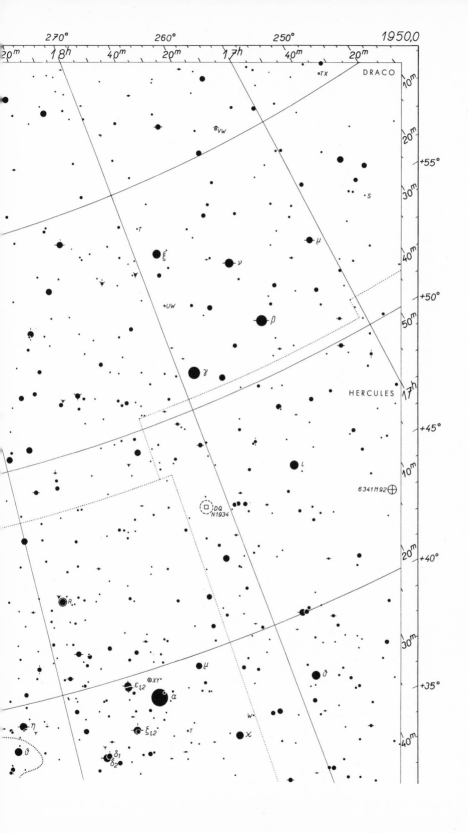

MAGNITUDINES STELLARUM

.	7,26 - 7,75 m	7,5
.	6,76 - 7,25 m	7,0
●	6,26 - 6,75 m	6,5
●	5,76 - 6,25 m	6,0
●	5,26 - 5,75 m	5,5
●	4,76 - 5,25 m	5,0
●	4,26 - 4,75 m	4,5
●	3,76 - 4,25 m	4,0
●	3,26 - 3,75 m	3,5
●	2,76 - 3,25 m	3,0
●	2,26 - 2,75 m	2,5
●	1,76 - 2,25 m	2,0
●	1,26 - 1,75 m	1,5
●	0,76 - 1,25 m	1,0
●	0,26 - 0,75 m	0,5
●	−0,25 - 0,25 m	0,0

DUPLICES ET MULTIPLICES

DUPLICES SPECTROSCOPICAE

VARIABILES   Max.- min.

•R	7,5 - <7,75 m
∘S	7,0 - <7,75 m
○RV	5,0 - <7,75 m

⊙ AF   4,5 - 6,0 m

⬤ V 365   4,0 - 4,2 m

N 1918   Nova −1,5 m

CUMULI GALACTICI

∷	< 1'
	1' - 2'
	3' - 5'
	6' - 10'
	11' - 20'
	21' - 30'
	31' - 40'
	41' - 50'
	51' - 60'

CUMULI GLOBULARES

⊕	0'1 - 2'0
⊕	2'1 - 5'0
⊕	5'1 - 10'0
⊕	> 10'0

NEBULAE PLANETARIAE

◎	1" - 10"
◎	11" - 30"
◎	31" - 100"
◎	> 100"

NEBULAE ANAGALACTICAE

∘	0'0 - 2'0
○	2'1 - 5'0
○	5'1 - 10'0
⬭	> 10'0

○ 3077 = NGC 3077 > 12,1 m

○ I.5332 = IC 5332   > 12,1 m

∘ sine numero < 12,0 m

NEBULAE DIFFUSAE

7000   □ < 10'

I.5067

NEBULAE OBSCURAE

ISOPHOTA GALACTICA

DIVISIO CONSTELLATIONUM

ECLIPTICA

AEQUATOR GALACTICUS
270°

THE KEY TO THE *Atlas of the Heavens* CHARTS

Stellar Magnitudes are represented by symbols which range by half magnitudes from 7.5 to the brightest stars. For instance, 0.0 stands for stars of apparent visual magnitudes between −0.25 and +0.25, while 7.5 stands for stars between 7.26 and 7.75. It is suggested that for ease and accuracy of comparing magnitudes a template be constructed which can be placed directly over the images on the chart. This might be drawn in India ink on tracing paper or made by punching holes the proper size in a thin sheet of plastic.

Double and Multiple Stars are next on the key, and are indicated by bars or lines extending out from the star image. A line straight through a star, giving two projections, one on each side, represents a visual double. Three, four, five, and six bars indicate stars with that number of visual components. Note that for visual systems the projecting line is in contact with the star image.

Spectroscopic Doubles. At the left in the key is first indicated a spectroscopic binary of two stars, but the projecting lines do not touch the star image itself. The second symbol represents a spectroscopic triplet. The third image in this key shows a regular visual double with one spectroscopic component; the fourth, with two spectroscopic components—a quadruple system. The last is a triple visual system with one spectroscopic component.

Variable Stars. All variables which attain a magnitude of 7.75 or brighter are indicated. The letter or number of the variable is given as shown by examples on the key, and the type and size of the image denotes its magnitude or its variation. The smallest star symbol with a variable's designation is for stars that reach the chart limit when at their brightest. Next, stars that attain 7.0 at maximum are shown by open circles the size of seventh-magnitude symbols. Similarly, stars reaching other magnitudes at maximum are indicated by open circles of commensurate size, as in the case of "RV" in the key, which attains a maximum in the 5.0 range.

When the range of a variable is within the limit of chart magnitudes, the symbol is composite, the outer circle indicating maximum brightness and the inner the magnitude at minimum. Where the range of the variable is very small, however, as in "V365" in the key, the white ring is made as narrow as it is possible to reproduce.

Novae are indicated by dashed open circles, the diameter equaling the magnitude at greatest brilliancy of the nova, and the date giving the year of its outburst. If any diffuse nebula is associated with a nova, it is indicated—see Nova Herculis, DQ, N1934, Chart V [a portion of which is reproduced here], where the associated nebulosity is less than ten minutes of arc in extent.

Concerning star symbols in general, it is important to note many instances on bright stars of what might at first seem a defect—a small white ring on the star disk. Vega is a good example, marked Alpha Lyrae on the chart. This star's symbol is almost one degree of declination in size, which would obscure the neighboring seventh-magnitude star. Therefore, in such cases, a ring of white around the fainter star permitted plotting its position. In the same region, Epsilon Lyrae is shown as a "naked-eye" double of two stars, with bars to indicate that each of the stars is again a telescopic double. The "1, 2" refers to Epsilon-1 and Epsilon-2, the designations of the two components. Delta Lyrae is shown as a naked-eye double, with one of the components a telescopic double and the other a spectroscopic binary. Stars that do not appear round should be examined closely, as it is probable they are composite images.

Galactic Clusters are shown for apparent diameters from less than one minute of arc up to sixty minutes (one degree), for several ranges of size. Do not confuse such clusters with novae: clusters are *dotted* circles, novae are *dashed*.

Globular Clusters of various sizes are represented by open circles with vertical and horizontal bars inside them.

Planetary Nebulae are represented from one second to greater than one hundred seconds of arc by two open, concentric circles. No indication of brightness is given.

Extragalactic Nebulae or *Galaxies* have a key given in two parts. The first shows that elliptical images in four size ranges mark these objects, up to ten minutes of arc. Those that are greater are shown in their proper sizes. For instance, at the left edge of Chart V is the Andromeda nebula, about two degrees along its major axis, and its companion galaxy NGC 205. The second part of this key explains the designations in other catalogues, such as *New General Catalogue* (NGC) and *Index Catalogue* (IC) objects, with the Messier number if a galaxy has one. Objects fainter than magnitude 12.0 are given without numbers, the chart limit for extragalactic nebulae being 13.0

Diffuse Nebulae (bright nebulosities) are given NGC and IC designations and their sizes and extents are indicated directly on the chart. The North America nebula (near Deneb on the chart) is used as an example in the key. Nebulosity smaller than ten minutes of arc is shown by a small square.

Dark Nebulae have light dotted lines to show the shape of the nebulosity.

Milky Way Boundaries are in heavy dotted lines.

Constellation Boundaries are represented by light lines of short dashes, and some constellations are labeled several times to avoid confusion.

The *Ecliptic* is a heavy dashed line.

The *Galactic Equator* is a line of alternate dashes and dots, with the galactic longitude marked at ten-degree intervals.

Positions of objects in the chart may be accurately measured from their plotted symbols. Right-ascension lines are straight, and a straightedge may be used to join markings from top to side of the chart, as well as from top to bottom. Right ascension is given in both time units and arc units. Declination lines are arcs of equally spaced circles. Consequently, a declination scale made to any degree of accuracy may be applied to any portion of the chart.

These "positions" of stars on the celestial sphere, and the two coordinates (right ascension and declination) correspond to what we see in the sky. "Position" on the celestial sphere is only a convenient way of describing direction; it leaves out the third dimension, distance from us, which is obviously very much larger for a faint star than for the flashing man-made lights on an airplane seen (momentarily) near it. How far is that star?   — T L P

Stellar Parallax

FREDERICK SLOCUM

(*The Telescope*, May–June 1935)

One of the fundamental problems of modern astronomy is the determination of the distances of stars. The only direct, rigorous method of solving this problem is by the application of the principles of terrestrial surveying.

Let us suppose that the terrestrial surveyor is confronted with the problem of finding the distance to an inaccessible, remote tower from a certain well-defined spot. From the early days of civilization it has been known that this problem requires the surveyor to form a triangle between the distant tower, the well-defined spot, and a point accessible from the well-defined spot and a known distance from it. If the surveyor then measured the angle formed at the tower by the two sides of the triangle that met there, a feat accomplished perhaps by noting the displacement of the tower relative to the still more distant landscape as he alternated between the two accessible vertices, he could derive the length of the side representing the desired distance.

The astronomical surveyor is confronted with an analogous problem, to find the distance from a well-defined spot in the universe, the earth, to an inaccessible, remote star. Because of the great distances of the stars a "base line" on the earth's surface yields a triangle so slender that the angle to be measured becomes smaller than his instruments can attain. However, the revolution of the earth about the sun carries the observer in six months to a point 186 million miles from his former position; that is, to the other side of the earth's orbit. Such a base line has been found sufficient to produce a measurable displacement of the nearer stars relative to those far beyond them [see Fig. 9].

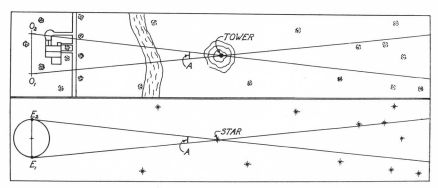

FIG. 9. Surveying stellar distances is analogous to surveying terrestrial distances. In the terrestrial problem, to find the distance from a certain well-defined spot O_1 to a remote, inaccessible tower requires that the surveyor know the length of a base line O_1O_2 and the value of the angle A which the base line subtends at the tower. In the astronomical problem the base line is a diameter of the earth's orbit E_1E_2 and the angle A must be measured.

In the writings of the early Greek philosophers the term *stellar parallax* appears in connection with the discussion as to whether the earth revolves around the sun or the sun around the earth. Aristotle [about 350 B.C.] pointed out that if the earth moved around the sun, the stars ought to show a parallax, that is, they ought to appear in different directions when observed from opposite sides of the earth's orbit. Since he could detect no such parallax, he claimed that the earth must be fixed in space. Aristarchus of Samos [about 200 B.C.] taught that the earth revolved around the sun and explained the absence of apparent parallax by assuming that it would be too small to detect.

[In A.D. 1497] Copernicus accepted this view when he wrote his book on the revolutions of the planets, but [forty-one years later] Tycho Brahe, at his great observatory in Denmark, equipped with far better instruments than his predecessors, could find no parallax. Partly for this reason and partly because he was loyal to the teachings of the Church he clung to the theory of the fixed earth.

[About A.D. 1600] Kepler and Galileo furnished the clinching arguments in favor of the revolution of the earth, and the latter suggested a method of measuring the annual parallax. With his newly invented telescope [in Italy], he discovered many double stars; in some cases a very bright star with a faint star apparently close to it. He assumed that one was bright because it was relatively near, the other faint because it was far away, and he suggested that careful measurements of the distance and direction of the brighter from the fainter ought to show an annual periodic change due to the difference in parallax of the two stars.

This method was actually tried by Sir William Herschel using one of his reflecting telescopes [in England]. In fact, he was working upon this very problem when he accidentally discovered the planet Uranus in 1781. As a result of several years' observations of many such pairs he discovered that some showed relative orbital motion, but he did not detect any annual parallax. . . .

It remained for Bessel at Königsberg, Germany, in 1838, to publish the first reliable result for the parallax of any star. He selected the star 61 Cygni because its rapidly changing position with respect to its neighbors (its proper motion) seemed to indicate that it might be relatively near. He measured the angular distance from this star to two fainter stars which he assumed to be very far away. These measures showed that 61 Cygni oscillates back and forth during each year, as expected from annual parallax. Similar visual observations were used on other stars with some success, but at the beginning of this present century such observations were discarded in favor of photography. The feasibility of this method was established by Kapteyn in Holland, but the details, as now generally used, were developed by F. Schlesinger [professor at Yale University until 1941].

By convention the parallax of a star is defined as half the full angle resulting from a change in the place of observation by a diameter of the earth's orbit, and the parallax of the nearest star, so far known, is only 0.75 seconds of arc.[1] This is equal to the displacement of a flagstaff ten miles away with respect to the distant landscape when one changes his place of observation by a little over two inches. Of course, the more distant the star the smaller its parallax.

___

[1] There are $360°$ (360 degrees) in a full circle, $60'$ (60 minutes of arc) in a degree, and $60''$ (60 seconds of arc) in a minute. Thus, $0''.75$ is $0.75/(60)(60)(360) = 1/1,728,000$ of a circle, or less than one millionth of the angular distance all the way around the sky.

The problem is then the exceedingly delicate one of deriving very small angles from observations subject to many possible errors. This, of course, requires a telescope of excellent quality and relatively long focal length. About a dozen of the largest telescopes in the world are now being used for this purpose. The procedure followed is nearly the same at all of these observatories.

At the Van Vleck Observatory [at Wesleyan University, in Middletown, Connecticut] a 20-inch refractor of 27.6-foot focal length is used for the determination of stellar parallax. It is used as a giant camera to take photographs through a yellow filter on 5-by-7-inch photographic plates loaded from the back with the film side against the filter.

In order to secure perfectly circular star images on the plate, great care must be taken in guiding the telescope during the exposure [keeping it steadily pointed at one group of stars]. An eyepiece with a magnifying power of 330 is used to view a star near the edge of the photograph. An illuminated cross of spider threads in the eyepiece is placed on the guiding

FIG. 10. The 20-inch visual refractor of the Van Vleck Observatory of Wesleyan University, used photographically for the determination of stellar parallax.

FIG. 11. The eye end of the Van Vleck refractor as adapted to photography. A indicates the guiding eyepiece; B, the guiding screws.

star and held there by turning screws which move the frame carrying the plateholder. The driving clock moves the whole telescope so as to counteract the rotation of the earth, but slight irregularities in the rate of the clock or atmospheric effects must be counteracted by hand guiding. It is possible to do this for a faint star more accurately than for a bright one.

If there should be any tendency for the stars to drift in one direction, the constant work necessary on the part of the observer in bringing the guiding star back to the cross threads will cause the bright stars to leave a photographic record of each little departure and so give for them somewhat pear-shaped images, difficult to measure with accuracy. It is therefore advisable to have all the stars that are to be measured as nearly as possible of the same magnitude. If the star whose parallax is desired is brighter than the reference stars, its brightness may be cut down by means of an occulting sector. The opening of the sector may be varied so as to reduce the light of a star by about one to six magnitudes. Still further reduction requires a filter with a neutral disk near the center capable of absorbing six magnitudes. This may be used in connection with the rotating sector so that, for example, the image of a first-magnitude star may be made to look like that of a tenth-magnitude star.

The parallax star is located near the center of the plate and an exposure of from five to ten minutes will generally be sufficient to yield four or more other stars well scattered over the plate. Such stars may be used as reference points from which to measure the real or apparent motions of the parallax star. Two exposures are made on each plate, the images being separated by two millimeters.

The maximum effect of parallax occurs at the time of year when the star is 90° east or west of the sun. It is seldom possible to secure photographs at exactly such times, but the parallax factor (the fractional part of the maximum displacement) can easily be computed. It is our practice to use plates with parallax factors larger than 0.60. . . .

In order that the displacement of a star due to parallax may be clearly separated from its proper motion and from other displacements, it is advisable to extend the observations over two or more years, taking groups of plates at intervals of about six months. The observatory has set as our minimum twenty plates, four at each epoch for five epochs.[2] . . .

The photographic plates are carefully developed and then the "negative" plates are measured by a micrometer [a microscope moved by a very accurately cut screw]. In spite of all precautions, the measurements include errors due to differences in the scale of the plates, differences in orientation, differences in atmospheric effects, and many other factors. All

[2] By *epoch* Slocum means several nights at about the same date.   — T L P

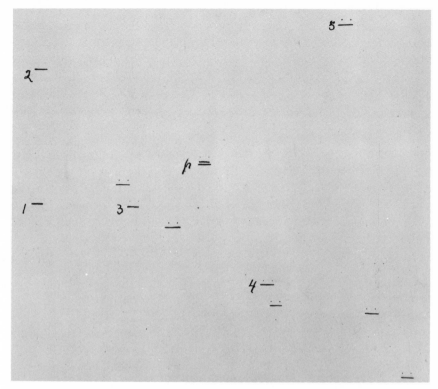

FIG. 12. The distance of Sirius was determined from parallax plates such as this one taken at Van Vleck Observatory. To allow measurement of its position with respect to the numbered faint stars, the Dog Star's light was reduced by a rotating sector. The two images of Sirius are doubly underlined.

the measurements are referred, by a simple mathematical process, to one plate as a standard, and the averages are analyzed for proper motion and parallax. The proper motion of each star increases uniformly with time. The parallax is proportional to the parallax factors for the different plates. The separation of these two motions by one star becomes then a mathematical problem of no great severity.

The resulting parallax will be the parallax relative to the faint comparison stars, which themselves possess small parallactic displacements. By statistical methods the average parallax of the faint stars can be calculated and added to the relative parallax to give the absolute parallax (relative to infinitely distant stars).

The bright star Sirius, for example, has a relative parallax of 0."379, which corresponds to a distance of approximately 50,540,000,000,000 miles. Yet Sirius is one of the nearest stars.

To avoid so many digits, larger units of distance are frequently used, such as the *light year* or the *parsec*. The light year is the distance that light travels in a year, found by multiplying the speed of light, 186,000 miles per second, by the number of seconds in a year. A light year is thus 5.8 million million miles. If a star had a parallax of one second of arc, it would be at a distance of 19 million million miles or 3.26 light years, whence the formula

$$\text{Distance in light years} = \frac{3.26}{p},$$

where p is the parallax of the star in seconds of arc. The parsec is the distance corresponding to a parallax of one second and

$$\text{Distance in parsecs} = \frac{1}{p}.$$

Thus Sirius is at a distance of 8.6 light years or 2.7 parsecs.

So far as is known at present, only five stars are nearer than Sirius, and only about a hundred are nearer than 10 parsecs or 32.6 light years.

This method of measuring distances by trigonometric parallax has its limitations. For stars about 300 light years distant the parallax is about $0''.01$, the angle which a foot rule would subtend at a distance of 4000 miles, or about 1/60,000 inch on the scale of the Van Vleck photographs. Measures of distances smaller than this on photographic plates are un- certain. There are other methods of estimating larger distances of the stars (one based on the apparent brightness), but most of them depend directly or indirectly upon the trigonometric measures of the nearer stars. Thus the measurement of trigonometric parallaxes becomes fundamental to these other methods.

In turn, distance is fundamental to the solution of many problems in astronomy: the linear dimensions of double-star orbits, the velocity of stars in space, the masses and densities of stars, the absolute luminosities of the stars in terms of the sun, the diameters of stars, star clusters, nebulae, and galaxies, and the extent of the sidereal universe.

■■■

Distances of the Stars

(*Sky and Telescope*, November 1964)

If we visualize our solar system as a whole amid the stars in space, its most remarkable characteristic is its extreme isolation. From the sun to its nearest stellar neighbor is about 7000 times as far as to the outermost known planet, Pluto. Truly, our sun's family of planets, comets, and interplanetary dust and gas is only a tiny island on a wide and lonely sea.

The light that left the sun eight minutes ago has just reached earth, but it must travel 4.3 years to reach Alpha Centauri, the zero-magnitude southern double star which, with its faint companion, is our closest neighbor. Thus it is natural to use the *light year* as a unit for star distances; it is the space that light traveling at 186,000 miles a second covers in one year....

Another distance unit is the *parsec*—corresponding to a parallax of one second of arc. For any star, the distance in parsecs is just the reciprocal of the parallax; Alpha Centauri, for instance, is 1/0.76 or 1.32 parsecs away. To convert parsecs to light years, multiply by 3.26.

It may be surprising to realize that more than two centuries ago—long before any stellar parallax had been measured—astronomers had a fairly good idea of the average distance of the brighter stars. The basic concept is simple. If some star is a physical duplicate of our sun, then the ratio of the apparent brightnesses of the sun and star will indicate the star's distance in terms of the sun's. It is a simple consequence of the law that the intensity of light is proportional to the inverse square of the distance from the source....

Such a rough calculation of a star's distance only works when the star has about the same candlepower as the sun. The computation would fail badly if we had chosen, for example, a very luminous supergiant star like Rigel. In fact, apparent brightness is a poor criterion for selecting nearby stars. Proxima Centauri is an eleventh-magnitude star at the same distance from us as zero-magnitude Alpha Centauri. Of the twelve nearest known stars, only four are of naked-eye brilliance: the sun, the two brighter members of Alpha Centauri, and Sirius.

Large proper motion is a more reliable earmark of vicinity. Any star whose position relative to its neighbors is changing by half a second of arc per year is very apt to be within fifty light years of the solar system.

The trigonometric parallax of a star, as determined from photographs taken with a long-focus refractor, has an uncertainty of about ±0.010 second of arc, irrespective of distance. For nearby Alpha Centauri this means that the distance is known to about 1 per cent. But for a star whose true distance is 100 parsecs this uncertainty is the same size as the parallax, and so the measurement leads to a virtually indeterminate result. Thus, the basic trigonometric parallax method gives useful results for individual stars only if they are well within 100 parsecs of the sun. Altogether, such measurements have been made for about six thousand stars.

Astronomers have used great ingenuity in devising a wide variety of methods for more distant stars. One group of these methods gives the average distance of a class of stars from observations of their motions. (Such a class might consist of all sixth-magnitude blue stars.) Spectroscopic measurements give the stars' line-of-sight motions in kilometers per second, while positional measurements of the same stars give their motions at right angles to the line of sight in seconds of arc per year. Suitable analysis of these data tells, in effect, how many kilometers correspond to one second of arc at the distance of the stars. The average distance of the class follows immediately.

The techniques already mentioned can be used to calibrate indirect methods for still remoter stars. Here the basic idea is that the distance can be calculated if we know both the apparent brightness and the intrinsic luminosity of a star. Many observable properties—spectrum line intensities, peculiarities of color, characteristic patterns of light variation—can be exploited to indicate the intrinsic luminosity.

Thus the astronomy of today has an arsenal of distance-measuring procedures. For a few hundred of the very nearest stars, precise information is available about individual ones. With greater and greater distances, the information becomes rougher and the variety of techniques less. But our plumb line can reach even the faintest stars observable in large telescopes.

....

Stars Nearer than
Five Parsecs

PETER VAN DE KAMP

(*Sky and Telescope*, October 1955)

Among the many different kinds of stars, astronomers want to know which are most numerous and which are most sparsely distributed. The naked-eye stars as a group cannot be used, because they do not make up a typical sample of the stellar population. A listing of naked-eye stars is overweighted in favor of very luminous objects which are conspicuous at great distances, and there are too few of the intrinsically very faint dwarf stars, for the latter can be discovered only if they are nearby.

Therefore, to find which kinds of stars actually are most numerous, it is best to make a stellar census within a relatively small volume around the sun. The list given in Table 1 is of all known stars within five parsecs— about sixteen light years—of the sun; it includes stars with parallaxes greater than 0″.195. The distance limit is arbitrary; it is chosen because it gives a sufficiently large and reasonably complete sample of stars.

Among these nearby stars, two facts stand out. The majority are faint; less than a dozen are visible to the naked eye. Double stars are common. Of the forty-two entries in the table, thirty are single stars, ten are double-star systems, and two are triple systems, leaving unseen companions out of consideration. If these were included, sixty stars would be involved, and only twenty-seven appear at present to be isolated individuals.

Thirty-six stars are of spectral type[1] M, which would indicate that the great majority of stars in our part of the Milky Way are intrinsically very faint red dwarfs. The list also contains five white dwarfs: van Maanen's star, CC 658, and the companions of Sirius, Procyon, and o^2 Eridani.

The reader may be familiar with most of the column headings. The *proper motion* of each star is its apparent change of position in the sky, expressed in seconds of arc per year. Because all these stars are near to us, they have large proper motions, the smallest being not quite half a second of arc per year. The *cross motion* is the star's velocity perpendicular to the line of sight, expressed in kilometers per second; cross motion can be obtained from the proper motion by taking the star's distance into account. The *position angle* of the proper motion (and the cross motion) is the direction toward which the star appears to move on the celestial sphere; it is counted from north (0°) through east (90°) and so on. The star's *radial velocity* is its line-of-sight motion and is expressed directly in kilometers per second, positive for recession and negative for approach. Cross motion and radial velocity are right-angle components of the star's space motion relative to the sun.

Following the usual astronomical convention, the letters A, B, and C, used here as column headings, refer to the components of a double or multiple star. The *absolute magnitude* of a star is the apparent magnitude it would have if it were viewed from a standard distance of 10 parsecs (32.6 light years); it is a convenient way of expressing the intrinsic bright-nesses of the stars. The values in the table are based on a visual absolute magnitude of +4.7 for the sun. The *luminosity* of a star is its intrinsic brightness in terms of the sun's as unity. Only three stars in this list outshine the sun: Sirius, Altair, and Procyon. The faintest star in the list is Wolf 359, but Ross 614B is probably even fainter. The faintest star known is of absolute magnitude +19.3, but it is too far away—19 light years —to be included here. . . .

---

[1] The "spectral type" mentioned here and listed under "Spectrum" in Table 1 is discussed in Chapter 3. — T L P

TABLE 1. KNOWN STARS WITHIN FIVE PARSECS*

No.	Name	R.A. 1950	Dec. 1950	Paral- lax	Dis- tance in light years	Proper motion	Cross motion km/sec	Posi- tion angle
1	sun	— —	— —	—	—	—	—	—
2	α Centauri	14ʰ 36ᵐ2	−60° 38′	0″760	4.3	3″68	23	281
3	Barnard's star	17 55.4	+ 4 33	0.545	6.0	10.30	90	356
4	Wolf 359	10 54.2	+ 7 20	0.421	7.7	4.84	54	235
5	Luyten 726-8	1 36.4	−18 13	0.410	7.9	3.35	38	80
6	Lalande 21185	11 0.6	+36 18	0.398	8.2	4.78	57	187
7	Sirius	6 42.9	−16 39	0.375	8.7	1.32	16	204
8	Ross 154	18 46.7	−23 53	0.351	9.3	0.67	9	106
9	Ross 248	23 39.4	+43 55	0.316	10.3	1.58	23	176
10	ε Eridani	3 30.6	− 9 38	0.303	10.8	0.97	15	271
11	Ross 128	11 45.1	+ 1 7	0.298	10.9	1.40	22	151
12	61 Cygni	21 4.7	+38 30	0.293	11.1	5.22	84	52
13	Luyten 789-6	22 35.7	−15 37	0.292	11.2	3.27	53	46
14	Procyon	7 36.7	+ 5 21	0.288	11.3	1.25	20	214
15	ε Indi	21 59.6	−57 0	0.285	11.4	4.67	77	123
16	Σ 2398	18 42.2	+59 33	0.280	11.6	2.29	38	324
17	Groombridge 34	0 15.5	+43 44	0.278	11.7	2.91	49	82
18	τ Ceti	1 41.7	−16 12	0.275	11.8	1.92	33	297
19	Lacaille 9352	23 2.6	−36 9	0.273	11.9	6.87	118	79
20	BD +5°1668	7 24.7	+ 5 29	0.263	12.4	3.73	67	171
21	Lacaille 8760	21 14.3	−39 4	0.255	12.8	3.46	64	250
22	Kapteyn's star	5 9.7	−45 0	0.251	13.0	8.79	166	131
23	Krüger 60	22 26.3	+57 27	0.249	13.1	0.87	16	247
24	Ross 614	6 26.8	− 2 47	0.248	13.1	0.97	18	131
25	BD −12°4523	16 27.5	−12 32	0.244	13.4	1.24	24	180
26	van Maanen's star	0 46.5	+ 5 10	0.236	13.8	2.98	59	155
27	Wolf 424	12 30.9	+ 9 18	0.223	14.6	1.87	40	278
28	Groombridge 1618	10 8.3	+49 42	0.222	14.7	1.45	31	249
29	CD −37°15492	0 2.5	−37 36	0.219	14.9	6.09	132	112
30	CD −46°11540	17 24.9	−46 51	0.213	15.3	1.15	25	138
31	BD +20°2465	10 16.9	+20 7	0.211	15.4	0.49	11	264
32	CD −44°11909	17 33.5	−44 16	0.209	15.6	1.14	26	218
33	CD −49°13515	21 30.2	−49 13	0.209	15.6	0.78	18	184
34	AOe 17415-6	17 36.7	+68 23	0.206	15.8	1.31	30	196
35	Ross 780	22 50.5	−14 31	0.206	15.8	1.12	26	120
36	Lalande 25372	13 43.2	+15 10	0.205	15.9	2.30	53	129
37	CC 658	11 42.7	−64 33	0.203	16.0	2.69	62	99
38	o² Eridani	4 13.0	− 7 44	0.200	16.3	4.08	96	213
39	70 Ophiuchi	18 2.9	+ 2 31	0.199	16.4	1.13	27	167
40	Altair	19 48.3	+ 8 44	0.198	16.5	0.66	16	54
41	BD +43°4305	22 44.7	+44 5	0.198	16.5	0.84	20	237
42	AC 79°3888	11 44.3	+78 57	0.196	16.6	0.87	21	57

* From the *Publications* of the Astronomical Society of the Pacific.

Radial velocity km/sec	Visual magnitude and spectrum			Visual absolute magnitude			Visual luminosity ⊙		
	A	B	C	A	B	C	A	B	C
0	−26.9 Go	—	—	4.7	—	—	1.0	—	—
− 25	0.3 Go	1 7 K5	11 M5e	4.7	6.1	15.4	1.0	0.28	0.000052
−108	9.5 M5	**	—	13.2	**	—	.00040	**	—
+ 13	13.5 M6e	—	—	16.6	—	—	.000017	—	—
+ 29	12.5 M6e	13.0 M6e	—	15.6	16.1	—	.00004	.00003	—
− 86	7.5 M2	**	—	10.5	**	—	.0048	**	—
− 8	−1.6 Ao	7.1 wd	—	1.3	10.0	—	23.	.008	—
− 4	10.6 M5e	—	—	13.3	—	—	.00036	—	—
− 81	12.2 M6e	—	—	14.7	—	—	.00010	—	—
+ 15	3.8 K2	—	—	6.2	—	—	.25	—	—
− 13	11.1 M5	—	—	13.5	—	—	.00030	—	—
− 64	5.6 K6	6.3 Mo	**	7.9	8.6	**	.052	.028	**
− 60	12.2 M6	—	—	14.5	—	—	.00012	—	—
− 3	0.5 F5	10.8 wd	—	2.8	13.1	—	5.8	.00044	—
− 40	4.7 K5	—	—	7.0	—	—	.12	—	—
+ 1	8.9 M4	9.7 M4	—	11.1	11.9	—	.0028	.0013	—
+ 14	8.1 M2e	10.9 M4e	—	10.3	13.1	—	.0058	.00044	—
− 16	3.6 G4	—	—	5.8	—	—	.36	—	—
+ 10	7.2 M2	—	—	9.4	—	—	.013	—	—
+ 26	10.1 M4	—	—	12.2	—	—	.0010	—	—
+ 23	6.6 M1	—	—	8.6	—	—	.028	—	—
+242	9.2 Mo	—	—	11.2	—	—	.0025	—	—
− 24	9.9 M4	11.4 M5e	—	11.9	13.4	—	.0013	.00033	—
+ 24	10.9 M5e	**	—	12.9	**	—	.00052	**	—
− 13	10.0 M5	—	—	11.9	—	—	.0013	—	—
+ 26	12.3 wdF	—	—	14.2	—	—	.00016	—	—
− 5	12.6 M6e	12.6 M6e	—	14.3	14.3	—	.00014	.00014	—
− 27	6.8 K5	—	—	8.5	—	—	.030	—	—
+ 24	8.6 M3	—	—	10.3	—	—	.0058	—	—
—	9.7 M4	—	—	11.3	—	—	.0023	—	—
+ 10	9.5 M4e	**	—	11.1	**	—	.0028	**	—
—	11.2 M5	—	—	12.8	—	—	.00058	—	—
—	9 M3	—	—	10.6	—	—	.0044	—	—
− 17	9.1 M3	—	—	10.7	—	—	.0040	—	—
+ 9	10.2 M5	—	—	11.8	—	—	.0014	—	—
+ 15	8.6 M2	—	—	10.2	—	—	.0063	—	—
—	11 wd	—	—	12.5	—	—	.0008	—	—
− 42	4.5 Ko	9.2 wdA	11.0 M5e	6.0	10.7	12.5	.30	.0040	.0008
− 7	4.2 K1	5.9 K5	—	5.7	7.4	—	.40	.083	—
− 26	0.9 A5	—	—	2.4	—	—	8.3	—	—
− 2	10.2 M5e	—	—	11.7	—	—	.0016	—	—
−119	11.0 M4	—	—	12.5	—	—	.0008	—	—

** Indicates unseen companion.

In further explanation of Table 1, note the variety of star names. Barnard, Wolf, Luyten, Lalande, Ross, Groombridge, Lacaille, Kapteyn, Krüger, and van Maanen are astronomers' names, and the number following a name ("Wolf 359") is the number of the star in a list published by that astronomer. "BD" stands for the Bonner Durchmusterung (see p. 7) of stars in the northern sky, organized in strips around the sky parallel to the equator; BD +5°1668 is the 1668th star listed in the strip between 5° and 6° north of the celestial equator. "CD" stands for the similar catalogue made at Cordoba, Argentina. The Greek letters indicate the sequence of bright stars in the constellation named (in the Latin genitive case); α Centauri is the brightest star in the constellation Centaurus (see p. 4); 61 Cygni and 70 Ophiuchi are fainter stars in Cygnus and Ophiuchus. Some of the brightest stars (Sirius, Procyon, Altair) have individual names dating far back in history.

The right ascension ("R.A.") and declination ("Dec.") are coordinates in the sky like longitude and latitude on the earth. Declination is measured like latitude in degrees north (+) or south (−) from the celestial equator, an imaginary line halfway between the poles (see p. 7). Right ascension is measured like east longitude, eastward from a point called the vernal equinox, where the sun crosses the celestial equator about March 21 each year. These celestial coordinates of stars (unlike the moon, sun, and planets —see Wanderers in the Sky) are very nearly fixed, but change slightly due to proper motion and a slow change of the vernal equinox; hence they must be dated.

The magnitude scale of stellar brightness (discussed in Chapter 2) starts at 0 for the brightest stars in the sky and increases to 5 for stars 1/100 as bright, to 10 for stars 1/10,000 as bright, and so on. Each magnitude difference corresponds to a ratio of 1/2.512 in brightness, and the daytime sun, at magnitude −26.9, appears over 40 billion times brighter than the brightest stars. However, this is largely due to the enormous difference in distance; if the sun and the stars were all lined up at the same distance, 10 parsecs, they would have the computed "absolute magnitudes" listed, or the "luminosities" reckoned in fractions or multiples of the sun.

The spectra of stars (see Chapter 3) are classed by letter (and number subdivisions) in a sequence from O-type hot blue stars through B, A, F, G, and K to M-type cool red stars. The two labeled "wd" are white dwarfs (see p. 231). The hot stars have much higher surface brightness (energy output per unit area) than the cooler ones, as shown in the next article. — T L P

....

A Model of the Solar Neighborhood

A. E. WHITFORD AND J. W. SLOWEY

(*Sky and Telescope*, October 1955)

A model showing the size, color, and location in space of stars known to be within five parsecs of the sun has recently been constructed at the University of Wisconsin, as a laboratory exercise by students in the elementary astronomy course. . . . Placing a star in the model involves specifying its direction from the sun in celestial coordinates, and finding the distance of the star from its parallax. . . .

The students started with a table giving the name, right ascension and declination, the parallax, apparent visual magnitude, luminosity, and the spectral class for each star known to be closer than five parsecs, data given by P. van de Kamp's table [Table 1]. This table lists several stars that are sure to be familiar, such as Alpha Centauri, Sirius, Procyon, and Altair. The majority, however, are faint and have unfamiliar designations, such as Wolf 359 and Groombridge 34.

Each pair of workers was given the task of mounting two or three stars on the model. First the diameter of each star was calculated from the relation,

$$d = (L/B)^{1/2},$$

where d is the diameter, L the luminosity, and B the surface brightness (visual light per unit area), all expressed in fractions or multiples of the sun. The luminosity can be taken directly from Table 1, and the surface brightness, B, from a table such as Table 2.[1]

---

[1] If the stars were ideal black-body radiators, and if the luminosity included all the light (ultraviolet and infrared as well as visual), $B = (T/5750°)^4$, where T is the temperature of the star's surface in centigrade degrees above absolute zero ($-273°C$); $5750°$ is the absolute temperature of the sun. Note that the surface area of a star is r^2 times the surface area of the sun, where r is the radius of the star in terms of the sun's radius. The tabulated values of B leave out the ultraviolet and infrared light missed in the visual luminosity.

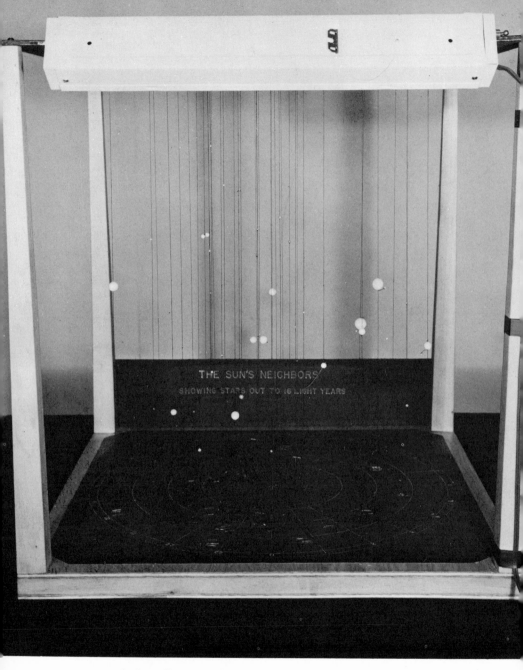

FIG. 13. A three-dimensional model showing the arrangement in space of the known stars within five parsecs of the sun, which is centered in the frame. The double just below the sun is Alpha Centauri (the faint star Proxima does not show in the picture). University of Wisconsin students made this model.

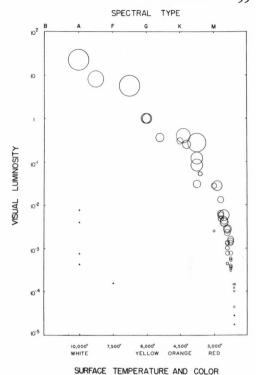

SPECTRAL TYPE

SURFACE TEMPERATURE AND COLOR

FIG. 14. The spectrum-luminosity relation for the stars closer than five parsecs. Sizes of the circles indicate the relative diameters of the stars. The star of smallest known mass, Ross 614B, could not be plotted, as its spectral type is unknown. This diagram (courtesy of Peter van de Kamp, Sproul Observatory) was made from the data in Table 1.

TABLE 2.   SURFACE BRIGHTNESS OF STARS RELATIVE TO THE SUN

Type	B	Type[1]	B	Type[1]	B
Bo	32.4	F5	1.91	dMo	0.043
B5	17.8	dGo	1.02	dM2	0.039
Ao	9.8	dG5	0.74	dM4	0.0354
A5	5.5	dKo	0.44	dM6	0.0170
Fo	3.23	dK5	0.117	dM8	0.0135

[1] d stands for "dwarf star." Most of the stars closer than 5 parsecs are dwarf stars.

To represent the sizes of the stars, a convenient scale was chosen, using a one-centimeter sphere for the sun. The students selected beads of the proper diameter and dipped them in fluorescent lacquer of a color to match the spectral type. An appropriate set of colors is for A stars, white; F, light yellow; G, yellow; K, orange; M, red. Fluorescent lacquers are obtainable from outdoor advertising firms and theatrical supply houses.

For most of the stars, a string of "pearls" from the five- and ten-cent store has a sufficient range in size. The largest stars, such as Sirius A and Procyon A, are hardwood beads turned out on a lathe. The smallest dwarfs require very fine beads, such as those used in Indian beadwork.

While the lacquer is drying, one may calculate the location of the star in the model. Since the stars are suspended on vertical black threads, it is natural to compute the projected coordinates in the equatorial plane, and the height above or below that plane. If D is the distance of the star, δ the star's declination, r the projected distance on the equatorial plane, and h the vertical distance from the equatorial plane, then

$$r = D \cos \delta;$$
$$h = D \sin \delta.$$

It is convenient to use a scale of distances where five centimeters equal one parsec (corresponding to 1.53 centimeters per light year). The supporting frame will then need to be about two feet square. A polar coordinate grid marked in right ascension and parsecs (or light years) is pasted to both the upper and lower decks of the frame; the equatorial plane is midway between them.

Starting with the sun at the center, the stars are then hung in place on taut threads. A vertical ruler showing parsecs (or light years) above and below the horizontal plane is helpful in adjusting the height. The upper end of each thread is secured with Scotch tape, and the lower with a stapler.

To illuminate the model, a 15-watt tubular fluorescent lamp is obtainable with a built-in black-light filter. It gives excellent diffuse illumination. The technical designation is F15T8/BLB, and it can be ordered from any dealer in fluorescent lighting equipment.

When the room lights go out and the black light is turned on, the threads disappear and the stars, now showing brilliant colors, seem to be floating in space. The student has before him a sample of a stellar population. It contains no giants, and only four stars intrinsically brighter than the sun. The majority of the stars are faint red dwarfs, whose actual preponderance is graphically presented. The considerable fraction of double- and triple-star systems is also impressive. The thinning out of the stars in the outermost part of the model indicates our incomplete knowledge of even the nearby stars.

In one respect the model gives a distorted view, since it is necessary to choose different scales for distances and diameters. Consider what would happen if Arcturus chanced to be within the five-parsec limit. Its diameter in the model would be about a foot, and a good number of the other stars would be engulfed by it. The wide disparity of scales is unavoidable; if

THE SUN'S NEIGHBORS

SHOWING STARS OUT TO 16 LIGHT YEARS

FIG. 15. This black-light view of the model shows the nearby stars apparently suspended in space. The sun is at the center, with the double star Alpha Centauri just below; Altair is at the far left. Sirius and Procyon are the largest stars on the right. The model is viewed from the direction right ascension 0 hours, declination $+15°$.

the scale adopted for the diameters had been used for the distances, stars on opposite sides of the model would have been 1300 miles apart. . . .

The completed model makes an eye-catching demonstration on public nights. The photographically inclined may attempt color shots, or even stereoscopic pictures.

For purposes of this introduction, it must be noted that astronomers have established without any doubt that the energy radiated by the sun and stars comes from nuclear reactions deep in their interiors. No other source of energy can account for their prodigious output. In particular, when allowance is made for its distance, the sun (with luminosity L = 1) is found to be radiating about 10^{26} (100 million billion billion) calories per second, or 3.8×10^{33} ergs per second. At this rate, chemical reactions, such as hydrogen burning in oxygen, would burn out—burn up the whole mass of the sun—in a few million years, whereas geologists have good evidence that the sun was shining on the earth several billion years ago about as strongly as at present.

The astronomers seized upon Einstein's 1905 conclusion from his relativity theory that mass, m, in grams can be considered equivalent to energy in ergs, $E = mc^2$, where c is the velocity of light, 3×10^{10} cm/sec, a very large number. At the conversion rate of $(3 \times 10^{10})^2 = 9 \times 10^{20}$ ergs per gram, less than 1/10,000 of the sun's mass would be used up in a billion years. The relativity theory was confirmed by several laboratory experiments, and by 1935 several nuclear reactions had been studied, using beams of high-speed atoms. Then Hans Bethe, a physicist at Cornell, noticed that high-speed hydrogen nuclei (protons) combine with carbon, oxygen, and nitrogen nuclei on impact, converting mass to energy at a rate that would match the sun's energy output under conditions like those near the center of a star (temperatures of 20 million degrees). The overall effect of these and other nuclear fusion reactions is to combine four hydrogen nuclei into one helium nucleus. Since a helium atom has a mass about 1 per cent smaller than four hydrogen atoms, these nuclear reactions could be the mechanism whereby a star of hydrogen could convert 1 per cent of its mass to energy. If the sun started as almost pure hydrogen, it could radiate at the observed rate of 3.8×10^{33} ergs/sec for over 100 billion years before all of its hydrogen (2×10^{33} gms) was converted to helium. Similar calculations show that the luminosity of many other stars can be explained in the same way.

In 1945 the release of large amounts of nuclear energy was proved possible in another way.   —T L P

....

Atoms, Stars, and Cosmic Bombs

ROBERT R. COLES

(*Sky and Telescope*, April 1946)

In his announcement of the first use of the atomic bomb in combat President Truman said, "It is the harnessing of the basic power of the universe. The force from which the sun draws its power has been loosed against those who brought war to the Far East."

Whatever else may result from this event, it has already inspired tremendous popular interest in every branch of physical science, as reflected in the press, on the radio, and in increased planetarium attendance. And in so doing, it has helped, more perhaps than anything else, to stress the value of research in pure science and to emphasize the important interrelation of physics, chemistry, and astronomy.

Through great telescopes, man explores the universe beyond the earth. This he views as a dynamic system, complexly organized and of such dimensions that a mere recitation of the figures involved staggers the imagination. At the other extreme is the realm of the atom—submicroscopic— also of great complexity, and so minute that it is impossible for most of us to comprehend its littleness.

Once these two (the stellar universe and the atom) were considered far apart and almost unrelated. Today we know that they are closely bound together and that research in either field provides material useful in the other. The fact that atomic energy is the basic power in the universe is a truth that has become increasingly apparent through the years.

But what is this mysterious thing that we call "atomic energy"? Judging from some recently published popular accounts, one might believe that man had suddenly discovered something entirely new and out of this world.

In one sense, hundreds of everyday phenomena result in the release of atomic energy. Such commonplace happenings as the burning of coal, the combustion of gasoline vapor in an automobile engine, and the electrolysis of water are familiar examples. In each of these energy is released. This energy results from changes in atomic structure. But here it is the outer parts—the electrons in the atoms—that are involved. Through a chemical reaction, the arrangement of these electrons is changed in the building up of various compounds or in the breaking down of other compounds into the elements of which they were composed. But the terrific effects that followed the atomic bombing of Hiroshima in August 1945 resulted from the splitting of the inner parts, or nuclei, of the atoms, with the release of almost unbelievable quantities of energy. This is more properly known as *subatomic energy*.

As everyone knows, the atomic bomb did not spring into existence full blown. It resulted from a vast two-billion-dollar government-sponsored project that was established under the pressure of war. But the amazing success of this project would have been impossible except for the groundwork of earlier research in atomic physics. The dawn of this science came during the last decade of the nineteenth century, with two events of far-reaching significance. The radioactive properties of uranium were discovered by H. Becquerel in 1896, and the far more radioactive radium was isolated by the Curies in 1898. These revolutionary achievements meant that the atom could no longer be considered as representing the ultimate in the structure of matter.

Almost immediately after the discovery of radium, many scientists in Europe and America began experimental work in atomic physics. Sir Ernest Rutherford found that radium gave off *alpha*, *beta*, and *gamma* rays; but the alpha rays were later shown to consist of particles identical with the nuclei of helium atoms (possessing two positive charges), the beta rays were actually fast-moving negative electrons, and the gamma rays were electromagnetic radiation (of the same nature as light) of extremely high frequency and great penetrating power. Evidently, the radium atoms spontaneously decomposed to form other elements and to release some of the fundamental particles which compose the nuclei of all atoms.

Radium is only one of some two-score radioactive nuclei in the three natural radioactive series; the final disintegration of each of these series produces the common element lead. It was not until 1919, when Rutherford bombarded nitrogen with alpha particles, that artificially radioactive elements were produced. The helium nuclei combined with the nitrogen to produce oxygen and hydrogen, and thereafter many more elements yielded to the bombardment of various particles produced by man-made electrostatic generators, by cyclotrons and other so-called *atom smashers*. In these operations, scientists succeeded in actually transmuting elements and learned at first hand of the stupendous quantities of energy that are locked in the heart of the atom.

But theory had been waiting for just such results. In 1905 Einstein suggested that the tremendous energy of radioactive decay might in part be accounted for by the conversion of some of the mass of an atom into energy. This required a restatement of the laws of the conservation of energy and matter, and the experiment of the atomic bomb has made very practical use of the fact that matter and energy are different forms of the same phenomenon.

In 1939 another epoch-making step was taken, which led directly to the atomic bomb. Two German scientists succeeded in producing a complete split, or *fission*, of a uranium nucleus into two parts of the same order of mass. We had only succeeded in "chipping" the atom before this, with relatively small releases of energy. Uranium fission made possible the development of chain reactions among large masses of uranium atoms; also it led to the production of neptunium and plutonium, two new elements (93 and 94). Recently, elements 95 and 96 have also been produced. [The number is now up to 104.]

Since the release of the atomic bomb story, such words as U-235, isotopes,

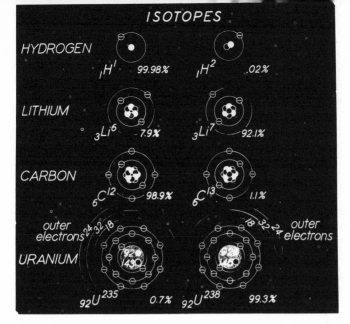

FIG. 16. Isotopes of an element have the same number of ring electrons and therefore the same chemical properties. They differ in the number of neutrons in their nuclei and have different masses. The percentages of isotopes which make up ordinary samples of some elements as found in nature are shown in this diagram.

deuterium, chain reaction, neptunium, and plutonium have found their places in everyday conversation. To the average citizen, without scientific background, they may seem rather vague in meaning, and the general picture of how they fit together may be confused, but of their importance in the scheme of things there can be no doubt. All this was settled with the explosion of the first atomic bomb.

The discovery of subatomic energy belongs within the past half century, but the stellar universe scintillates with visual evidence of atomic energy changes that have been going on for countless millions of years. For centuries man had speculated on the source of solar energy, lately realizing that if the explanation could be found for the sun it would probably apply to most other stars in the sky as well.

The ancient theory that the sun was on fire had to be discarded for the simple reason that the sun is too old; if its energy were generated by ordinary chemical combustion, it would have burned itself out long before now. Also, chemical compounds which are the products of combustion cannot exist at the tremendously high temperatures that prevail in the sun's interior. The famous Helmholtz contraction hypothesis, proposed in 1854, also had to be discarded in view of the sun's age. This proposal was that the sun maintained its temperature by continual gravitational contraction,

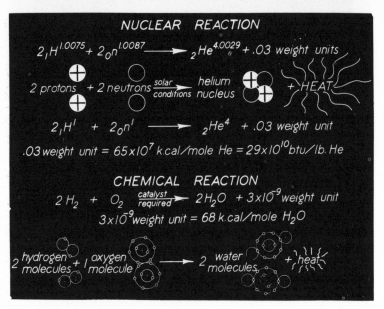

FIG. 17. A nuclear reaction, whereby the sun gets its energy, and a chemical reaction, showing the formation of water, are here compared. Note the tremendously greater energy per mole released in the nuclear reaction.

but it gives out energy at such an enormous rate that it would have to contract too fast to live long that way.

Finally, research in nuclear physics suggested the theory that subatomic action taking place in the deep interior of the sun transmutes elements, with a consequent change of matter into energy. The currently accepted mechanism is the *carbon cycle*, proposed by Hans Bethe, of Cornell University, in 1938. What occurs is a series of reactions which return to the point of starting after six steps. Carbon acts as a catalyst in changing four hydrogen nuclei into one helium nucleus. This nucleus weighs less than its original separate components; the lost mass appears as the energy by which the sun shines.

So far as the stars are concerned, this also seems to explain the energy production of those belonging to the main sequence on the spectrum-luminosity diagram [see Fig. 59]. Other explanations are needed, however, for other stellar types, but that nuclear reactions are involved there is little doubt.

Strong evidence pointing to nuclear-fission processes in the stellar universe comes from the presence of cosmic rays. These mysterious radiations (particles or photons) have very great penetrating power, much greater, indeed, than either X rays or gamma rays. They have been known to penetrate more than fifteen feet of lead. They are stronger high in the atmosphere than near the surface of the earth, and the prevailing theory

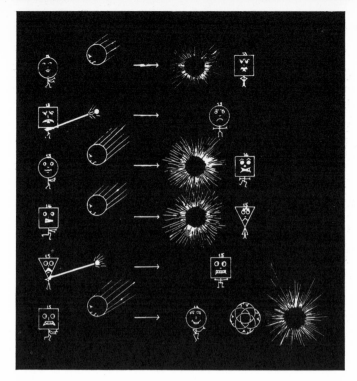

FIG. 18. The carbon cycle of solar-energy generation, as conceived by Cecilia Payne-Gaposchkin of Harvard. Carbon of atomic weight 12 is the first actor on the scene (top line, left). Hydrogen nuclei (protons) are the fast-flying fellows in acts 1, 3, 4, and 6. In the same acts, gamma-ray bursts appear, while in acts 2 and 5 positrons are ejected. Carbon 13, nitrogen 13 and 14, and oxygen 15 also take part, but in act 6, rejuvenated carbon returns to the scene along with a helium nucleus in place of the four protons used in the cycle.

is that they may result from some tremendous energy-matter transformations in the cosmos—perhaps from the bursting of super-atomic bombs on the far horizons of space. Such explosions have been observed in the bursting of the supernovae. Perhaps the cosmic rays detected on earth at the present time were ejected during vast star explosions that took place millions of years ago.

What is believed to be the debris of a supernova that burst forth in past ages may be seen through the telescope today as the famous Crab nebula in Taurus [see Fig. 90]. Comparison of photographs at long intervals shows that it is actually expanding; some 900 years ago it was probably a point of light, comparable to a star. Supporting these calculations is the record of a Chinese astronomer who observed an exceptionally bright star in that same part of the sky in the year 1054. This coincides very nicely with the theory. So here we may be viewing the debris of a tremendous cosmic bomb that burst before the days of the Norman Conquest!

The study of nuclear reactions has continued at an accelerating pace, and the military applications now include fusion reactions in the "hydrogen bomb." Unsavory as these weapons may be, the research that went into them greatly benefited astronomers' understanding of stellar interiors and led to entirely new studies. One of these is the search for neutrinos, very small uncharged particles released during the nuclear reactions shown in Figures 17 and 18. Physicists were forced to assume the ejection of neutrinos in explaining tracks of electrons shot out of some radioactive atoms. These tracks can be photographed in special cloud chambers, and they show the motions of electrons, positrons, protons, and other submicroscopic atomic nuclei that bounce off each other and "kick back" like so many elastic balls.

In several cases, the tracks showed that there must be another particle, which left no track. For instance, when a neutron ejects an electron and

TABLE 3. NUCLEAR REACTIONS RESPONSIBLE FOR ENERGY GENERATION IN THE SUN*

The PP Chain

$$H^1 + H^1 \rightarrow D^2 + \beta^+ + \nu$$
$$D^2 + H^1 \rightarrow He^3 + \gamma$$
$$He^3 + He^3 \rightarrow He^4 + 2\,H^1$$

or

$$He^3 + He^4 \rightarrow Be^7 + \gamma$$
$$Be^7 + e^- \rightarrow Li^7 + \nu + \gamma$$
$$Li^7 + H^1 \rightarrow 2\,He^4$$

or

$$Be^7 + H^1 \rightarrow B^8 + \gamma$$
$$B^8 \rightarrow Be^8 + \beta^+ + \nu$$
$$Be^8 \rightarrow 2\,He^4$$

The CNO Cycle

$$C^{12} + H^1 \rightarrow N^{13} + \gamma$$
$$N^{13} \rightarrow C^{13} + \beta^+ + \nu$$
$$C^{13} + H^1 \rightarrow N^{14} + \gamma$$
$$N^{14} + H^1 \rightarrow O^{15} + \gamma$$
$$O^{15} \rightarrow N^{15} + \beta^+ + \nu$$
$$N^{15} + H^1 \rightarrow C^{12} + He^4$$

* In some of the proton-proton series, later reactions depend on earlier ones. Greek letter symbols are β^+ (positron), γ (gamma ray), and ν (neutrino). (Table by Hubert Reeves, *Sky and Telescope*, May 1964)

turns into a proton, the kickback of the proton is not exactly opposite to the electron's track. In this way it was established that invisible neutrinos (designated by *v* in the nuclear reactions listed in Table 3) must be ejected also. That is, neutrinos should be added to the "actors" shown in Figure 18.

A large number of experiments by physicists and calculations by astronomers of the conditions inside the sun and stars showed that several other nuclear reactions might serve to convert hydrogen to helium, the most important in the sun's interior starting with the proton-proton reaction as shown in Table 3. Both this set of reactions and the CNO cycle (carbon cycle) release neutrinos, most of which pass through the outer layers of the sun and stream out through space, carrying energy with them. Because they are so small and uncharged, neutrinos pass right through matter—the whole earth, for instance—and are extremely difficult to detect. Very recently, a neutrino detector has been developed by Raymond Davis of Brookhaven National Laboratory, Long Island, New York. He uses a large tank of carbon tetrachloride in which a few of the passing solar neutrinos convert chlorine atoms to radioactive argon gas, which can be separated from the liquid carbon tetrachloride and detected in minute amounts by radioactive counters.

Large neutrino detectors with several thousand gallons of carbon tetrachloride are now being installed in underground caves and vaults where they will detect nothing else but the penetrating neutrinos and thus furnish direct evidence of nuclear reactions going on inside the sun.

—T L P

The Sun

Although it may seem antithetical to the nighttime stars, the daytime sun is just an average sort of star, close enough for detailed study. Its dominant position among the planets has been discussed in other volumes of this series (Wanderers in the Sky and The Origin of the Solar System). The fact that our sun has a system of planets is of concern here only because of its implications about the formation of the sun and of other stars like it. Such similar stars may also be accompanied by planets, and would probably look very like our sun if we could get as close a look (from 93 million miles). —TLP

Our Nearest Star, the Sun

(Sky and Telescope, March, May, July, September 1962)

All around us, enveloping the earth and reacting with its atmosphere, are atomic and subatomic particles that have their origin at the sun. We usually think of our nearest star as a heavenly body some 93 million miles away, but it is now known that solar gases fill the intervening space and that the earth is actually immersed in the extremely tenuous outer reaches of the sun's atmosphere. The solar particles make themselves known through magnetic storms, aurorae, cosmic rays, and weather phenomena, mostly in ways that are far from completely understood.

TABLE 4.   SOLAR STATISTICS

Sun's diameter	865,000 miles
Sun's mass	333,000 earths
Average density	88 pounds per cubic foot (1.4 times water density)
Surface gravity	28 times the earth's
Surface temperature	5800° Kelvin
Central temperature	15,000,000° Kelvin
Apparent magnitude	−26.9 (visual)
Absolute magnitude	+4.9 (visual)
Spectral class	dG2

Cautious visual inspection of the sun through heavily smoked glass or a very dense dark filter reveals a perfectly round disk, smooth and bright to its edges, where it seems to be sharply bounded. Although this, the *photo-*

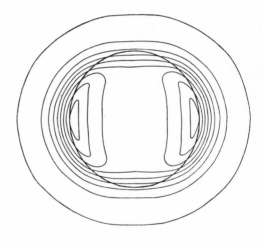

FIG. 19. Intensity contour lines indicate the general appearance of the sun at a radio wavelength of 20 centimeters. The emission is stronger near the edge of the visible disk than at its center. (Courtesy of the Radiophysics Laboratory, Sydney, Australia)

sphere, is often referred to as the solar surface, it is unlike the earth's surface in that it is completely gaseous.

Thus, the sun's apparent disk is simply the result of our being unable to see farther into the opaque hot gases that constitute the sun's main body. A similar effect can be noticed when walking through a thick fog: there always seems to be a dense wall of cloud ahead, but it is never reached because it only marks the limit of vision.

The solar disk, about half a degree in diameter, that is observed by eye is quite different from the sun as "seen" by other radiation detectors. Could our eyes view centimeter radio waves, we would see a much larger sun. It would also be somewhat elliptical. Our impression of the sun's appearance is further limited by the earth's atmosphere, which scatters the photosphere's glare into the surrounding sky and overwhelms the faint outer solar regions. Were there no scattering, we could see these outlying parts without resorting to special instruments or waiting for a total eclipse of the sun.

Lying just outside the photosphere is the *chromosphere*, named for its reddish color. Fiery wisps, called prominences, protrude from it and are often seen beyond the edge of the moon during an eclipse. Extending still farther from the sun's center is the *corona*, visible to several million miles above the photosphere at some eclipses. The corona is composed of highly ionized gases that indicate a very great temperature (millions of degrees) and of dust particles that reflect sunlight. The latter are well distributed throughout the principal plane of the solar system, forming the zodiacal light and the very dim zodiacal band in the nighttime sky.

Essentially, all the energy used today by man stems from the sun's radiation—tidal energy and nuclear reactions being the two outstanding exceptions. Since the earth intercepts only one part in 2.2 billion of the total solar radiation, it is evident that our daytime star is indeed a powerful source. The amount of energy received from the sun can be measured with a *pyrheliometer*, a heat-absorbing device. About 1/30 calorie per second falls on each square centimeter outside the earth's atmosphere. Multiplying this by the number of such areas needed to cover a sphere of radius equal to the earth-sun distance gives the total energy flowing out from the sun each second. The resulting rate is equivalent to a horsepower of 5×10^{23} (five followed by 23 zeros).

On the average, each gram of solar material releases two ergs of energy per second. (An erg is about the energy of a flying mosquito; one horse-

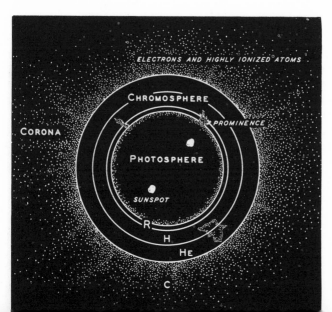

FIG. 20. The principal outer layers of the sun, depicted by University of Colorado scientists. The reversing layer is R, while in the chromosphere H stands for a predominance of hydrogen, He for helium.

power is about 7.5 billion ergs.) A high explosive, such as TNT, yields some 10^{11} ergs per gram, but only for a very short time, whereas it is fairly certain that the sun has been radiating at approximately the same rate for at least three billion years. In this period it has produced a million times the energy that could be derived chemically by blowing up an equal mass of TNT. Hence, solar energy cannot be attributed to even the most energetic chemical reactions.

Nor can the heating of the sun by contraction produce the observed radiation, although it is known that every star in the early stages of its formation obtains energy in this way. If the sun were to contract its diameter by only eighty yards a year, its present photosphere's temperature of about 5800° Kelvin could be maintained. Earlier, the shrinkage was faster, and 20 million years ago the sun would have filled the earth's orbit.

Since there is evidence that life has existed on the earth for a billion years or more, we must look to some other uniform source of radiation for very long periods. There is now no doubt that the key is given by Einstein's famous equation $E = mc^2$. This simply says that if we could transform a body of mass m into its equivalent in energy, the latter would be equal to the product of the mass and the square of the speed of light (c). For one gram, the result is 9×10^{20} ergs, since the speed of light is about 3×10^{10} centimeters per second.

The results of complete conversion of matter into energy are staggering. For example, if a teaspoon of water were annihilated in one second, it would produce nearly 600 billion horsepower, or 400,000 times the total electrical power produced in this country annually. Even in three billion years the sun has had to convert only 0.002 of its mass to produce the observed radiation. But how does it do this? The key is found within the atom, in the realm of nuclear physics, and in the solar interior, where temperatures of millions of degrees prevail.

In such a hot environment, the atoms comprising the sun are in extremely rapid motion, and incessant collisions take place. These encounters are so violent that the very cores of the atoms are damaged. Some of these nuclei are forced to expel subatomic particles, changing their weights and their electrical charges; in other words, they form new elements. This transmutation of matter has been going on in the universe of stars for countless eons; man has just very recently discovered it and learned how to exploit it in atomic and hydrogen bombs.

In one set of events, known as the *proton-proton reaction*, four hydrogen nuclei (called protons) combine to form an atom of helium [see p. 42]. . . .

In relatively cool stars like the sun, the proton-proton reaction plays an important part, but as the central temperature increases with the evolution of a star, other events can occur and release energy at even faster rates. The first series to be discovered, by Hans Bethe in 1938, is the *carbon cycle* [illustrated in Fig. 18]. Here, carbon, nitrogen, and oxygen form intermediate elements in the transformation of hydrogen to helium atoms, the carbon acting as a kind of catalyst that is recovered each time the cycle runs its course.

The tremendous energy that is produced by such reactions, deep in the interior of the sun, is in the form of gamma rays and very short X rays. It gradually works outward through the solar material, exerting pressure that keeps the sun from collapsing under the compression of its own gravity. The radiation maintains the high internal temperature and the photosphere's white heat, and finally is radiated into space over a wide range of wavelengths.

Rabbits in Siberia, tree rings, and wars, though seemingly unrelated, all have been suspected at one time or another of a connection with sunspots.

In 1610, soon after the telescope was invented, Galileo began recording these temporary dark patches on the surface of the sun. Since that time sunspots have been diligently studied by amateur and professional astronomers alike. A wealth of information about them has been gathered, but still their exact nature is puzzling.

Sunspots are about 2000° centigrade cooler than the surrounding photosphere. Their temperature is therefore far greater than white-hot steel, and they look dark only by contrast with their even brighter surroundings. Often occurring in groups, sunspots are rarely seen close to the sun's equator, and almost never in solar latitudes higher than 45° north and south. The lifetime of an average small sunspot is less than a day, but larger ones last longer. About half of all groups persist for two weeks or more.

A sunspot first appears as a small dark pore in the brilliant surface of the sun. Originally one or two thousand miles in diameter, it grows rapidly if it survives, in exceptional cases becoming nearly 100,000 miles across. Normally, two spots appear together in almost the same latitude, but as far as 50,000 miles apart. As they develop, each may become surrounded by a number of lesser spots, the original pair and their retinues being defined as a single group.

The western end of such a group, leading as the sun rotates, usually becomes dominated by a single large spot, while the trailing eastern end is often a clustering of smaller ones. As the group decays, the leader may remain visible after the others have vanished.

A well-developed spot has a dark umbra, or inner part, surrounded by a lighter penumbra. In some cases the penumbra is encircled by a bright ring,

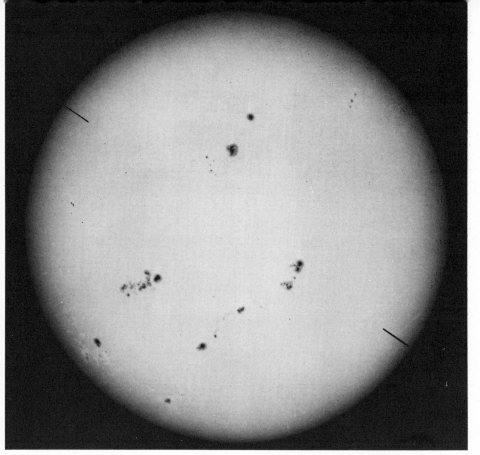

FIG. 21. On August 14, 1960, Philip J. Del Vecchio photographed the sun
with a 2.4-inch refractor, using a fine-grain direct positive film for this 1/1400-
second exposure. The axis of the sun is marked with ink lines, and the tendency
of sunspots to occur in definite belts in middle latitudes is clearly seen. The
American sunspot number for this day was 237. (Courtesy Philip J. Del
Vecchio)

FIG. 22. Sunspots filmed by Jean Dragesco on July 18, 1961, with a 10-inch
reflector. He projected the image through a red filter and ½-inch Plössl ocular
onto Kodak Microfile film for the 1/1000-second exposure. As this group was
near the solar limb, the spots appear foreshortened. (Courtesy Jean Dragesco)

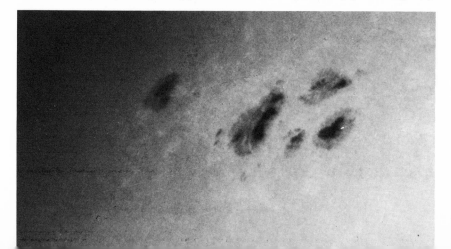

even lighter than the photosphere, and sometimes bright bridges cross the dark interior. Structure has long been observed in the penumbra, but only recently have observations from high-altitude stations and balloons made it possible to record detail within the umbra.

Even casual observations of the same sunspot on several successive days will show it steadily progressing across the disk. Evidently, the sun is slowly rotating, counterclockwise as viewed from the north. The sun does not turn as a rigid body, however. Instead, the period increases from the equator northward and southward. It is 25.0 days at the equator, 25.4 at latitude 15°, 26.3 at 30°, and 27.7 days at 45°. . . .

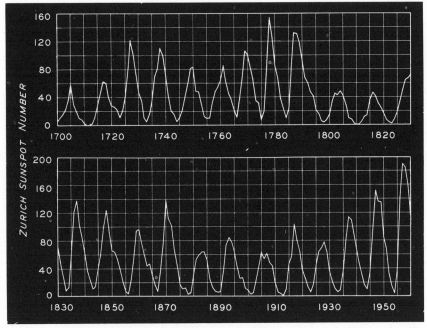

FIG. 23. Yearly mean sunspot numbers from 1700 to 1960. In 1962 the length of the sunspot cycle was nearer ten years than eleven, and maxima were very high, increasing with each cycle. (From *The Sunspot Activity in the Years 1610–1960* by M. Waldmeier, Schulthess, Zurich, 1961)

The number of spots on the sun's surface at any one time varies greatly. Nearly continuous records have been kept since 1749, and fragmentary data go back to 1610. They clearly show that there is a periodic rise and fall in this type of solar activity with approximately an 11-year cycle, averaging some 4½ years in the rise to maximum, about 6½ in falling back to minimum spottedness. . . . At several observatories, the spottedness is determined from day to day by photographing the sun and measuring the total area of the spots on the solar disk. . . .

Studies of such records indicate that the locations of the spotted zones on the sun change with the eleven-year cycle. The early spots in a new cycle appear in higher latitudes, near 30° north and south. Subsequent spots are found closer and closer to the equator, the majority being near latitude 15° at the time of maximum. Later spots in the cycle are seen still closer to the equator, until at minimum the last of a cycle may be observed at about 8° north and south, while some forerunners of the next cycle start to be noted in high latitudes.

Beginning in 1908 George Ellery Hale and Seth B. Nicholson recorded data on the magnetic properties of sunspots. They found that in pairs of spots the magnetic polarity of the preceding spot was opposite to that of the following. Furthermore, if the preceding spots in the northern hemisphere had north polarity, those in the southern hemisphere had south polarity. The cycle that reached a maximum in 1917 showed just this arrangement.

The next cycle, however, displayed reversed polarities. Preceding spots in the north had south polarity, those in the south had north. Subsequent observations have shown a general reversal of polarity with the start of each new spot cycle. Thus, the period of the magnetic alternation is about twenty-two years.

The eleven-year cycle has important effects upon our planet. Among the best established solar-terrestrial relationships are those involving changes in the earth's magnetic field, properties of the upper atmosphere, and the frequency of auroras. In each case, there is a variation that goes hand in hand with the eleven-year cycle of solar activity.

Less certain are attempts to trace corresponding cycles in weather phenomena. The meteorology of the lower atmosphere is so complex that true correlations are hard to unmask. Even less direct effects have been proposed. It has been suggested that the rabbit population of Siberia, the quality of pelts from fur-bearing animals, the stock market, and the occurrence of wars may be correlated with sunspots.

Strictly speaking, none of the terrestrial changes mentioned are caused by sunspots themselves; even in the bona-fide cases of sun-caused periodicities, we should look rather to the general solar activity, of which the sunspots are only one manifestation.

With conventional methods, such as eyepiece projection of the sun's image, an observer can record sunspots but is unable to see a great deal of other solar activity. The bright glare of the photosphere produces scattered light in our sky that masks faint details in the atmosphere of the sun.

The solar spectrum consists of a bright continuous rainbowlike background, called the continuum, upon which are superimposed many dark Fraunhofer lines. These are caused by the absorption of light in cooler gases just above the photosphere where the continuum originates.

To watch the activity of these gases, our view must be limited to a narrow range of wavelengths that includes one of the stronger Fraunhofer lines. By limiting the span of wavelengths in this way, we reduce the continuum's unwanted glare and accentuate the visibility of solar features that either emit or absorb that spectral line selectively.

Several instruments can be used to isolate the desired wavelengths. Many large solar observatories use the spectroheliograph—a spectrograph specially arranged to scan the sun's image with a moving slit. More convenient for small observatories and amateurs is a monochromator, a telescope accessory containing a narrow-band filter.

Usually these instruments are designed for the hydrogen-alpha line at a wavelength of 6563 angstrom units. In this deep crimson light, the sun's face appears mottled. On the lumpy-looking surface (which is actually at a level well above the photosphere) may be seen many dark scratchy lines, bright patches, and some dark spots. From time to time a small area may flash to temporary brilliance, often attaining as much as ten times the intensity of its surroundings.

The dark, irregular lines are *filaments*, the bright patches *faculae*. The latter are better observed in the violet light of calcium but can also be seen in white light near the sun's limb. The sudden brightenings are called *flares*, and may become so bright that they can be seen without a monochromator, but this is very rare.

Faculae, like sunspots, are indicators of solar activity. They are, however, longer lived—often appearing before spots do in a particular region and lasting long after the spots have disappeared. They develop and decay slowly; a facular region has never been observed to disappear suddenly.

In or near the active areas delineated by faculae and spots, flares may occur. These are circular if they are small, but the more extended ones assume wispy irregular shapes. Classified by size, flares range from importance 3+, covering more than 1200 millionths of the visible hemisphere, to importance 1−, those less than 100 millionths. In addition, *microflares* are observed, extremely small but with intensities comparable to larger ones. They are, perhaps, the most numerous of all; at Pic du Midi Observatory, B. Lyot recorded seventeen of them in one hour.

Flares are more frequent when solar activity is at a high level. To predict approximately the daily number of flares of importance 1, 2, and 3, multiply the sunspot number by 0.044, 0.015, and 0.002, respectively. Thus, with a sunspot number of 150, we should expect about nine of these flares per day, two of which would be of importance 2.

A typical flare reaches maximum brilliance in five to ten minutes, then begins a slower decline that may last as long as an hour or more. Sometimes the same area will again brighten several hours or days later.

Since 1956, measurements of X rays have been made from above the earth's atmosphere during a number of flares. These studies have shown that solar X rays increase with flaring, the largest flares producing the shortest wavelengths.

In addition to spewing energy into space, flares seem to propagate some sort of a disturbance parallel to the solar surface. Moving pictures show how filaments are affected as the disturbance spreads outward from a flare.

By inserting an occulting screen in the light path of a monochromator to block the brilliant solar disk, we can see the fainter prominences that at the sun's limb often extend outward from the chromosphere into the corona. Although they may not appear to move, time-lapse motion pictures show complex internal streaming and extensive changes in their overall shapes.

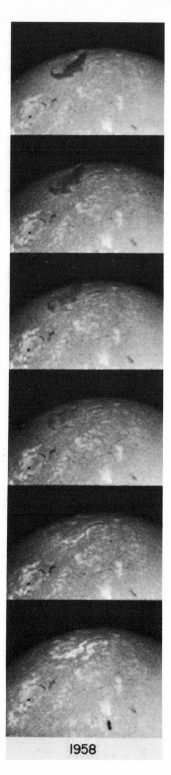

FIG. 24. Less than 1½ hours separate the top and bottom frames in this series from the flare-patrol records of Sacramento Peak Observatory on September 1, 1959. In the top two pictures a large dark filament is seen near the sun's edge, but it fades out quickly in the middle frames. However, in an adjoining region of the sun a strong flare (importance 2+) appears, seen in the lowest picture as a pair of bright sinuous filaments. (Courtesy Sacramento Peak Observatory)

1958

It was noticed many years ago that there seemed to be two different types of prominences. They were called *quiescent* if their general appearance was changing slowly or not at all, and *eruptive* if they showed violent action. Detailed studies with motion picture equipment have led to more extensive classification systems, and have proved that material is in motion even in the quiescent cases. . . .

Moving prominences are characterized by material becoming luminous near their tops and streaming down in majestic curves toward active areas on the sun's surface. . . .

Often, active prominences take the form of a loop or loops. These may sway back and forth or may be still, with material flowing around the loop or pouring down from the top. Moving prominences sometimes subside into the chromosphere, occasionally dissolve suddenly without any clear reason, or may fly into the corona, sometimes reaching velocities exceeding that of escape from the sun.

Since a great number of different phenomena are associated with centers of activity on the sun, it is interesting to trace the life history of a typical center.

A tiny patch (facular spot) brightens and elongates, signaling the start of a center of activity. In some cases, sunspots may appear within a few hours. By the second day the faculae have increased in size and brightness, and usually the first spot is seen near the western end of the region. The initial signs of flare activity begin between the second and fifth days, and the magnetic field that originally appeared with the faculae and became bipolar with the earliest spots begins to spread.

After five days both preceding and following spots have developed, together with a number of small ones between them. Some short-lived filaments have become visible, and flares erupt, generally between the main spots. Some of the flares may be accompanied by surges of material into the corona. A typical surge prominence begins four minutes after a flare and rushes upward to a height of some 35,000 miles in about thirteen minutes. Then it falls back along the same trajectory, the return taking twenty-four minutes.

On the eleventh day flare activity reaches a maximum and sunspot development is about complete. The size and brightness of the faculae continue to increase, however, and the magnetic field displays a variable distribution.

Some sixteen days later the faculae are still increasing in size, their brightness remaining constant. Nearly all the spots except the western one have disappeared. There are few if any flares, and a stable filament has formed on the poleward side of the faculae. At this time the magnetic flux reaches its peak.

FIG. 25. Looped prominences often contain material "raining" downward on the sun. (High Altitude Observatory photograph)

The filament continues to increase in length as the magnetic field fades, the faculae decrease in brightness, while the last of the spots disappear. After about a hundred days the faculae have dissolved, the filament reaches maximum length and is nearly parallel to the equator. Subsequently, the filament grows shorter and may drift slightly poleward. Finally, after six to nine months, the last vestige of the center of activity has vanished.

The sun radiates into surrounding space a fantastic range of wavelengths in the electromagnetic spectrum, all the way from radio waves that are 10 meters or more in length to gamma rays on the order of 10^{-14} meter (a million billion times shorter). For many years our only means of studying the sun's energy was by visible light with wavelengths around 10^{-7} meter (together with the near ultraviolet and infrared), but recently we have learned how to observe some of the other solar radiations.

Corpuscular emission from the sun—sometimes called solar cosmic rays —can convey information about our daytime star and about interplanetary space. [See Vol. 2, *Neighbors of the Earth.*] But some particles cannot penetrate the earth's atmosphere, and these must be studied with artificial satellites and space probes. Similarly, much important radiation cannot reach ground-based instruments. Short-wavelength ultraviolet light and X rays are unable to pass through the blanket of air that insulates us from space, but they can be recorded from high-altitude balloons and space platforms.

At the longwave end of the spectrum, radio energy coming from the sun was independently detected in 1942 by J. S. Hey in England and G. C. Southworth in the United States. Since then, electromagnetic waves ten million times longer than those of visible light have provided a wealth of new data.

Since the sun generates radio waves in a number of different ways, it is extremely difficult to ascertain exactly how and where a particular radiation originates. However, the signals we receive can be divided roughly into three categories: *quiet sun, slowly varying component,* and *bursts.* The first is a background radiation upon which the others are superimposed, and its intensity corresponds to a source temperature of about a million centigrade degrees. The centers of the sun's radio and optical disks coincide, but the former grows brighter toward the edge instead of becoming darker.

The existence of the slowly varying component has been deduced from statistical analyses of the received intensity of radiation. It appears to rise and fall with the sunspot cycle, and may originate in condensations of the corona above spots.

Perhaps the most interesting features of the radio sun are its bursts. Intense but relatively short-lived salvos of energy are received at nearly all radio wavelengths, particularly near the time of peak sunspot activity. They seem to be associated with flares. The complex spectra of the bursts can best be studied by recording intensities at a number of wavelengths at the same time. . . .

Several different types of solar noise bursts have been recognized:

Type I (formerly known as a noise storm) is characterized by pips over a wide range of frequencies. They have bandwidths of about four megacycles and durations of a few seconds. Some sort of large-scale oscillation of solar material probably produces them.

Type II is a fairly rare narrow-band radiation that shows a slow decrease in frequency with time—about half a megacycle in a second. It has been suggested that this type is caused by either corpuscular streams or shock waves moving outward through the solar atmosphere at some 1500 kilometers per second.

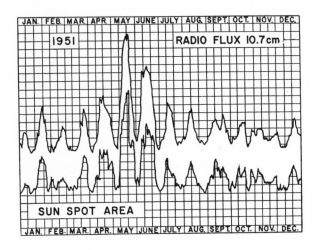

FIG. 26. The slowly varying component (top curve), recorded at 10.7 centimeters by A. E. Covington and W. J. Medd at the Canadian National Research Council, is compared with the daily average sunspot area (lower curve). (From *Journal* of the Royal Astronomical Society of Canada)

Type III bursts occur generally in groups of two or three, with a total duration of less than sixty seconds. Their rapid frequency drift (of the order of twenty megacycles each second) would correspond to particles moving with speeds around 200,000 kilometers per second, if they can be explained in a manner similar to type II.

Type IV is perhaps synchrotron radiation, like that produced by electrons moving at nearly the speed of light in man-made accelerators or in the Crab nebula. This differs from type I continuum emission in having no detailed structure and a higher frequency. It seems to appear after intense slow-drift bursts of type II, and lasts from ten to 150 minutes over a band up to thirty megacycles wide.

U bursts are named for their characteristic shape on the records. The frequency drops fairly rapidly with time, reaches a minimum, and then starts to increase again. Occurring in groups, these strange bursts are probably associated with flares.

After this summary of facts about the sun it is worthwhile to review just how some of the basic data were obtained, and to relate them to observations of the stars. It is quite difficult to compare the sun's brightness, or apparent magnitude, with that of a star some million million (10^{12}) times fainter. Star brightnesses are measured accurately relative to one another, but the precise energy—the fraction of an erg received from a star each second—has only been derived from the much greater (and more easily measured) amount of energy received from the sun, together with the measured ratio of solar brightness to star brightness described below. This huge ratio is expressed in magnitudes, each five magnitudes corresponding to 100 times fainter. That is, from solar magnitude, -26^m, to a star of magnitude $+4^m$ is $30^m = 6 \times 5^m$, and the star is $(1/100)(1/100)$ $(1/100)(1/100)(1/100)(1/100) = (1/100)^6 = 10^{-12}$ as bright as the sun.
—TLP

....

The Sun's Brightness

(*Sky and Telescope*, December 1956)

Joel Stebbins, Lick Observatory, reported recently on how he and G. E. Kron had measured the apparent magnitude, color, and temperature of the sun. These three data are of basic importance in astrophysics. Nevertheless, it is exceedingly difficult to place the sun accurately on the stellar-magnitude scale, because it is ten billion times brighter than the next brightest star, Sirius.

With a new device for reducing the sun's light by a known amount without changing its quality, and with the aid of a photoelectric cell, Stebbins and Kron first compared the sun quantitatively with a standard lamp and with an electric furnace that served as a source of black-body radiation. Then the lamp, shining through a pinhole set up on one of the peaks of Mount Hamilton, was observed with a telescope 2000 feet away, and this artificial star was compared photoelectrically for brightness and color with actual stars.

The apparent visual magnitude of the sun was found to be −26.73 on the international system, with a probable error of ±0.03, and its color index came out +0.53. The sun is actually about 10 per cent less bright than the generally accepted value, but the color index agrees exactly with that of other stars whose spectra match the sun's.

Thus, Stebbins and Kron found the sun's photovisual absolute magnitude to be +4.84—this is the apparent magnitude it would have if seen from a distance of 10 parsecs. When the color index of +0.53 is applied, the photographic absolute magnitude comes out +5.37.

Comparison of the sun with the lamp and the electric furnace at 3000° absolute suggests that the sun has a surface temperature of 6400°. On the same scale, the Lick astronomers find the temperature of the hottest blue stars, such as those in Orion, to be as high as 25,000°.

All of these results are not too different from previous determinations, but the use of the photoelectric cell has improved upon the accuracy of earlier visual and photographic methods.

The earth's atmosphere is not mentioned in this brief description, but it caused Stebbins and Kron a good deal of trouble. Both the sunlight and the starlight they measured passed through the air above Mt. Hamilton, California, but at different times. The clarity or transparency of the sky was probably changing. The amount of atmospheric absorption can be determined over a short period of time by measuring the change in brightness of the sun or a star as it rises higher or sinks lower in the sky. This has to be done for several different colors, since the air removes more blue than red from light passing through it. For this reason, too, the comparison of sun and stars with a lamp just 2000 feet away requires a color correction.

This difficulty and others can be avoided by making measurements from balloons, rockets, or artificial satellites above the earth's atmosphere. Volume 1 of this series, Wanderers in the Sky, shows (on p. 128) the improved clarity of photographs of the sun taken from a balloon at 80,000 feet, well *above winds and unsteady air. But instruments must be carried a good deal higher in order to measure all the solar radiation, unaffected by absorption in the earth's atmosphere. Ultraviolet light of wavelength 2850 A or less is completely absorbed by a layer of ozone (o_3) about seventy miles above the surface. This ozone layer was a barrier to astronomical observations of the sun's ultraviolet spectrum until about 1950, when rockets opened up a whole new field of study.* — T L P

....

Rocket Ultraviolet Solar
Spectroscopy

WILLIAM A. RENSE

(*Sky and Telescope*, August 1958)

Above the earth's blanket of air there is a vast range of radiations from the sun, moon, planets, stars, nebulae, and other celestial objects that do not penetrate the atmosphere to reach observers on the ground. These radiations often hold the key to improved understanding and new discoveries about the astronomical universe.

Rockets that carry instruments high enough to reach these radiations before they are absorbed serve as small observatories above the atmosphere that sample the intrastellar radiation. In a sense, the rocket programs represent man's first step to move his observatories spaceward.

Observations of the ultraviolet solar spectrum from rockets are an effort to unlock some of the mysteries concerning the sun's radiation at wavelengths shorter than about 2850 angstroms. An appreciable payload has to be lifted at least above the ozone layer of our atmosphere, and preferably much higher. The instruments must in some way be pointed at the sun and equipped with radio transmitters to telemeter the data they record, or must have parachute mechanisms so the records can be examined directly when the rocket has returned to earth.

Rocket research in this field got under way in 1946 when a successful flight was organized by a Naval Research Laboratory group. Since that time many other successful attempts have been made by NRL, as well as by the Air Force Cambridge Research Center (AFCRC) and the University of Colorado. . . .

The Aerobee rocket has played the major role in solar ultraviolet spectroscopy. At first, however, the V-2 and the Viking were employed, and later the Deacon, Cajun, Asp, and Loki. Early Aerobees were small, and reached about seventy miles, but two later types, Intermediate Aerobee and Aerobee-Hi, carry typical payloads to heights of around 130 miles, where their instruments can detect considerably more of the solar ultraviolet radiation. . . .

FIG. 27. An Aerobee-Hi roars upward at Holloman Air Force Base, New Mexico, as the launching tower is wreathed in smoke from the rocket's exhaust. The tower is tilted slightly to prevent a misfire from falling back on the launching site. (U.S. Air Force photograph)

Some of the rockets have a solid-fuel booster to assist starting. After take-off, this is dropped, then the rocket's liquid fuel burns out, and the missile coasts upward to the top of its trajectory. At about forty miles, where air resistance is nearly negligible, the doors on the nose cone are ejected automatically and the detecting instrument exposed.

In most experiments an electronic "sun seeker" automatically points the instrument directly at the sun. During much of this part of the flight, the rocket spins rapidly around its longitudinal axis, about once each second, and wobbles like a top (precession) in a period of about two minutes. These are the important motions the sun seeker must neutralize.

The rocket moves very slowly when near maximum height, but gains speed rapidly during descent. At this time, if film has been exposed, it is rolled up into a light-tight, shockproof cassette, and the whole instrument is automatically tucked into the nose cone. At a suitable time the nose cone is separated from the rest of the rocket by an explosion, both parts then being slowed by the denser lower air because they are aerodynamically unstable. Automatic release of a parachute provides for safe landing of the nose cone, with its instrument and sun seeker, on the desert floor. . . .

For photographing solar ultraviolet radiation from a rocket, a concave-grating spectrograph is commonly used. Sunlight passes through a slit onto the grating, where it is dispersed and focused on the film. The slit, grating, and film are all on a circle (called the Rowland circle), which has a diameter equal to the radius of curvature of the concave grating. . . .

Before the time of rocket spectroscopy, the sun's ultraviolet spectrum had been observed only down to about 2850 angstroms. The earth's lower atmosphere, especially the ozone layer, masked the spectrum beyond this point. When the first rocket pictures were taken at heights well above the ozone layer, astronomers found that down to about 2000 angstroms the spectrum was like that in the visible region—continuous radiation of the photosphere crossed by the dark Fraunhofer lines of absorption in the solar atmosphere.

An important new discovery in this region was the two emission lines in the center of the absorption lines of ionized magnesium at about 2800 angstroms. However, the continuous radiation in the 3000-to-1800-angstrom region is less than that expected from the photosphere's temperature of 6000°.

In the solar spectrum between 2650 and 2500 angstroms comparison of the dark lines with the bright ones that come from the light of an iron arc in the laboratory make it clear that many of the solar absorption lines in this spectral region are due to iron. The known wavelengths of these iron lines allow measurement of the wavelengths of all the other lines. About

1500 new lines in the solar ultraviolet are now being measured by this method.

One of the most striking features of the new spectrograms is the sudden drop in intensity in the continuum around 2000 angstroms. This effect was unexplained for some time, but it is now known to be caused mainly by the absorption by aluminum and calcium beyond their series limits. Only for these elements do the limits lie in the correct spectral region, and both metals are relatively abundant in the sun's atmosphere.

The truly exciting part of the new spectra lies below 1900 angstroms, where many emission lines occur, the most prominent being Lyman alpha of hydrogen at 1216 angstroms. The emission lines, mostly due to ions, are believed to originate in the hotter regions of the chromosphere. The spectrum of the sun is very faint in the accompanying spectrogram of this region [Fig. 29], and it contains absorption as well as emission lines.

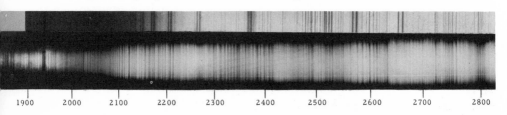

FIG. 28. The upper spectrum (negative) is of impure aluminum, photographed in the laboratory. The lower spectrum (positive) is of the sun; the weakening around 2000 angstroms appears to be partly caused by aluminum vapor in the solar atmosphere. Calcium vapor also contributes to this effect. (University of Colorado spectrogram)

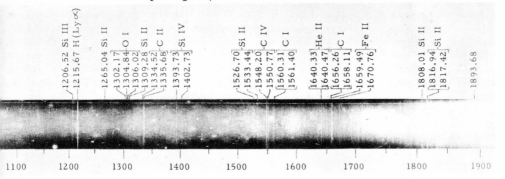

FIG. 29. The solar spectrum between 1100 and 1900 angstroms, photographed from an Aerobee-Hi rocket on August 6, 1957, at an altitude of about 150 kilometers. This 89-second exposure shows many identified emission lines, due to hydrogen, helium, carbon, oxygen, silicon, and iron. (In a June 1958 flight, the spectrum was photographed to wavelengths as short as 100 angstroms.) (University of Colorado spectrogram)

The half width of the Lyman-alpha (Ly α) line is about one angstrom, an important finding astrophysically because it indicates something of the temperatures, pressures, and depths of the hydrogen layers that emit this radiation. Photographic and photon-counter intensity measurements indicate that Lyman alpha may vary during the sunspot cycle. Values from 0.1 to 6 ergs per square centimeter per second have been measured. This line's intensity may also depend on the day-to-day aspect of the solar disk, varying by a factor of as much as two or three.

In Figure 30 the left photograph shows the sun in Lyman-alpha light, photographed by a specially designed rocket camera with lithium-fluoride optics. The center and right views, taken at McMath-Hulbert Observatory on the same day as the rocket picture, show the sun in ionized calcium light at 3934 angstroms (the K line) and Balmer hydrogen-alpha at 6563 angstroms, respectively. It will be seen that enhanced Lyman-alpha radiation occurs in those areas that contain hydrogen-alpha and ionized-calcium plages [bright areas in the chromosphere, in regions of sunspots].

If we take as an average value three ergs per square centimeter per second for the intensity of Lyman-alpha radiation, a simple calculation shows that this is about two millionths of the total solar-energy output in the visible region. Small as this is, however, solar Lyman alpha may play an important role in some phenomena of the earth's upper atmosphere, such as the formation of ionization layers, because such shortwave energy has strong ionizing powers. . . .

Until June 4, 1958, there was a gap in the data from a little below 1000 angstroms down to the soft X-ray region. Rockets had not been able to

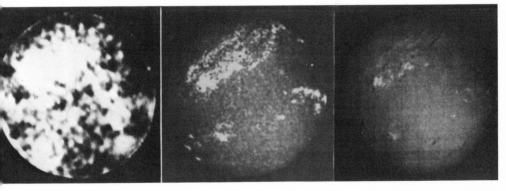

FIG. 30. Three views of the sun, in far-ultraviolet, violet, and red light, in which the same active region of the solar surface can be recognized. At the left is a rocket-camera photograph in Lyman-alpha light at 1216 angstroms. (University of Colorado) The other two photographs (courtesy McMath-Hulbert Observatory) are spectroheliograms in ionized-calcium light at 3934 angstroms (center) and in hydrogen-alpha radiation at 6563 angstroms (right).

carry suitable instruments high enough to be clear of the heavy absorption effects of the molecular nitrogen in the atmosphere. Also, spectrographs become much less sensitive in this range, requiring longer exposures and a reduction in the background of scattered light. (Photon counters cannot be used because no window materials transparent at these wavelengths are known.)

Astrophysicists had predicted interesting possibilities for this region. For example, that there might be some very intense lines originating in the solar corona. They expected that strong lines of neutral and ionized helium would be present, and that the Lyman continuum stretching below 912 angstroms might be detectable.

Then on June 4, the University of Colorado group successfully flew (in an Aerobee-Hi rocket) a specially designed grazing-incidence spectrograph that closed the gap between 1000 and 100 angstroms. A strong He II line at 303.8 angstroms was photographed. This is the resonance line in the spectrum of ionized helium that corresponds to hydrogen Lyman alpha. The He I resonance line at 584 angstroms is very weak compared to He II at 303.8.

It was with some surprise that rocket spectroscopists, by means of special photon counters, had measured appreciable amounts of solar X rays between 1 and 100 angstroms. Most of this occurs between 40 and 100 angstroms, is fairly constant, and is observed on all occasions. But the emission at shorter wavelengths is more variable in character; for example, at *very* short wavelengths it is much stronger at the time of solar flares.

A large part of the sun's X-ray emission corresponds to that of a gray body at 500,000° absolute, but the X-ray flux at very short wavelengths may at times indicate as high as 4,000,000°. These results are not completely explained, although the corona, with its high temperatures and highly ionized atoms, may be a source. Cosmic rays are known to be emitted by the sun, and X rays are likely to be associated with them. . . .

....

Ultraviolet Radiation from Solar Activity Centers

(*Sky and Telescope*, August 1963)

Following its launching on March 7, 1962, NASA's orbiting solar observatory operated continuously for sixty-six days, then intermittently for the rest of last year. Among the equipment its stabilized platform carried was a scanning monochromator that recorded the solar spectrum in the extreme ultraviolet, between 50 and 400 angstroms.

Each scan of this spectral range took eight minutes; between six and seven thousand spectra were gathered in all. Iron lines were prominent at 284 and 335 angstroms and a strong helium line was observed at 304 angstroms.

From a study of about one third of the spectra, W. M. Neupert of NASA's Goddard Space Flight Center found that increases in ultraviolet flux can be traced to bright areas in sunspot regions (plages). The development of plages was followed through nearly three solar rotations. The enhancement varied from line to line, the greatest flux increases being associated with the lines of Fe XV and Fe XVI (iron atoms that have lost 14 and 15 electrons, respectively).

The intensity ratio of these lines was found to be nearly constant, however. Using this ratio, the Goddard scientist derived a coronal temperature of 1,750,000° K for the quiet sun (at a time when the relative sunspot number is zero). The probable error of this temperature is ±100,000°, arising mainly from the uncertainty in calibration.

Solar Physics News

OTTO STRUVE

(*Sky and Telescope*, September 1962)

At California Institute of Technology, R. B. Leighton and his associates R. W. Noyes and G. W. Simon have spent the last several years developing a powerful new method of studying motions of material in the sun's atmosphere. . . .

Here is another instance of how an important and exciting new astronomical idea had to be followed by a long period of almost routine work to exploit the advance. In solar physics, the past few years have seen several breakthroughs. Among these have been Martin Schwarzschild's balloon-borne telescopes and the Naval Research Laboratory's work on the extreme ultraviolet radiation of the sun by means of rockets and artificial satellites. . . .

The Pasadena workers used a familiar instrument, a Hale spectroheliograph, attached to the 65-foot tower telescope on Mount Wilson. In the

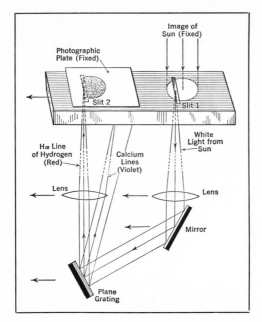

FIG. 31. How a spectrohelio-graph works is shown schematically. At upper right, the image formed by a long-focus telescope is scanned by Slit 1. The scanning motion is shared by the lenses, mirror, grating, and Slit 2. A monochromatic image of the sun builds up on the fixed photographic plate. The picture is taken at a wavelength selected by adjusting Slit 2. (From *Astronomy* by W. T. Skilling and R. S. Richardson, Holt, New York, 1939 and 1947; courtesy Holt, Rinehart and Winston)

ordinary operation of a spectroheliograph (Fig. 31), the sun's image is focused on the slit, and a prism or grating produces a spectrum in the focal plane of the camera. A narrow second slit placed just in front of the photographic plate, is adjusted to block out all but a narrow strip of the spectrum, usually admitting only the violet K line of calcium or the red H-alpha line of hydrogen. The two slits and the dispersing unit are driven at a suitable scanning speed across the solar image, which remains stationary, as does the photographic plate.

Used in this conventional manner, the spectroheliograph records the difference in brightness of various solar features at a selected wavelength. It does not indicate (except indirectly) differences in line-of-sight velocity. . . .

Leighton and his associates have added some special features to the Mount Wilson spectroheliograph (Fig. 32). One is a beam splitter, whose purpose is to produce two simultaneous spectroheliograms. With it they employ a line shifter, which has two glass blocks that may be tilted in opposite directions by equal amounts. Usually, the blocks are adjusted so that one solar image is produced by the red wing of a Fraunhofer line (say 0.1 angstrom from the line center), while the other image is produced by the violet wing.

A positive transparency is made of the first-mentioned of the two images and superposed on the negative of the other (from the violet wing). The gradations in brightness, for example of solar faculae, are practically identi-

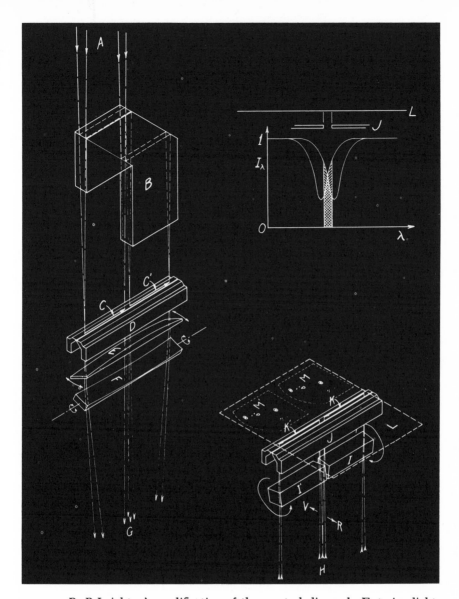

FIG. 32. R. B Leighton's modification of the spectroheliograph. Entering light, A, traverses beam splitter, B, to form duplicate images, C, C'. Following the entrance slit, D, are lenses, E and F, to correct tilt and curvature. The split light beam then goes to the collimator and grating; at lower right it returns from the camera lens. Two monochromatic solar images, M, M', at slightly different wavelengths, are formed simultaneously on the fixed plate, L, by light, H, that has passed through two glass blocks, I, I', and the second slit, J. At upper right cross-hatched areas show portions of the spectrum-line profiles that reach plate L through slit J. (California Institute of Technology diagram)

cal on the two original negatives, and therefore cancel out when the positive is placed over the negative. The superimposed pair would show no structure, appearing uniformly gray, provided there were no radial velocity differences on the sun. But any Doppler effect [see p. 137] would shift the spectrum and the absorption line. For example, if a particular area were receding, its light in the violet image would come from farther out in the line's wing and be brighter, while in the red image the area would be represented by the fainter light nearer the line's center (Fig. 33). The superimposed positive and negative therefore show a denser-than-average region when the motion is away from the observer, and lighter than average where the radial velocity is of approach.

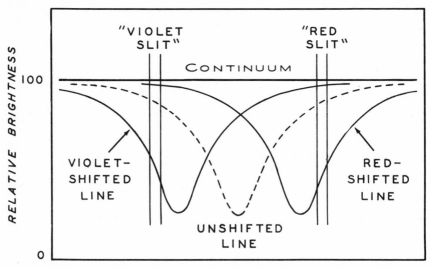

FIG. 33. The dashed curve is the profile of a solar absorption line; solid curves show the profile as displaced in approaching and receding areas of the sun's disk. Note, in each case, the relative intensities passing the slit in its two positions. Compare with the explanation in the text of how a "canceled" plate is made.

A good demonstration is provided by Figure 34, a typical "canceled" photograph of the sun in the wings of the calcium line at 6103 angstroms. Here the sun's axial rotation is strikingly demonstrated by the east-west density gradient across the disk. But for further investigation it is better to suppress this strong gradient. For this the authors used a *line tilter*, a double-convex lens that compensates for the slanting of the spectral lines caused by solar rotation. A recent photograph, corrected in this manner, is Figure 35.

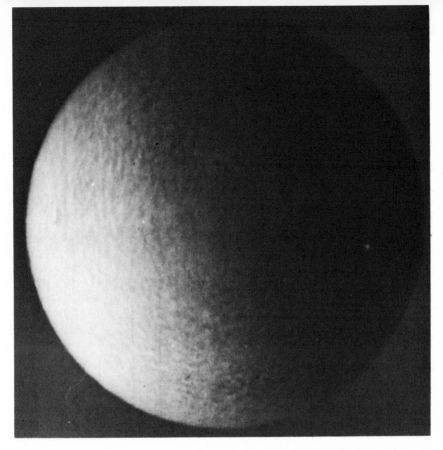

FIG. 34. Solar rotation is dramatically shown in this "canceled" plate taken on June 25, 1960, at the Mount Wilson Observatory. The approaching part of the solar disk appears bright, the receding part dark, in this superposition of a positive and negative spectroheliogram. (*Astrophysical Journal* engraving, courtesy Mount Wilson and Palomar Observatories and the University of Chicago Press)

Here the sun's disk appears overspread with mottled dark and light patches many thousands of kilometers in size. In the center region they are mostly absent, just where motions vertical to the sun's surface would produce the greatest Doppler effect. Toward the solar limb, however, where our line of sight is more nearly parallel to the photosphere, the mottling becomes quite pronounced. Evidently the large-scale motions of the gas are predominantly horizontal over the sun, with bright areas in this picture indicating material approaching us, dark areas that which is receding.

We notice that the brightest and darkest areas seem to form pairs, with the dark ones always on the side away from the sun's center. Evidently, these are enormous cells, gas flowing outward from the center of each cell

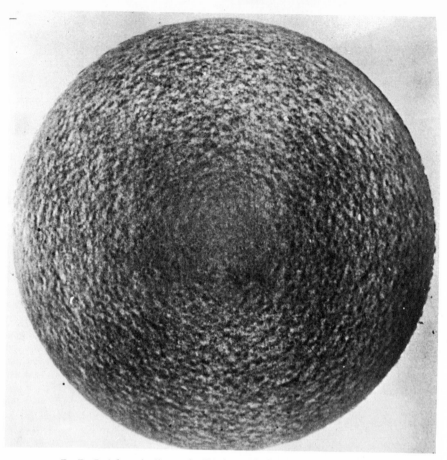

FIG. 35. R. B. Leighton's "canceled" plate of the sun on June 10, 1962, was prepared with the line-tilter lens in place, thereby removing the effects of solar rotation. This makes visible a disk-wide pattern of approaching (bright) and receding (dark) currents of gas. Note what Leighton calls supergranules, cells having bright parts toward the sun's center and dark edges toward the limb. Motions are parallel to the solar surface, hence do not show in the middle of the disk.

to its edge; the cells appear elongated because of foreshortening as we look at them slantwise toward the sun's limb. A typical large cell of this "supergranulation" has a lifetime of several hours, according to Leighton and his co-workers. They have succeeded in pictorially recording the large-scale velocity fields reported by A. B. Hart in 1956, and for the entire solar surface instead of only the equatorial latitudes to which her work had applied.

The new studies also help explain the dynamics of the brightness-velocity correlation of solar granulation. They confirm previous findings by others that brighter elements move upward in the lower levels of the atmosphere. When a pair of plates taken with the 17-centimeter solar image of the 65-foot tower are compared, the image from the red side of the line profile always has more contrast in its small-scale features than does the one taken on the violet side. . . .

But the small-scale motions give a very different result, illustrated in the lower right panel of Figure 36. This is a doubly canceled plate, and near its left edge there is the expected featureless gray appearance; the pattern

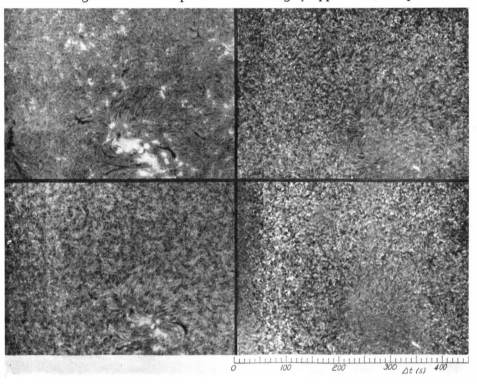

FIG. 36. A method of studying rapid changes in solar velocity fields is presented in these Leighton photographs. At the upper left is an ordinary spectroheliogram, taken in the core of the hydrogen-alpha line. Below it is a similar picture, but at a wavelength 0.35 angstrom longer. At upper right is a "canceled" plate formed by combining this second picture with another at a shorter wavelength; the black-and-white rice-grain pattern shows small-scale rising and falling motions. At lower right is a doubly canceled plate, the $\triangle$t scale marking for each part of the picture the number of seconds that elapsed between occurrences of the velocities being compared. Here, gray indicates that the velocity is little changed after the lapse of $\triangle$t seconds, while pronounced rice-grain pattern means a large change.

of vertically moving material can hardly have changed much between the end of the first run of the slits and the beginning of the return run. But the gray is replaced by a prominent rice-grain effect when about a minute has elapsed between exposures, indicating that the velocities have changed drastically and can no longer be suppressed by the double cancellation. These hydrogen cells evidently have very short lives. . . .

Undoubtedly, these fluctuations, best seen near the center of the sun's disk, are connected with the previously known up-and-down motions of the solar granules and of the material in the spaces between them. The amplitude of the oscillations is about 0.4 kilometer per second and decays rapidly, but in some cases three complete cycles can be observed before the motion becomes too small to be recorded. The characteristic lifetime of such motions is 400 seconds, and the areas involved are some two or three thousand kilometers in extent, with smaller elements at lower atmospheric levels.

The measurements reported by Leighton and his co-workers are in quite satisfactory agreement with results by other investigators who have measured photographs of solar granulation or high-dispersion spectrograms. The authors note: "The presentation of the data in *pictorial form* has proved of great value in discovering important qualitative relationships which have heretofore been hidden from us."

It is this pictorial form of presentation that is especially intriguing and finds other useful applications in astrophysics. Many variable stars have been discovered by superposing two photographs of the same star field, one a positive and the other a negative, taken at different times. . . .

Brightness

and

Luminosity

....

From the brightest object in the sky we turn (on the rotating earth) at nightfall to stars that are fainter by 25 magnitudes and more—by a factor of over ten billion (see p. 58). This striking contrast is partly explained by distance, which has a powerful effect on brightness (p. 25). There are two other simple reasons for different brightnesses of stars: (1) there may be obscuring material between us and faint stars, and (2) the stars may differ intrinsically; that is, they would be brighter or fainter than the sun if placed side by side with it. This intrinsic brightness is called "luminosity," L, and can best be measured in units called "suns." That is, $L = 0.5$ refers to a star half as bright as the sun. Luminosity can also be expressed in magnitudes (see p. 30).

In order to find the true luminosities of the stars, the effects of their different distances and of different amounts of obscuring material must be removed from measurements of their brightnesses. A great deal of progress has been made over the past thirty years, both in the accuracy of brightness measurement and in sorting out the effects of distance and obscuration. One of the results of such studies is a knowledge of the sizes of stars— their diameters in miles. — T L P

73

■■

Little Stars and Big Ones

C. A. FEDERER, JR.

(*The Sky*, September 1937)

. . . Let us look up at the night sky as if we were the first human beings to see it. First, we see thousands of tiny points of light which differ from each other only in brightness and color. None of them seems to move, so we call them "fixed." . . .

With the aid of the telescope, the spectroscope, and other instruments, astronomers now tell us definite facts about the distances of the stars, their motions, their masses, their temperatures, and their physical and chemical constitutions. But the crowning achievement of all has been the measurement of the sizes of the stars. All the other facts have just been stepping stones in securing this final result. Every bit of knowledge which has been obtained, and every thought process has played its part in leading to the answer to the question men have asked each other for centuries, How large are the stars? . . .

The sun is the only star in the sky which appears to us as more than just a point of light. It owes its greater apparent size to its nearness. The true disk of no other star can be seen in the largest of existing telescopes. Present telescopes make the stars appear brighter, but do not magnify them so as to make them appear larger. . . .

Because of its nearness, we have been able to measure the size of the sun directly. It is about 864,000 miles in diameter, which makes it occupy over a million times the volume of the earth. However, it is just an average-size star. Like all stars, the sun is so hot at its surface that it is incandescent. Its great temperature prevents it from solidifying, so instead of being, like the earth, partly solid and partly liquid, it is in a gaseous condition throughout. We believe it is shining at the expense of the material of which it is composed; about five million tons of its mass are being converted into energy each second. Yet it is so large that it may go on expending light and heat at this rate for thousands of millions of years in the future.

Stars are like the lights of a city as seen from a mountain top. Some are brighter than others; some are near, some far away. Along a boulevard, where the street lamps are probably all of the same brightness, or candlepower, those which are farthest from the observer appear faintest. But an isolated light far beyond the end of the same street may appear brighter than any of those nearer because its actual luminosity is many times greater. Thus, the apparent brightness of a luminous object depends on two things, its distance and its real brightness. . . .

Astronomers refer to real brightness as absolute magnitude. Sirius is twenty-six times as luminous as the sun. Canopus, although it appears fainter than Sirius in the sky, is at least 40,000 times as luminous as the sun. But the companion of Sirius, a very strange star, is only 1/300 the sun's brightness. It is found that there is an astonishing difference in the luminosities of the stars. Some are actually a million times brighter than others. When this was discovered, Hertzsprung suggested that we call the stars of great luminosity *giants*, and the faint ones *dwarfs*. These names have stuck. While not originally intended to convey any reference to the actual sizes of the stars, because their sizes were not then known, we shall see that they are well named in this respect, too.

What about that other characteristic of the stars which we observed on our first sight of them? Can their colors tell us anything that will help in measuring them? Strange as it may seem, the answer is Yes. Have you ever watched a piece of metal being heated in a forge? First, it is cold and dark. Then, as its temperature rises, it glows a dull red. The red turns to an orange or yellow color, and then, when the metal is hottest, it is white, or even blue. There are stars in the sky corresponding to each of these colors. Antares is red; Arcturus is orange; Capella and the sun are yellow; Sirius is white; while Spica is blue white. Does this indicate that the surfaces of some stars are hotter than others? We believe it does.

Several independent methods of studying the colors and the spectra of the stars confirm this conclusion. The spectroscope plays a very important part here. Blue stars have surface temperatures of 44,000° Fahrenheit or about 25,000° centigrade. White stars are at about 11,000°C; yellow stars, like the sun, about 6000°C; while the red stars have comparatively cool surfaces, about 3000°C. But here on the earth this last is considered a very high temperature indeed, and we do not wonder that even the red stars are shining brightly.

From this it is evident that the color of a glowing surface, be it on earth, or on a star, is a result of its temperature. But the temperature also determines something else. The radiator in your home is useless until it becomes hot. The amount of heat it radiates into the room depends directly upon its temperature. When the sides of a stove burning wood or coal become red hot they radiate heat very rapidly. This principle of heat radiation, too, will help us to measure the stars.

By the color of a star we have been able to tell its surface temperature, and by this temperature we can compute the amount of light and heat it radiates from each part of its surface. The actual figures astound us. Each square foot of the sun's surface is constantly radiating energy equal to 8000 horsepower. The total radiation over its whole surface is so enormous we cannot really comprehend it, but we can express it—in horsepower it is the number five followed by twenty-three ciphers.

We are now ready to draw our conclusion from the foregoing facts—to estimate the sizes of many of the stars. Let us use the famous star Capella as an example. This is really a double star; its color is the same as that of the sun—spectral class G [see Chapter 3], so we may assume its surface temperature to be 6000° centigrade, and its radiation per unit area equal to the sun's. But from measurements of its distance and its apparent magnitude, we find that the real brightness of one of the two stars composing it, which we may call Capella A, is 150 times that of the sun. Therefore, in order to achieve such a great total luminosity, this star, Capella A, must have 150 times the surface area of the sun. This means that its diameter is twelve times the sun's or about ten million miles. It occupies a volume over 2 billion times that of our tiny earth.

In a similar fashion the red stars Antares and Betelgeuse, already called giants because of their high luminosity, are found to be "supergiants" in size. Antares is actually one of the brightest stars near the sun. But its red color indicates low temperature and low radiation per unit of its surface area. For it to shine so brightly, then, its total surface must be enormous. Its calculated diameter is 400 million miles. It is 100 million times the size of the sun!

Hardly less remarkable is the extremely low density of such red giants. Antares averages about 1/3000 the density of the air around us—it would be considered a good vacuum here on the earth. Comparison with the companion of Sirius made it seem almost incredible that they could both be stars. Sirius' companion is a white star, and thus has a high temperature and great radiation per unit area of its surface. Yet it is very faint, so the only way to reconcile its color with its low luminosity is to conclude that it must be very small. Its diameter is probably only 30,000 miles—no greater than that of Uranus. It is called a white dwarf, at the other extreme from the red giants on the density scale. A cubic inch of the material of the companion of Sirius weighs a ton!

When the densities of the red giants and the white dwarfs were first determined in this way, they seemed so paradoxical that doubt was thrown on the validity of this method of calculating stellar diameters. But, fortunately, support for both extreme cases came just when it was needed.

The enormous sizes of Antares and Betelgeuse were confirmed by measurements of their actual apparent diameters with the 20-foot interferometer attached to the 100-inch reflecting telescope at Mount Wilson Observatory. A 50-foot interferometer is now being used, and has given us measures of some of the lesser giants. The interferometer measurements are based on principles almost entirely independent of those used in calculating stellar diameters.

Confirmation of the great density of the companion of Sirius comes from its spectrum, the dark lines of which are shifted considerably toward the red. The amount of this shift is predicted by the theory of relativity, and should be greatest for the densest stars. How the numerous paths of scientific research meet, how they lead us to the truth, is revealed here again! One of the tests of Einstein's famous theory is also proof of the validity of the process by which astronomers learn that there are both little stars and big ones.

The two methods described by Federer remained as the only ones for measuring the diameters of stars until very recently. The first, most widely used, depends on measurement of the surface temperature and the total luminosity of a star in all colors or wavelengths of the ultraviolet, visible light, infrared, and longer wavelengths it radiates. For an ideal hot body, theory and laboratory experiments show that the luminosity, L, should be related to the surface temperature, T, and the surface area $4\pi R^2$ (where R is the radius of the star) by the Stefan-Boltzmann equation, $L = 4\pi R^2 \sigma T^4$. The constant σ is known, so the radius of a star can be calculated from L and T.

The Michelson 20-foot interferometer can be used to measure the angular size of a star image by adjusting two mirrors reflecting light from the same star into a telescope (Fig. 38) so that "fringes" in the star image disappear. These fringes—dark bands across the fuzzy star image—are caused by interference of the light waves coming to the image by two different routes from a point source. The size of the star in effect provides two point sources—its two half disks separated by about one star radius—and when the mirror separation is correct, the two fringe patterns fill each other in. As noted in the following article, this method has been successful on only six large nearby stars. —T L P

....

The Stellar Interferometer
at Narrabri Observatory

R. HANBURY BROWN

(Sky and Telescope, August 1964)

During the past few years a novel type of astronomical instrument—a stellar intensity interferometer—has been under development at Narrabri Observatory in Australia. Its purpose is to measure the apparent angular sizes of stars.

FIG. 37. A new type of astronomical instrument—an intensity interferometer—has been built at Narrabri Observatory in Australia. Here, standing on the movable carriage of one of two 22-foot reflector arrays, are (right) R. Hanbury Brown, University of Sydney, and E. P. Ney, University of Minnesota, who assisted in the program. (University of Sydney photograph)

If we determine the angular diameter of a star, then from its parallax we can calculate its physical size, and from its light flux its temperature can be deduced. Both size and temperature are of fundamental importance to stellar astronomy, and in particular, to understanding stellar structure. Our present knowledge of the sizes is mostly indirect, gained from theoretical models or from observations of eclipsing binaries. However, for a very few stars direct angular-diameter measurements have been made, and astronomy textbooks usually quote the results for six stars observed with the 20-foot Michelson interferometer on the 100-inch telescope at Mount Wilson about forty years ago. The resolving power of that interferometer was limited by the maximum separation of its mirrors to about 0.02 second of arc. Consequently, all six stars are relatively large, cool, and nearby.

In a subsequent Mount Wilson attempt to extend the measurements to more stars, a larger instrument was built, with a maximum separation between the mirrors of 50 feet, but it was not successful and observations were discontinued about 1930.

If we inquire why this work was not carried further, we find two major difficulties in extending the resolving power of Michelson's interferometer. Figure 38A shows a simplified outline of the instrument. Light from the star reaches the observer by reflection at two separate mirrors, M_1 and M_2, and forms an interference pattern of alternate bright and dark bands crossing the focal image of the star. The angular diameter of the star is measured by separating the two mirrors until this interference pattern disappears. The diameter in radians is approximately equal to the wavelength of light divided by the spacing between the mirrors.

The first difficulty in designing a very large Michelson interferometer is the requirement that the light paths via the two mirrors must be very precisely equal: roughly speaking, they should differ by less than a wavelength. In practice, this requirement sets such stringent limits to any differences in flexure and thermal expansion between the two arms of the instrument, and demands such precise guiding, that a large instrument is both difficult and expensive to construct.

The second obstacle is the fact that the interference pattern is not stationary in the focal plane. Atmospheric scintillations introduce random and very rapid phase changes in the light paths from the star to the two mirrors, thereby distorting and displacing the pattern. This makes the instrument very difficult to use and demands extremely steady seeing.

Probably an improved version of the Michelson interferometer could now be built by using modern devices such as narrow-band filters and photoelectric detectors. Nevertheless, it is uncertain how to overcome atmospheric scintillation, nor does it seem likely that an instrument of reasonable cost could be built with sufficient resolving power to measure the very small disks of the hot stars of types O and B.

Both of these major limitations of the Michelson interferometer are avoided in the *intensity interferometer* (Fig. 38B). Light from a star is received on two separate mirrors, M_1 and M_2, and is focused on photoelectric detectors D_1 and D_2. The output currents of these detectors contain a steady, or DC, component, which is rejected, together with a fluctuating, or AC, component extending over a wide range of frequencies.

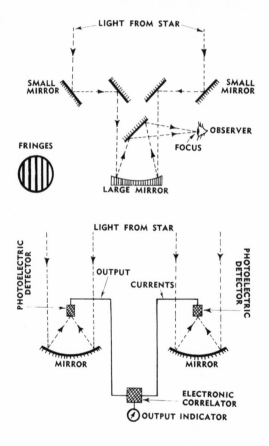

FIG. 38. The arrangement (A) of an astronomical Michelson interferometer, and (B) of the intensity interferometer. (From *The Universe of Time and Space*, edited by S. T. Butler and H. Messel, Pergamon Press and The Macmillan Company, New York, 1964)

It is convenient to think of these fluctuations as consisting of two distinct parts: *shot noise*, due to the discrete charges of the photoelectrons, and *wave noise*, due to fluctuations in the intensity of the incident light. Shot noise we can regard as being completely uncorrelated in the two detectors, but wave noise is correlated if the light falling on the two detectors is mutually coherent. Generally speaking, two light beams are said to be mutually coherent if after combination in a suitable optical system (such as a Michelson interferometer), they can be made to interfere.

This correlation between the wave-noise components is measured by amplifying the fluctuations in the outputs of the two detectors and then evaluating their cross product in an electronic correlator. The correlation is repeatedly determined for several different separations between the two mirror-detector units, and from the results we can find the angular size of the star.

The Michelson interferometer combines the light fields at two separated mirrors to form fringes, and the observer measures the visibility of these fringes for different mirror spacings. On the other hand, with an intensity interferometer we "detect" the light at each mirror, extract the rapid fluctuations of intensity electrically, and then measure the correlation between these fluctuations as a function of mirror spacing. The relationship between the two observations is strikingly simple, for the correlation measured with the intensity interferometer is directly proportional to the *square* of the fringe amplitude or fringe visibility in a Michelson interferometer with the same mirror spacing.

What advantages does an intensity interferometer offer? First, there is no need for high mechanical precision either in constructing it or in guiding it on a star. Any difference between the star-to-detector light paths, or in the electrical paths from the detectors to the correlators, needs only to be less than the wavelength of the highest *electrical* frequency transmitted from the detectors to the correlator. Since a convenient value for this frequency is about a hundred megacycles per second, corresponding to a wavelength of three meters, it is vastly simpler to build an intensity interferometer than one of the Michelson type. We can construct an extremely large interferometer without running into acute and very costly mechanical problems.

A further attraction is that the intensity interferometer does not seem significantly affected by atmospheric scintillation. Both theory and the few observations that have been made support this conclusion. This valuable property can be explained in terms of the limited range of electrical frequencies that are accepted by the correlator. If we restrict the highest frequency to 100 megacycles, the atmosphere can affect the observed correlation only if it introduces a *differential* time delay into the star-to-detector light paths of at least one billionth (10^{-9}) of a second. It is unlikely that the minor atmospheric irregularities responsible for scintillation can produce such a sudden effect.

Another advantage is that the results of the measurement are presented as printed numbers on a chart. Thus they are almost completely objective and independent of the observer's judgment and skill.

Nevertheless, the intensity interferometer is rather complicated, and it is big. Very large mirrors are needed to reduce observing times to a few hours, even for bright stars. However, these large mirrors can be relatively crude by astronomical standards, since their principal function is to collect starlight on a photocathode, not to form an optical image.

The Narrabri stellar intensity interferometer is an attempt to put the peculiar advantages of such an instrument to work in astronomy, specifically to measure the tiny disks of the hotter stars. The first stage was to build a crude pilot model with 61-inch-diameter searchlight mirrors at Manchester University in England. In 1955 this measured the angular diameter of Sirius as 0.0068 ± 0.0005 second of arc. After this successful test, it was decided to build a full-scale instrument as a joint project of Manchester and Sydney universities.

The instrument itself was built in the United Kingdom and then installed at Narrabri, which is in flat pastoral country about 700 feet above sea level some 300 miles north of Sydney. Our observatory forms part of the Chatterton Astronomy Department of Sydney University.

Design of the instrument had the limited objective of measuring the angular sizes of all stars brighter than about apparent magnitude +2.5 accessible from our latitude of 30° south. We assumed that it must be possible to determine the correlation for one base-line spacing with about 10 per cent accuracy in a single observing period of not more than eight hours. For brighter stars the times would, of course, be much shorter. It is hoped by this program to improve the temperature scale for the hot stars and to gather some new information about particular stars. For example, it may disclose double stars that lie in the present gap between visual and spectroscopic binaries, or it may prove possible to check theories of the structure of hot bright-line stars such as Gamma Velorum.

Figure 39 shows the layout at Narrabri. Two large reflectors are mounted on trucks which run on a circular railway track with an inside diameter of 600 feet and a gauge of 18 feet. Each reflector is controlled by a computer that calculates continuously the star's direction. To follow the star in azimuth the trucks move around the track, and to follow it in elevation the reflectors tilt about horizontal axes. In addition, the turntable carrying each reflector permits aiming directly at the star. The separation between the two reflectors can be varied from about 30 to 618 feet, and the trucks move so that this base line remains at right angles to the star's direction. This last feature is important because it ensures that the light reaches each mirror at the same time.

One minor complication, introduced by the garage over the southern part of the track, is that all travel of the reflectors must take place without

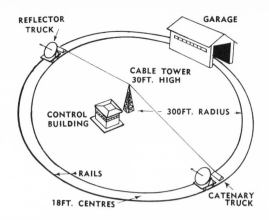

FIG. 39. The general layout of the instrument at Narrabri. (From *The Universe of Time and Space*, edited by S. T. Butler and H. Messel, Pergamon Press and The Macmillan Company, New York, 1964)

passing through the garage. Thus, for stars that transit north of the zenith, the reflectors look outward from the track, while for stars that transit south the reflectors look inward.

The computer and control system would be able to point the reflectors with an accuracy of two or three minutes of arc if the tracks were perfectly flat. But irregularities in the track, together with the clearances between the wheel flanges and the rails, introduce errors up to ±15 minutes. A photoelectric guiding system on each truck corrects these errors by making small adjustments to turntable angle and reflector elevation. The guiding phototube is mounted at the reflector's focus, alongside the main photoelectric detector, in such a way that it also compensates for any pointing errors due to flexure of the long mast supporting the equipment at the focus.

The pointing accuracy of both reflectors is monitored continuously during observation by means of a television camera at the focus, arranged to display the stars in the field of view on a monitor at the control desk. At wind speeds less than about twenty miles per hour, the overall pointing accuracy of each reflector is about ±1 minute of arc with the complete system operating and the trucks in motion. . . .

Very large but optically crude, each reflector is made of a light alloy frame about twenty-two feet in diameter, which is paraboloidal to ensure that all the light reaches the focus at the same time. On this framework are 252 hexagonal mirrors, each mounted on an adjustable three-point suspension for focusing. . . .

These small mirrors are of glass, front-coated with aluminum and protected with silicon dioxide. They are all of spherical figure, and at their nominal focal length of eleven meters focus all the light from a distant point source into a circle about one centimeter across. Each mirror has an electric heating pad cemented to its back to prevent the formation of dew.

FIG. 40. Twin light collectors on the circular track at Narrabri Observatory, New South Wales, Australia. A number of the small mirrors have been removed, for recoating, from each of the 22-foot reflectors. A boom thirty-six feet long supports a photoelectric detector at the focus of each reflector. This equipment has been used to measure the angular diameter of the star Vega. (University of Sydney photograph)

The equipment at the focus is supported thirty-six feet from the mirror by a steel pole held by stainless-steel guy rods. The photoelectric detectors are in light-tight boxes, screened electrically and magnetically, into which light can be admitted through a shutter actuated electrically by the operator at the control console. Converging starlight from the reflector is first rendered parallel by a negative lens three inches in diameter, and then goes through an interference filter with a bandwidth of 80 angstroms centered at a wavelength of 4385. It is then focused by an aspherical positive lens through an iris diaphragm onto the cathode of a fourteen-stage photo-multiplier. The output of the phototube is transmitted to the correlator through a coaxial aluminum cable suspended from the catenary. . . .

The control building near the center of the track houses the console, correlator, and much auxiliary equipment, such as rotary converters and an air-conditioning plant. Contained in the control console are the computer, the electronic circuits associated with star guiding, and all the switches and indicators needed to control the two moving trucks and reflectors. . . .

The correlator accepts the noise outputs from the two photomultipliers, multiplies them together, and records their product every one hundred seconds. It also measures the anode and cathode currents of the photomultiplier averaged over one hundred seconds and records them as well. Although the idea is simple, the correlator was the most difficult part of the instrument to develop.

In principle, the limit to the interferometer's sensitivity is set by statistical fluctuations in the correlator output, which in turn are determined by the statistical fluctuations in the output currents of the photoelectric detectors. Experience shows that the main problem in approaching this limit is to make a correlator that is free from spurious drifts in output. Our aim at Narrabri is to improve the correlator until such drift is negligible in observations lasting all night. This goal is not yet reached, and further modifications of the system are being made. . . .

The whole instrument was ready for initial tests in July 1963. Ideally, we should have measured Sirius again, but the minimum spacing between the two reflectors is too great to allow a satisfactory measurement. Hence we chose Vega, a similar but more distant star.

The results of this successful trial are shown in Figure 41. The angular diameter of Vega was deduced to be 0.0037 ± 0.0002 second of arc. From the known distance of this star, its linear diameter is then 3.2 ± 0.2 the sun's. A comparison with the sun yields 9200° ± 300° Kelvin for the effective surface temperature—in good agreement with recent estimates by several astrophysicists. The temperature of Sirius from the 1955 experiment was 9400° ± 400°.

FIG. 41. The circles mark correlations for Vega measured at five different separations of the reflectors, with vertical bars that indicate relative uncertainties in the data. The theoretical curve (dashed) is for an angular diameter of 0.0037 second of arc, with the star's limb-darkening coefficient taken as 0.7, a probable value for an Ao star.

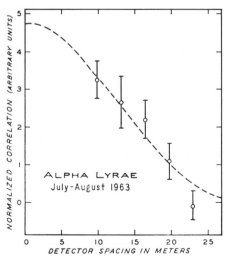

Broadly speaking, the results of the first test on Vega were satisfactory, and the whole system worked reasonably well in view of its many novel and untried features. But the electronic correlator proved to be insufficiently stable and rather too complicated to maintain; also, the overall sensitivity was almost one stellar magnitude poorer than anticipated. Both these troubles are now being investigated. Already the correlator stability has been improved, and the loss of sensitivity has been traced to the photomultipliers. Replacing them by more highly developed models soon to become available should improve the sensitivity by roughly one magnitude. It should then be possible to measure stars as faint as +2.5 to +3.0; meanwhile the instrument will be fully occupied in measuring the brightest stars.

The equipment described in this article was designed in collaboration with R. Q. Twiss and the firms of Dunford and Elliott (Sheffield), Ltd., and Mullard, Ltd. Financial support for the project has been provided by the British department of scientific and industrial research, the University of Sydney, and the U.S. Air Force. H. Messel organized and sponsored the project in Australia. C. Hazard, J. Davis, L. R. Allen, and Graham Gifford did most of the testing of the interferometer and made the observations of Vega.

Distance Modulus

GEORGE S. MUMFORD

(*Sky and Telescope*, May 1965)

The distance of a nearby star can be determined directly by measuring its parallax—the change in its apparent direction as viewed from different parts of the earth's orbit. This straightforward procedure is useful only for stars fairly near the sun, because the parallax angles for more distant objects are too small to be accurately measured.

In order to push deeper into space, indirect methods are needed. Two of these are analogous to experiences that almost anyone has every day. First, when you judge how far away a tree or house is, you make use of the fact that the farther away something is the smaller it appears. If you knew the actual size, the distance could be computed from the apparent size.

Harlow Shapley did just this in his classic study of globular clusters. He was able to determine the real diameters for the nearby clusters, and found them to be roughly equal. On the assumption that more distant ones were also similar, he could derive a relation between apparent size and distance, the scale being provided by the closest objects.

A second, related procedure depends on brightness. In estimating the distance to a streetlight at night, you use the idea that the fainter it looks, the farther away it is. This concept is the basis of astronomical methods of finding brightness distances.

Imagine that a point source of light emits E ergs of energy per second. As the light travels away from the source, it spreads over larger and larger areas until, at a distance D from the center, it is spread over a sphere of surface area $4\pi D^2$. Thus, each unit area of this sphere receives a light energy, or *luminous flux*, of $E/4\pi D^2$ ergs per second.

Now let us compare the luminous fluxes F_1 and F_2 received at respective distances D_1 and D_2 from the source. Since E is the same in both cases:

$$F_1/F_2 = (D_2/D_1)^2.$$

This formula expresses the well-known principle that the intensity of light varies inversely as the square of the distance from the source. For instance, if you double your distance from the source, it will appear only one quarter as bright.

In astronomy, we generally use magnitudes instead of luminous fluxes. By definition, if two stars differ in brightness by five magnitudes, the luminous flux of one is 100 times that of the other. For a difference of one magnitude, the flux ratio is the fifth root of 100 (or approximately 2.512), which is also the number whose logarithm is 0.4.

Therefore, if m_1 and m_2 are the apparent or observed magnitudes of two stars whose fluxes are F_1 and F_2, we have

$$0.4(m_1 - m_2) = \log (F_2/F_1)$$

or

$$(m_1 - m_2) = 2.5 \log (F_2/F_1).$$

Combining this relation with the one stated above gives us a simple formula connecting magnitude difference and distance ratio:

$$m_1 - m_2 = 2.5 \log (D_1/D_2)^2$$
$$= 5 \log (D_1/D_2).$$

This tells us that if we could view Sirius, for example, from ten times its actual distance, it would appear five magnitudes fainter, that is, magnitude +3.6 instead of its actual −1.4.

Similarly, if we should observe a star of magnitude +3.6 that we knew (from spectroscopic evidence) to be physically similar to Sirius, the formula would indicate that this star is ten times as far as Sirius. Here we have a powerful method for plumbing the depths of space. Once the distance of a single object of known apparent magnitude is available, we can calculate the distance of any other that has the same intrinsic luminosity.

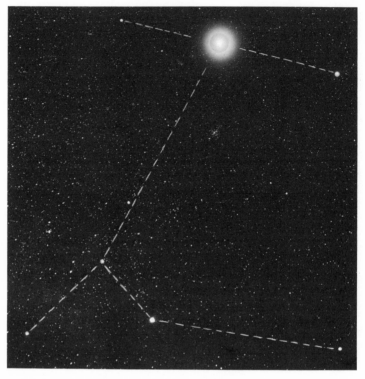

FIG. 42. Sirius, the brightest star in the constellation Canis Major, is of visual magnitude −1.4 and is 8.7 light years distant. (Harvard College Observatory photograph)

This restriction to similar objects is important. Barnard's famous star [p. 241] of great proper motion has an apparent magnitude of about 9.5, and thus is 10.9 magnitudes fainter than Sirius. The formula would indicate Barnard's star to be 150 times as distant as Sirius, yet in reality the former is the nearer of the two! Barnard's star is a small, cool red dwarf which has only 1/50,000 the intrinsic brightness of Sirius. It is evident that this method of finding brightness distances must be limited to like stars.

In essence, we do this when we compare the apparent magnitude of a star with its *absolute magnitude*—its brightness at the standard distance

FIG. 43. Barnard's star (arrowed), although as faint as magnitude 9.5, is one of the nearest stars, at 6.0 light years. The two photographs seen here in near coincidence were taken only eleven months apart, yet the motion of Barnard's star is evident. (Sproul Observatory photograph)

of 10 parsecs. Take m_2 as M, the absolute magnitude, and D_2 as 10 parsecs; drop the subscripts from m_1 and D_1. The previous equation can then be rewritten:

$$m - M = 5 \log (D/10),$$

where m is the apparent magnitude and D is the distance in parsecs.

The quantity on the left side of the equation is termed the *distance modulus*. It depends, in the simplest case, only on the difference between the apparent and absolute magnitudes of a star. Once this difference is known, the distance can be evaluated. (In practice, we must allow for the possibility that the object's light is dimmed by material between it and the observer. This can be done with a correction term [as on p. 96], but here we will ignore this complication.)

A few years ago, H. C. Arp of Mount Wilson and Palomar Observatories published a study of many novae that appeared in the Andromeda galaxy, Messier 31. For some of these, the apparent magnitude at maximum has been plotted against the observed rate of fading in magnitudes per day, as shown by the triangles in Figure 44. Because M31 is quite far from us in comparison with its thickness, we may assume here that all its novae are at the same distance. Thus, the plot indicates that there is a relation between the *intrinsic* brightness of a nova and its observed rate of decline, such that the intrinsically brighter ones fade more rapidly.

For a number of novae in our galaxy, both the apparent magnitudes at maximum and the distances are available, so their absolute magnitudes at maximum are known. We can make a plot of these novae like that for the Andromeda galaxy, except that the ordinates are now absolute magnitudes. If we assume that the novae in the two systems are intrinsically similar, we can slide the graphs vertically for the best fit, which corresponds roughly to $m = 16.0$ and $M = -8.2$. Hence, the distance modulus, $m - M$, is 24.2 magnitudes for Messier 31. Solving our formula gives about 69,000 for $D/10$, or a distance in parsecs of 690,000. Even though we have disregarded obscuring matter and some other complications, this result is only a little larger than the currently adopted distance. . . .

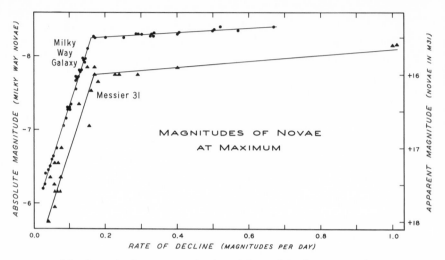

FIG. 44. Messier 31's distance can be found from this chart, as explained in the text. Each plotted point marks the maximum brightness of a nova. The triangles for M31 are from H. C. Arp, the dots for our galaxy from Cecilia Payne-Gaposchkin.

The formula for absolute magnitude, M (or distance modulus m − M), given above is equivalent to the "inverse-square law" of brightness, $B = L/D^2$, with m measuring B, and M measuring L, both in the logarithmic magnitude scale (see p. 30). The measured parallax, p, can be used in place of distance, $D = 1/p$ in parsecs. The presence of obscuring material, ignored here, would make m − M larger (see p. 96).

Since $L = BD^2$, stars of low luminosity must have small B (brightness) or small D (distance) or both. The search for nearby faint stars is difficult because the accurate photographs necessary for the measurement of parallax ($p = 1/d$) do not show very faint stars. However, some of the nearby stars have faint companions, recognized by their common proper motion accumulated over many years. Figure 45 shows one of these, discovered by G. Van Biesbroeck in 1939 using the 82-inch telescope at the McDonald Observatory in Texas. Accompanying a ninth-magnitude star of known distance (5.7 parsecs, from parallax $p = 0''.18$), it is about the faintest star in Figure 45, with m = 18.0. Thus, its absolute magnitude is M = m + 5 + 5 log p = 18.1 + 5 − 5 log. 5.7 = 23.1 − 5(0.76) = 19.3. For the sun, M = 4.9, so this star is 19.3 − 4.9 = 14.4 magnitudes less luminous than the sun, and its luminosity is L = 0.000002 (2 millionths of the sun).

There are others that may have even smaller luminosities. —TLP

FIG. 45. One arrow points to BD +4°4048, a 9.2-magnitude star which has a yearly proper motion of 1.44 seconds of arc. The other arrow points to an eighteenth-magnitude star which travels through space with the first star. From the distance of the brightest star, 19 light years, the faint companion is found to be of absolute magnitude 19.3. The photograph was taken at the prime focus of the 82-inch reflector at the McDonald Observatory by G. Van Biesbroeck. (McDonald Observatory photograph)

Two Very Faint Stars

(*Sky and Telescope*, December 1960)

The earliest plates made with the 48-inch Schmidt telescope for the Palomar Observatory–National Geographic Sky Survey were taken a little more than a decade ago. They are now old enough that by repeating photography of the same areas changes in position of many stars should be revealed. With this in mind, W. J. Luyten, University of Minnesota, repeated five plates in the fall of 1958, as a guest investigator at Mount Wilson and Palomar Observatories, and in 1960 Milton L. Humason obtained one more plate.

To find which stars had moved against the general background of stars, Luyten placed the old and new plate of a pair in a blink comparator, recognizing fast-moving stars by their apparent jumping back and forth as he alternately viewed one plate and then the other. In all, on the six pairs of plates, some 1100 stars showed appreciable proper motions.

Two of the most interesting of these may be the faintest star known and the faintest white dwarf. Luyten writes:

"A star, LP 464-53, at right ascension 0ʰ17ᵐ.0, declination +12°38' (1950 coordinates), with a proper motion of one second of arc annually, shows faintly on the red plates—red magnitude about +20.2—but is invisible on the blue plate of the Sky Survey pair. Probably it is a very faint red dwarf. Assuming that its photovisual magnitude is around 20.5, and its parallax of the order of 0.1 second of arc (roughly thirty light years), its absolute magnitude is also +20.5. This, therefore, appears to be the least luminous star now known, fainter even than Van Biesbroeck's companion to BD +4°4048 [see Fig. 45], and about two million times fainter than the sun. If it could be viewed from 93 million miles (as we see the sun), it would be only one fourth as bright as the full moon.

"The second object, LP 321-98, is at $12^h39^m.8$, $+30°14'$ (1950), not far from the north galactic pole, and has a proper motion of 0.55 second annually. But while its photographic magnitude is +20.2, the photovisual magnitude is 19.5; hence its color is almost the same as that of the sun, and it seems to be a degenerate star or white dwarf. Again it is the faintest of its class, with an absolute magnitude around +18, or some 180,000 times fainter than the sun, and probably possessing a density of many tons per cubic inch."

The magnitudes (brightnesses) of these very faint stars were estimated roughly from the images on photographs. Much more accurate methods of measuring brightness have been developed during the past thirty years, using photoelectric cells. The light of a star, focused by a telescope, falls on the photosensitive cathode of a photocell and causes a small electric current to flow, due to electrons ejected by the light. This current is amplified electronically and measured with an accuracy better than 1 per cent. This measured current is proportional to the brightness of the light falling on the cell. With one telescope and constant conditions (clarity of the sky, temperature of the photocell, and electrical voltage used in the amplifier), these measurements give relative brightnesses of the stars, after some calculation.

However, different colors of light affect the photocell in different degree, and different cells have different color sensitivity. Hence, star brightnesses are measured separately for different colors, blue and yellow being the first two measured. (Colored glass inserted in front of the photocell cuts out the light not measured.) Expressed in magnitudes, these are designated B (blue) and V (visual). Together with U (ultraviolet), they were accurately defined in terms of color (wavelength intervals in the spectrum) by Harold L. Johnson and W. W. Morgan in 1954, and the "UBV system" is widely used among astronomers. Several other systems are also used, differing only in the bands of wavelengths used in measuring the relative brightnesses of stars.

The spectral types and luminosity classes listed in the following article are estimated from details in the spectra of the stars (see Chapter 3), and it was previously known that spectral types were correlated with color.

Blue stars have spectra of types O, B, and A, whereas red stars are of spectral types K and M.

Extreme color differences are readily apparent to the eye, but an accurate measure of color is the ratio of brightness in red light to brightness in blue light, B_{red}/B_{blue}, or the difference between blue magnitude and red magnitude (since $\log(B_{red}/B_{blue}) = \log B_{red} - \log B_{blue}$). Hence the difference $B - V$ is a measure of color called the color index. —T L P

....

The Fifty Brightest Stars

HAROLD L. JOHNSON

(Sky and Telescope, August 1957)

Many lists of the brightest stars have been made. None, however, has had the advantage of being based upon accurate photoelectric observations. Inasmuch as such determinations of bright stars have now become available, a new list, containing the fifty brightest stars, is presented here (Table 5).

TABLE 5. THE FIFTY BRIGHTEST STARS

	Bayer designation	Name	Spectrum	V	B—V	B
1	α Canis Majoris	Sirius	A1 V	−1.43	+0.00	−1.43
2	α Carinae	Canopus	F0 Ia	−0.73	+0.15	−0.58
3	α Centauri	(Alpha Centauri)	G2 V	−0.27*	+0.66	+0.39*
4	α Bootis	Arcturus	K2 IIIp	−0.06	+1.23	+1.17
5	α Lyrae	Vega	A0 V	+0.04	+0.00	+0.04
6	α Aurigae	Capella	(G0)	+0.09	+0.80	+0.89
7	β Orionis	Rigel	B8 Ia	+0.15	−0.04	+0.11
8	α Canis Minoris	Procyon	F5 IV-V	+0.37	+0.41	+0.78
9	α Eridani	Achernar	B3 V	+0.53	−0.16	+0.37
10	β Centauri	(Beta Centauri)	B0.5 V	+0.66*	−0.21	+0.45*
11	α Orionis	Betelgeuse	M2 Iab	+0.7**	+1.87	+2.6**
12	α Aquilae	Altair	A7 IV, V	+0.80	+0.22	+1.02
13	α Tauri	Aldebaran	K5 III	+0.85**	+1.52	+2.37**
14	α Crucis	(Alpha Crucis)	B0.5 V	+0.87*	−0.24	+0.63*
15	α Scorpii	Antares	M1 Ib	+0.98**	+1.80	+2.78**
16	α Virginis	Spica	B1 V	+1.00	−0.23	+0.77
17	α Piscis Austrini	Fomalhaut	A3 V	+1.16	+0.09	+1.25
18	β Geminorum	Pollux	K0 III	+1.16	+1.01	+2.17
19	α Cygni	Deneb	A2 Ia	+1.26	+0.09	+1.35
20	β Crucis	(Beta Crucis)	B0.5 IV	+1.31	−0.23	+1.08
21	α Leonis	Regulus	B7 V	+1.36	−0.11	+1.25
22	ε Canis Majoris	Adhara	B2 II	+1.49	−0.17	+1.32
23	α Geminorum	Castor	(A0)	+1.59*	+0.05	+1.63*

TABLE 5.   THE FIFTY BRIGHTEST STARS (continued)

	Bayer designation	Name	Spectrum	V	B—V	B
24	λ Scorpii	Shaula	B2 IV	+1.62	−0.23	+1.39
25	γ Orionis	Bellatrix	B2 III	+1.64	−0.23	+1.41
26	β Tauri	Elnath	B7 III	+1.65	−0.13	+1.52
27	β Carinae	Miaplacidus	Ao III	+1.65	+0.00	+1.65
28	γ Crucis	(Gamma Crucis)	M3 II	+1.67	+1.53	+3.20
29	ε Orionis	Alnilam	Bo Ia	+1.70	−0.18	+1.52
30	α Gruis	(Alpha Gruis)	B6 V	+1.75	−0.14	+1.61
31	ζ Orionis	Alnitak	O9.5 Ib	+1.78*	−0.21	+1.57*
32	ε Ursae Majoris	Alioth	(Aop)	+1.78	−0.02	+1.76
33	γ Velorum	(Gamma Velorum)	WC7+B3	+1.80*	−0.24	+1.56*
34	α Persei	Mirfak	F5 Ib	+1.80	+0.48	+2.28
35	α Ursae Majoris	Dubhe	Ko III	+1.80	+1.06	+2.86
36	ε Sagittarii	Kaus Australis	B9 IV	+1.82	−0.04	+1.78
37	δ Canis Majoris	Wezen	F8 Ia	+1.84	+0.66	+2.50
38	η Ursae Majoris	Alkaid	B3 V	+1.87	−0.20	+1.67
39	θ Scorpii	(Theta Scorpii)	Fo I-II	+1.87	+0.37	+2.24
40	β Aurigae	Menkalinan	(Aop)	+1.90	+0.03	+1.93
41	δ Velorum	(Delta Velorum)	A2 V	+1.92*	+0.03	+1.95*
42	γ Geminorum	Alhena	Ao IV	+1.93	+0.00	+1.93
43	α Trianguli Australis	(Alpha Tri. Aus.)	(K2)	+1.93	+1.41	+3.34
44	α Pavonis	(Alpha Pavonis)	B2 V	+1.96	−0.20	+1.76
45	β Canis Majoris	Murzim	B1 II-III	+1.97	−0.23	+1.74
46	ε Carinae	(Epsilon Carinae)	Ko+B	+1.97	+1.13	+3.10
47	α Hydrae	Alphard	K3 III	+1.98	+1.44	+3.42
48	α Arietis	Hamal	K2 III	+2.00	+1.15	+3.15
49	α Ursae Minoris	Polaris	(F8)	+2.01**	+0.60	+2.61**
50	β Ursae Minoris	Kochab	K4 III	+2.02	+1.47	+3.49

* Visual double star with brightness difference less than five magnitudes; the magnitude given is for both components measured together.
** Variable star with range of V: Betelgeuse, 0.4 to 1.0; Aldebaran, 0.75 to 0.95; Antares, 0.90 to 1.06; Polaris, 1.96 to 2.05.
Spectra in parentheses are from the *Henry Draper Catalogue*.

The columns give the number in order of brightness; the Bayer letter designation; the star's proper name, if any; and then its spectral type and luminosity class on the MKK (Morgan-Keenan-Kellman) system; the apparent visual magnitude V; the color index B — V; and the blue magnitude B.

An asterisk following the magnitude of a star indicates that it is a visual binary whose separation is too small to be noticed by the unaided eye; in these cases the combined magnitudes and colors are given. Stars marked with a double asterisk vary in light, their ranges being given in the footnote. Two variable stars of large range, Omicron Ceti (Mira) and Eta Carinae, which are sometimes brighter than second magnitude at maximum light, are omitted from the table.

The probable errors of the magnitudes, V, are approximately ±.015 to ±.020 magnitude. Therefore, the order of the ten brightest stars in the list is very unlikely to be changed by additional observations; even among the twenty brightest stars the order is probably not significantly in error. For the faintest stars in the list, however, observational errors may change the order of brightness. In fact, some of those at the very foot of the list may not actually belong among the first fifty, while other stars should perhaps have been included instead.

The magnitudes and colors of the northern stars are all from photoelectric observations, mostly from the published data of Johnson and Morgan (*Astrophysical Journal*, 117, 313, 1953), and Johnson and Harris (*Astrophysical Journal*, 120, 196, 1954), and from unpublished observations by these authors. The magnitudes and colors of the southern stars depend primarily upon the photoelectric and photographic observations taken at the Royal Observatory, Cape of Good Hope, South Africa (*Cape Mimeogram* No. 1). Southern observations by Eggen (*Astronomical Journal*, 60, 65, 1955) were included but were given lower weight.

It has been necessary, of course, to transform the observations of the Cape Observatory and of Eggen to the **UBV** system, since they were published in other systems. These transformations were determined from stars, mostly not among the fifty brightest, that are common to the several catalogues. In some cases, these transformations are not strictly linear, and compensation had to be made for the nonlinearity.

The visual magnitudes, V, are on the system of the international photovisual magnitudes [magnitudes measured from photographs made with filter and film emulsion chosen to simulate the spectral response of the human eye] of the north-polar sequence. They average about 0.1 magnitude brighter than the magnitudes of the *Henry Draper Catalogue*. The color indices, **B−V**, represent the international color indices about as well as the international colors are defined. In accord with the original definition of the international system, the zero point of the color indices is placed at Ao V, while **B−V** is +1.00 at Ko III. The blue magnitudes, **B**, contain no ultraviolet short of 3800 angstroms, approximately, in order to minimize the difficulties of transformation from one similar system to another, and may be considered to be "photographic" magnitudes.

The comments above on "transforming" from one system of magnitudes and color indices to another display the basic difficulty in measurements of brightnesses: unless the same colors of light (wavelength intervals) are measured, two observers will get different results on the same set of stars, no matter how accurately they measure. The differences between, say,

Johnson's **B**, **V** and someone else's **G** (green instead of blue), **O** (orange instead of yellow) would depend on color index, a red star showing up brighter in **G**, **O** than in **B**, **V**. The "transformations" mentioned by Johnson are formulae expected to give **B**, **V** in terms of **G**, **O** and **G**—**O**:

$$B = aG + b(G—O)$$
$$V = cO + d(G—O)$$

where a, b, c, and d are constants determined from several cases where **B**, **V**, **G**, and **O** are all measured for the same star.

As the next article shows, five new magnitude measurements have since been added, in the red (**R**), and infrared (**I**, **J**, **K**, **L**). The catalogue of 1324 stars is not reproduced here because of space limitations. It is an important and useful list of accurate magnitudes and colors that now serve as standards for further observations. As Johnson estimated (p. 95) the early list of the fifty brightest stars in Table 5 needs few corrections. In all but ten cases the **V** magnitudes are within $0.^m02$ of the 1965 values. Two stars should be added to Table 5 ahead of α Arietis, which then becomes number 50: γ Leonis K0 III, **V** = 1.98, **B**—**V** = 1.15, and β Ceti K1 III, **V** 2.00, **B**—**V** = 1.00. There are four more between α Ursae Minoris and β Ursa Minoris: β Andromedae, σ Centauri, κ Orionis, and α Andromedae. Note that the new values of **V** are accurate to $\pm 0.^m017$, less than 2 per cent error in the brightness:

When these values of **B**—**V** (and other values, for fainter stars) are plotted against spectral type ("Spectrum," column 3 in Table 5), it is found that for B-spectrum stars **B**—**V** is almost —0.2, for A stars about 0.0, for F stars about +0.4, for G stars about +0.7, for K stars about +1.2, and for M stars about +1.7. This increase in redness from B stars through A, F, G, K, and M is to be expected as a result of the differences in temperature, as shown in Chapter 4 (p. 149). But many of the fainter stars have colors redder than this, an effect of the interstellar dust, which reddens their light just as smoke would. For instance, a faint F star, which should have **B**—**V** = +0.4, may actually have **B**—**V** = +0.6, in which case it is said to have a "color excess" of 0.2. Of course, the "smoke" also dims the starlight, and it has been found that this dimming, in magnitudes, is about three times the color excess. From infrared measurements like the ones described below, Harold Johnson found in 1966 that in some regions the dimming is as much as five times the color excess ("CE"). Hence the distance modulus (p. 90) is increased to

$$M - m = 5 + 5 \log p + 3(CE)$$

or more. — T L P

Five-color Photometry
of Bright Stars

BRAULIO IRIARTE, HAROLD L. JOHNSON,
RICHARD I. MITCHELL, AND WIESLAW Z. WISNIEWSKI

(*Sky and Telescope*, July 1965)

Astronomers have long agreed on the need for more accurate apparent magnitudes of the naked-eye stars. These are, in general, the stars for which other kinds of information are most complete. But as far as brightnesses are concerned, until fairly recently the best available data were still the visual measurements made some seventy years ago at Harvard and Potsdam Observatories.

Excellent as this old work was by the standards of its time, the Harvard and Potsdam photometric catalogues of stars failed to meet most later needs. At best, the probable error of an individual observation was nearly ±0.1 magnitude, and in the Harvard work there were large systematic errors depending on spectral type, amounting to several tenths of a magnitude for faint red stars. Furthermore, astronomers felt a growing need for measurements of star colors as well as brightnesses.

By the 1940s, improvements in photoelectric photometry provided much more powerful methods. With care and a good sky, stars could be measured to an accuracy of about ±0.01 magnitude. By inserting standardized color filters in the photometer, it became possible to measure ultraviolet, blue, and yellow magnitudes of stars. In particular, the filter types used by H. L. Johnson, W. W. Morgan, and D. L. Harris, III, became adopted generally, and served to define the new **U**, **B**, and **V** magnitude system.

The **U** magnitudes refer to ultraviolet starlight of around 3600 angstroms wavelength. The blue magnitudes, **B**, have an effective wavelength of 4300, and may be considered as "photographic" magnitudes. They contain no ultraviolet light short of 3800 angstroms, approximately, in order to minimize the difficulties in comparing and combining the results of different observers. Finally, the **V** magnitudes refer to yellow light of about 5400 angstroms, and are in effect visual magnitudes. They average about 0.1 magnitude brighter than the Harvard visual values.

More recently, photoelectric measurements of stars have also been made in the **R** (red) and the **I** (infrared) systems, corresponding to around 7000 and 9000 angstroms, respectively. At still longer effective wavelengths are other kinds of magnitudes, determined with lead sulfide cells: J (12,500 angstroms or 1.25 microns), K (2.2 microns), and L (3.6 microns).

Having so many kinds of accurate stellar magnitudes has greatly widened the concept of star color. Fifty years or more ago, when astronomers were limited to visual and photographic methods, the *color index* of a star meant merely its photographic magnitude minus its visual magnitude: $CI = m_p - m_v$. This index is about 0.0 for white stars (spectral type Ao), about +1.0 for orange stars (Ko), and +2 or more for very red stars. For many practical purposes today, we can regard the difference $B - V$ as equivalent to the traditional color index.

Similarly, the difference between any two magnitudes for the same star provides another color index. The catalogue that accompanies this article [not reproduced here] lists $U - V$, $B - V$, $V - R$, and $V - I$ indices for the star 33 Piscium as +1.91, +1.04, +0.77, and +1.32; adding the first two of them to the V magnitude (4.61) of 33 Piscium gives $U = 6.52$ and $B = 5.65$ for this star. Subtracting the last two indices from V gives $R = 3.84$ and $I = 3.29$. Thus 33 Piscium (a giant star of spectral class K1) appears progressively brighter as we consider its magnitudes from ultraviolet to infrared.

Systematic photoelectric measurement of all these kinds of magnitudes for all naked-eye stars is an enormous task that is still unfinished. . . .

During the last two years, staff members of the Lunar and Planetary Laboratory (University of Arizona) and astronomers of the Observatorio Astrofísico Nacional (Tonantzintla, Mexico) have participated in a cooperative program of photoelectric photometry of the brightest stars, obtaining measurements of more than 1300 bright stars in five broad wavelength bands—U, B, V, R, and I. The stars selected are those brighter than 5.0 on the Harvard visual system. The catalogue is complete to this limit for all of the sky north of declination −30°, and almost complete between −30° and −50°. A few stars fainter than fifth magnitude have also been included.

Collection of Data

The photoelectric observations on which this catalogue is based began in January 1963, with the 21-inch reflector of the Lunar and Planetary Laboratory in Arizona's Catalina Mountains, 8250 feet above sea level. That same July our 28-inch telescope at 8450 feet came into use on this program. In January 1965, just two years later, we completed the measurements at this station, in latitude 32° north. At Tonantzintla (7500 feet elevation, latitude 19° north) observations were begun in February 1963 and have continued through this May.

Lunar and Planetary Laboratory staff members who took part in the observing included Harold L. Johnson, Richard Mitchell, David Stein-metz, Kent Underwood, Michael Wirick, and Wieslaw Z. Wisniewski. The Tonantzintla observations were made by Braulio Iriarte, E. E. Men-doza, and Johnson.

Descriptions of our **UBV** and **UBVRI** photometers have been published in several places, for example in Chapter 7 of *Astronomical Techniques* (edited by W. A. Hiltner, University of Chicago Press, 1962), and *Communications* of the Lunar and Planetary Laboratory (1, 73, 1962). The Catalina photometer contains the original 1P21 photomultiplier tube and filters that defined the **UBV** system.

The Tonantzintla photometer uses a 7102 photomultiplier. Because of the red sensitivity of this tube, a special filter had to be added to cut the red leaks of the **B** and **V** filters. **U** measurements could not be made.

An important aspect of our program is the automatic data-collection system, made possible by a highly routine observing procedure. Beforehand, an IBM card is punched for each star, listing an identification number, the right ascension and declination, spectral type, and visual brightness. (For a faint star, a finder chart may be pasted on the unused portion of the card.) At the time of observation, the identification and coordinates are punched from the card into a paper tape record. On this tape are then punched the photometric measures of the star, the sky background bright-ness, and the time. Finally, the observer characterizes the observation as good or bad by means of push buttons.

The tape records from several nights are converted to IBM cards, which are fed into a computer. This computer is programed to correct the ob-servations for atmospheric extinction and to convert them to the standard **UBVRI** system. Many astronomers now use computers to reduce their photometric observations.

Some Further Comments

The original **UBV** system is defined by northern stars, many of which cannot be reached by southern hemisphere observers. Therefore our new **UBV** measurements, extending to declination −50°, provide additional checks on the photometry in the southern sky.

Recently the Cape Observatory published two lists of **UBV** magnitudes for most of the bright southern stars (in *Bulletin 64* of the Royal Observa-tory, and in a mimeogram entitled *Photometry from 1961 to 1963*). Both lists are internally consistent and are close to the original **UBV** system. The accompanying charts (Fig. 46) comparing Cape and Catalina data show the mutual consistency of these two series. This comparison is made for equatorial stars that were observed at approximately equal altitudes from Arizona and South Africa.

CATALINA MINUS CAPE

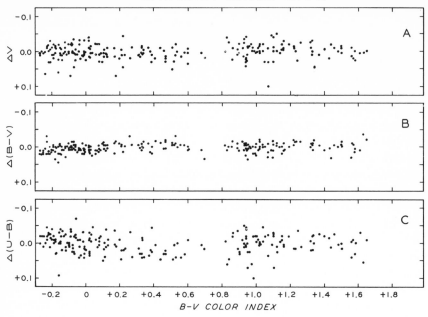

TONANTZINTLA MINUS CAPE

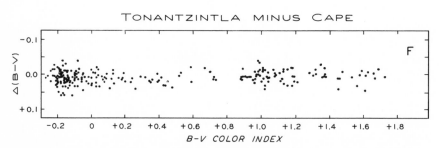

FIG. 46. Each of these charts is a plot of the difference between **V**, **B−V**, or **U−B** measured at Catalina Observatory, Cape of Good Hope Observatory, or Tonantzintla Observatory and the same quantity measured at another of these three observatories.

CATALINA MINUS CAPE — 1961–63

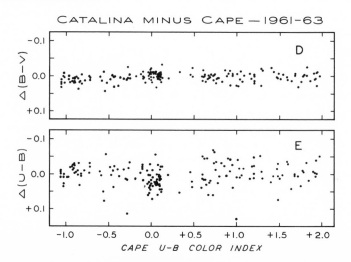

However, for the bluest stars, the Cape **B — V** values (Fig. 46B) tend to be more negative than values in the Johnson-Morgan standard system. The Tonantzintla comparison (Fig. 46F) confirms this systematic effect for stars from declinations —30° to —50°. The effect is clearest in Figure 46D, in which the Catalina values are compared with those from the Cape mimeograms, this time the **B — V** differences being plotted against **U — B** values.

From Figure 46D comes a simple rule for the correction of the Cape **B — V** color indices: If **U — B** is negative, apply —0.015 (**U — B**) to the Cape **B — V** value. If **U — B** is positive, no correction is applied.

This precept is the only correction needed for the Cape southern photometry. Although the systematic effect seems to come from a difference in the ultraviolet transmissions of the **B** (blue) filters, no corrections seem needed for the Cape **U — B** measures, since they fit the **U — B** system reasonably well.

It should be remembered that the new Catalina-Tonantzintla observations do not define the **UBV** system. Its formal definition is the data for 108 standard stars, published by Johnson and Harris in the *Astrophysical Journal*, 120, 196, 1954.

According to the new data, Vega (H.D. 172167) is 0.04 magnitude brighter than the standard value. Perhaps the star is variable. Such differences have been carefully checked; they are not due to arithmetic errors, and instead may represent statistical uncertainty, with some contribution from stellar variability.

The precision of measurement can be evaluated in two ways. The repeatability of the measures of nonstandard stars gives the internal probable error of an observation; comparison with independent data furnishes the external error.

Here are the probable errors of a single observation of each type at Catalina, in units of ±0.001 magnitude: V, 17; U — V, 20; B — V, 9; V — R, 16; V — I, 16. The corresponding probable errors for a single Tonantzintla observation are 35, —, 20, 23, 23. (The dash is used because ultraviolet measurements were not made at Tonantzintla, as pointed out previously.) . . .

The fifty brightest stars are not necessarily the fifty most luminous. Many of them, such as Alpha Centauri (see p. 25), may be bright because they are nearby. Conversely, most luminous stars may appear faint in our sky because they are far from us. The luminosities of stars of known parallax (nearer than 1000 parsecs, or 3300 light years) range as high as L = 40,000 suns (p. 75) or M = —5.6. Is this the largest? How bright can a star be?

The search for highly luminous stars is simplified when a large number are at the same distance from us—the brightest are expected to stand out and be easily recognized in clusters, clouds, and other galaxies of stars. However, there is a basic difficulty with this method due to "foreground stars" between us and the distant group which would be reckoned falsely as highly luminous if assumed to be at a larger distance (that of the group) than they really are. The problem is to identify members of a group or cloud by some other characteristic, such as the motion or radial velocity shared by all stars in the group. The Doppler shift in wavelength due to radial velocity (see p. 137) can be used, as described in the following note. The instrument used in South Africa photographs two spectra of each star, one with red to the right, the other with red to the left and blue to the right. The separation between the same feature in these two spectra is a measure of the wavelength shift, and thus of the radial velocity. — T L P

....

Supergiants in the Large Magellanic Cloud

(Sky and Telescope, July 1962)

A new objective-prism spectrograph has been installed at Haute Provence Observatory's Zeekoegat station, near Oudtshoorn, South Africa. Designed by C. Fehrenbach, this instrument can be used to determine radial velocities for a large number of stars on one double-exposure plate, the objective prism being rotated 180° between exposures.

The first plate taken with the new equipment at Zeekoegat was of the Large Magellanic Cloud, in December 1961. It is a four-hour exposure, two hours for each position of the prism, and contains more than 250 spectra. Miss M. Duflot, director of the station, and Fehrenbach report that because of the cloud's apparent radial velocity of +250 kilometers per second, the distinction between cloud member and nonmember stars is discernible at a glance.

As a result, the French astronomers have been able to identify ten stars belonging to the Large Cloud that are perhaps ten times brighter than any supergiants known in our galaxy. Similar to three red super-supergiants found by A. D. Thackeray and his co-workers a few years ago, the new discoveries have absolute magnitudes of about —9, some 400,000 times more luminous than the sun.

3

Stellar

Spectra;

The Analysis

of Starlight

Almost all that we know about stars comes from measurement of their faint light—the direction from which it comes, the overall brightness, the color, and changes of these measurable quantities in time. (In the case of the sun, streams of particles are detected, and radio emission, neutrinos, gamma rays, and cosmic rays may add to what the light can tell us.) Color has been discussed briefly (Chapter 2), and frequent references have been made to spectra, absorption lines, wavelengths of light, and Doppler shifts in wavelength. This chapter is devoted to the basic principles of stellar spectroscopy—the experimental facts and logic used in reasoning out the nature of a source of light from a detailed analysis of its color. —TLP

••

The Atom in Astronomy

LEO GOLDBERG

(*The Telescope*, May–June 1937)

Visual examination of a star, either with a telescope or with the naked eye, provides little information about its real physical nature. The very nearest stars are so distant that they appear as mere points of light, even when scrutinized through the most powerful telescopes now in existence. To be sure, a considerable amount of knowledge may be gleaned from direct visual or photographic observations. Such observations yield important information about the relative brightnesses of the stars, their colors, their distribution in space, the distances of the nearer objects, and their motions across the sky. But we would be completely ignorant of the chemical composition of the stars, their sizes, and the conditions of temperature and of pressure in their atmospheres if we were forced to rely entirely on such equipment. Fortunately, astronomers have at their disposal an exceedingly valuable detective, the spectroscope, which analyzes the light emitted by a star, identifies the kinds of atoms that are supplying it, and determines the physical conditions under which the atoms are operating.

The discovery of the principle of the spectroscope dates as far back as 1666, but its application to the sun and stars was delayed for nearly a century and a half. In that year, Sir Isaac Newton performed a classical experiment, which may be regarded as the forerunner of modern spectroscopy. On passing sunlight through a prism of glass, he found that the beam was spread out into a band of colors, or spectrum, ranging from red at one end to violet at the other. His conclusion was that white light is composed of a mixture of all the colors of the rainbow, and that each kind of light is refracted, or bent, by a different amount in going through a

FIG. 47. How the prism breaks up light into colors. (From *Introduction to Astronomy*, by Cecilia H. Payne-Gaposchkin, Prentice-Hall, New York, 1954)

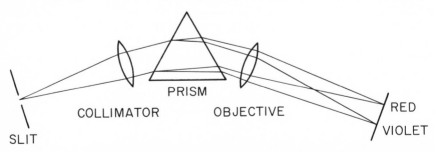

prism. The prism separates the colors. Violet light is refracted most and red light least. Hence they appear at opposite ends of the spectrum.

This discovery, one of the most significant in the history of physics and of astronomy, was essentially ignored until 1802, when Wollaston inaugurated a series of spectroscopic discoveries that have continued at an increasing rate to the present day. On examining the spectrum of sunlight that had been admitted to a darkened room by means of an exceedingly narrow crevice, Wollaston observed that the continuous band of colors was crossed by four dark lines. He erroneously interpreted these lines as the divisions separating the four elementary colors making up white light, namely, red, yellowish green, blue, and violet. Curiously enough, Wollaston noted also that if the light from the lower part of a candle flame were likewise examined by means of a slit and prism, a set of bright lines was formed, one of which corresponded to the dark line between the blue and the violet regions of the solar spectrum. Following closely upon Wollaston's researches, Fraunhofer published, in 1814, the results of his careful and detailed examination of the solar spectrum. His great map of the solar spectrum included 574 dark lines, the strongest of which he designated by letters: A, a, B, C, D, E, b, F, G, and H.

The question of the origin of the dark lines remained a puzzle for a number of years. It was at first thought that the earth's atmosphere was responsible for absorbing certain colors of sunlight, but this hypothesis was abandoned when it was learned that certain bright stars showed dark lines that were absent from the sun, and that indeed stellar spectra differed from each other with respect to the numbers and kinds of lines that could be seen. In addition, the light emitted by various terrestrial sources was of varying character with respect to the bright lines formed. The mystery was finally solved in 1859, when the results of the laboratory investigations of two Germans, Kirchhoff and Bunsen, were made known. These experimentalists showed that the radiation from a glowing rarefied gas possesses a spectrum of bright lines on a dark background, and that the numbers and positions of these lines are characteristic of the element emitting the light. No two elements exhibit identical spectra. Thus, nature has provided us with the means of fingerprinting the elements; even though they be mixed with one another, they may be separately identified and distinguished with the aid of the spectroscope. When the light source is an incandescent solid, liquid, or dense gas, the spectrum is a continuous one, ranging in color from red to violet. Furthermore, when light from such a source is allowed to pass through a cooler rarefied gas, which itself would emit a bright-line spectrum, the continuous spectrum is crossed by a series of dark lines whose positions coincide with those of the bright lines that the cooler gas would ordinarily emit when excited to incandescence. In other words, the vapor of a given element is transparent to light of all colors except those it is capable of radiating. The appearance of the sun's spectrum is then readily understood if we regard the sun as a dense hot central body surrounded by a cooler atmosphere. The continuous spectrum is radiated at the surface of the main body of the sun (the photosphere), and the dark lines are imprinted by the elements contained in its atmosphere (the reversing layer). By comparing the dark lines in the solar spectrum with the bright lines emitted by the same elements in the laboratory, the astrophysicist gains definite information concerning the chemical composition of the solar atmosphere.

The exciting results of Kirchhoff and Bunsen's experiments came at a time when astronomical research had become more or less standardized. A great deal of attention was being paid to the motions of the moon and of the planets, and great catalogues of star positions were being compiled. Kirchhoff's suggestion that the spectroscope might yield important information about the nature of stars was seized upon by a young English amateur, William Huggins. Huggins had been seeking for new methods of astronomical research, and as he wrote later in his career, Kirchhoff's discovery came to him as the discovery of a spring of water in a dry and thirsty land. He immediately applied himself to the spectroscopic examination of large numbers of stars. In 1864 he announced the discovery of lines belonging to some twenty elements and concluded that although stars differed from one another in the relative proportions of their constituent elements, they were essentially similar to the sun in construction, and that the universe was composed of the same materials as our own solar system. Meanwhile, the photographic method was being introduced into astronomy, and Huggins was once more a pioneer, when he foresaw the advantages of the dry over the wet plate. Large numbers of stellar spectra were photographed, and accurate measures were obtained of the positions of the lines. In addition, the ultraviolet region of the spectrum, invisible to the eye, was made accessible by the more versatile photographic plate.

Confronted with an increasing array of spectral observations, physicists were stimulated to inquire into the source of light. As to the nature of light there remained little doubt. The nineteenth century had witnessed a striking series of optical experiments by Fresnel, Young, and others, experiments that could be successfully explained only on the assumption that light was a wave motion. It is of little wonder that the concept of light as a wave motion was so universally accepted at that time when we consider that no physical theory, with the exception of Newton's law of gravitation, had so successfully withstood the onslaughts of one brilliant experiment after another as had the wave theory of light. The wave theory assumes that the color of the light is dependent on the length of the light wave. Along the spectrum from red to violet, the wavelength progressively decreases. With the knowledge that each element emits light only of discrete wavelengths, it was now natural to inquire into the structure of the atoms that so radiate. In the latter part of the century Maxwell proposed his electromagnetic theory of light, which appeared to be experimentally confirmed by the researches of Hertz and of Lodge. On this theory, light waves were of electromagnetic character, and it therefore seemed probable that atoms were vibrating electric systems. The discovery by J. J. Thomson that tiny electrified particles (electrons) were associated with atoms appeared to confirm the view of Sir Oliver Lodge, who wrote in 1888, "The whole subject of electrical radiation seems to be working itself out splendidly."

Various attempts were made to visualize an atom whose electrons could vibrate in a manner to produce the characteristic radiations that were observed. Rutherford introduced the notion that an atom was composed of a nucleus and of electrons revolving about the nucleus in planetary fashion. The latter idea was not considered tenable, however, for on the basis of classical mechanics, a moving charge would radiate energy, and hence the electron would tend to slow up and to fall into the nucleus. In addition such an atom would radiate light of all wavelengths, in contradiction to the observed fact that each element emitted light of discrete wavelengths. For example, the spectrum of hydrogen was observed to consist of a perfectly definite series of lines (Fig. 48), regularly spaced, with the separations between the lines decreasing progressively toward the ultraviolet. Balmer had shown empirically that an interesting mathematical relationship existed between the wavelengths of these lines, but he had made no attempt to explain their origin.

In 1913 Niels Bohr proposed a model of the hydrogen atom on the basis of the so-called quantum theory, and achieved the striking success of predicting the wavelengths of the hydrogen lines, in exact agreement with those observed. On the Bohr model, the hydrogen atom consisted of a nucleus of positive charge and of an electron that revolved about the nucleus in a circular orbit. Thus far, there was no essential disagreement with the Rutherford model. But now Bohr assumed further, in contra-

FIG. 48. The dark lines of hydrogen (white on this negative) in the spectrum of a star. The very faint lines arise chiefly from metallic atoms in the star's atmosphere. (Mount Wilson and Palomar Observatories photograph)

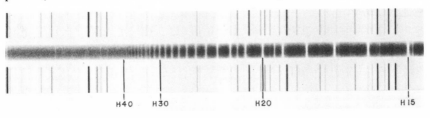

H 40   H 30   H 20   H 15

diction to the laws of classical mechanics, that the electron could occupy orbits of only certain discrete energies, and that no energy was radiated during the motion of the electron. An electron was allowed to "jump" from an orbit of high energy to one of lower energy, and in so doing, to emit a quantum, or photon, of light of a discrete wavelength. The wavelength is inversely proportional to the difference in energy between the two orbits involved in the jump. Thus a line in the violet, or short wavelength region of the spectrum, corresponds to a larger change of energy in the atom than a line in the red region.

The Bohr atom attained a wide popularity among physicists, chiefly because it accounted so well for many features of the observed spectrum. Certain difficulties soon became apparent, however, particularly in connection with attempts to extend the model to atoms with more than a single outer electron. In addition, physicists were becoming dissatisfied with the solar-system type of atom because of the artificial manner in which restrictions were imposed on the motion of the electron. It was becoming increasingly evident that an entirely new mechanics was necessary to account for the structure and behavior of atoms. This need has been supplied, largely through the work of de Broglie, Schrödinger, and Heisenberg in developing the theory of wave, or quantum, mechanics. In wave mechanics, the atom model is essentially mathematical. Attempts to visualize such a model inevitably lead to difficulties, but one significant point emerges from the theory, namely, the dual nature of waves and of particles. According to quantum-mechanical interpretation, an electron and a light quantum are each a combination of a group of waves and a particle. The nature of the particles and of the waves, as well as their interrelationship, remains as yet a mystery. Quite apart from philosophical considerations, the theory of quantum mechanics as applied to atomic processes appears to be in a highly satisfactory state.

The information that the physicist has made available concerning the structure of the atom has proved to be of inestimable value in ascertaining the physical conditions within stellar atmospheres. A star is a massive conglomeration of atoms, under certain conditions of temperature, pressure, and surface gravity. If we possess knowledge about the manner in which these conditions influence the emission of light by atoms in laboratory sources, we may apply our knowledge in the reverse order, and by examining the light emitted by a star via the spectrum, deduce the physical conditions under which the radiation is being sent forth. We know, for example, that if atoms are subjected to the influence of a magnetic field, each spectral line is split into several components. The magnitude of the splitting is dependent on the strength of the field. A minute splitting of this sort is observed in the spectrum of the solar disk. We conclude, therefore, that the sun, like the earth, is a huge magnet. Furthermore, when the spectra of sunspots are inspected, the splitting is highly conspicuous, indicating that the spots are centers of violent magnetic activity.

Measurements of intensities, both of the continuous background and of the dark lines, in stellar spectra, yield valuable information. The continuous background is not uniformly bright over the whole spectrum; the wavelength at which the radiation is strongest is governed by well-known laws, and depends on the temperature. For example, the spectrum of a red star (temperature 3000°C) is most intense in the red, that of the sun (temperature 6000°C) is strongest in the yellow region. As the temperature is increased, the maximum of spectral intensity shifts more and more toward the violet region, producing a corresponding change of color in the star. Such knowledge is extremely useful, since by measuring the position at which the radiation in a stellar spectrum is strongest, we are able to calculate the temperature of a star.

A knowledge of atomic structure is invaluable in any attempt to interpret the line spectra of stars. For the purposes of description, it is convenient to retain the orbital model of the atom, in which one or more electrons revolve about a nucleus. A bright line is produced when an electron jumps from an orbit of high energy to one of lower energy, but the jump is reversed in the stellar atmospheres. The radiation streaming from the photosphere is taken up by the atoms in the atmosphere and absorbed in the process of raising an electron from an orbit of low energy to one of higher energy. If the radiation is of sufficiently high energy, it may tear the electron completely away from the atom. Such a process is known as ionization, and the line spectrum of an ionized element is totally different from that of the same atom in the nonionized or neutral state. The various elements differ from one another with respect to their susceptibilities to ionization. Thus calcium requires a very small amount of energy to become ionized, whereas in the helium atom the electrons are very tightly bound, and require a large quantity of energy for ionization. Ionized helium accordingly shows up in the spectra of only the hottest stars, whereas ionized calcium may appear in the spectra of relatively cool bodies.

The measured intensities of dark lines are an index to the numbers of atoms producing the lines and hence to the abundances of the various elements present in stellar atmospheres. This conclusion is fairly obvious, for if a large number of atoms of a given element are present to absorb a particular radiation, a very dark line will result, since a large amount of energy will have been absorbed from the bright photospheric radiation. Conversely, a small number of atoms will produce a line of low intensity.

According to present indications, nearly all stars are essentially similar to each other in chemical composition. The conspicuous dissimilarities in the spectra of stars result not from differences in chemical composition but from differences in temperature, pressure, and surface gravity. The matter in the universe is thus even more uniform than Huggins supposed it to be.

The processes occurring in stellar atmospheres are by no means completely understood. But at least the broad outlines of the picture are accounted for, and the details are being rapidly filled in. It is indeed a triumph of human ingenuity that an understanding of the atom, a particle that is in the neighborhood of one billionth of a centimeter in diameter, has paved the way to a knowledge of the nature of stars, objects having diameters of the order of a million billion centimeters.

....

William Henry Pickering

ANNIE J. CANNON

(*The Telescope*, March–April 1938)

The death of William H. Pickering at Mandeville, Jamaica, on January 17, 1938, removes one of the few remaining astronomers intimately associated with the early photography of the sky. Born in Boston on February 15, 1858, in the family home on Mount Vernon Street, on Beacon Hill, he was an eighth descendant of John Pickering, who came from England to Salem about 1636 and built the Pickering house, standing now among Salem's famous colonial homes. He was also a great-grandson of Timothy Pickering, a friend and cabinet officer of George Washington. His mother was Charlotte Hammond, a descendant of William Hammond, who sailed from England about 1597 and settled in Wells, Maine, where he lived to the age of 105 years. Of sturdy English stock are the Pickerings!

After graduating from the Massachusetts Institute of Technology in 1879, William Pickering was an instructor in physics there for several years. In 1877 his brother, Edward C. Pickering, nearly twelve years his senior, and then professor of physics at the Institute, had been appointed director of the Harvard Observatory. It was a novelty, years later referred to by President Eliot as "my peculiar appointment," to put a physicist at the head of an astronomical observatory, but a novelty which the new developments of astronomy soon fully justified. Attracted by the great new era in astronomy, William abandoned teaching to undertake research

FIG. 49. William H. Pickering. (Photograph by Clyde Fisher)

at the observatory, and a few years later was made assistant professor of astronomy. Both Pickering brothers entered into the new problems with faith and enthusiasm.

William Pickering's advent to the observatory was at an auspicious time, for the recent improvements in the dryplate process of photography opened great possibilities for advancing astronomy along new lines. A crucial experiment was made when he took a photograph of the constellation Orion with a small camera attached to the tube of a telescope. The success was so evident that he suggested to his brother, the director, the importance of this method of astronomical research. Edward Pickering at once started a series of experiments which culminated in systematic photography of the whole heavens, and laid the foundation for the great Harvard collection of celestial photographs, now numbering 400,000 and containing the history of the sky for the last fifty years. . . .

The Harvard College Observatory and Miss Annie Cannon occupy a special place in any discussion of astronomical spectroscopy. Her article above shows how photography, destined to become so important in astronomy, was first linked to it there. The next excerpt, Miss Cannon's lecture in the series Harvard Observatory on the Air, broadcast by a Boston radio station in January 1941, shows the character of its author, a woman who contributed mightily to American astronomy and helped launch the strong tradition of women astronomers. Photography was used to record spectra as well as to map the skies, and Miss Cannon, after studying the spectra, categorized them in the classes O, B, A, F, G, K, M, R, N, S, although she was probably not responsible for the ditty "Oh, Be A Fine Girl, Kiss Me Right Now, Sweet" that helps all English-speaking astronomers to remember the sequence. — T L P

■■

The Story of Starlight[1]

ANNIE J. CANNON

(*The Telescope*, May–June 1941)

. . . Light coming through space with the marvelous velocity of 186,000 miles a second brings all the evidence we have of this great stellar universe. Light, whose radiations are unchanged whether but eight minutes on the way, as from the sun, or millions of years, as from distant galaxies, also brings to us knowledge which fifty years ago seemed almost beyond human thought. *Patient light!* Shining down on humanity these countless centuries until man became clever enough to wrest from its vibrations the secrets so closely concealed.

We can trace back the beginning of this new astronomy to 1666, when Isaac Newton bought at a country fair a crude prism, "to try therewith the phenomena of color." By many experiments he proved that white light is a mixture of differently refrangible rays. Since there was no English word to designate the beautiful band of multicolored rays produced by his prism, he took from the Latin the word *spectrum*, meaning an appearance. No word is heard more often in modern astronomy than this word *spectrum*. No starry appearance is more eagerly sought.

Newton did not fail to realize the importance of his experiments; for

[1] One of the series of radio talks *Harvard Observatory on the Air* given over station WRUL [Boston], January 18, 1941.

FIG. 50. Annie J. Cannon in 1925 when she received the degree of Doctor of Science from Oxford University.

thus he reported to the Royal Society his new "theory of light and color": "It is in my judgment the oddest if not the most considerable detection which hath hitherto been made in the operations of nature."

Odd, indeed, it did seem to the thinkers of that day, for Newton was persecuted by criticism and discussion. Even as late as 1790, the poet Goethe, who aspired to be a scientist, considered that "the idea of white light being composed of colored lights is quite inconceivable, mere twaddle, admirable for children in a gocart."

It was actually two hundred years before Newton's work was carried to fruition, and then those magical dark lines which traverse the spectra of all stars were forced to yield secrets enough to fill many chapters in the Story of Starlight. With the interpretation of the meaning of dark lines in stellar spectra, a new field of human thought and endeavor arose. Various astronomers began to supplement their telescopes with an instrument which by some such device as a wedge-shaped piece of glass, a prism, separates light into its component colors. The Italian astronomer Father Secchi observed the spectra of a large number of stars and placed them in four great classes. William Huggins, of London, assisted by his gifted wife, studied in detail some of the brighter stars. There was not at that time any method of distinguishing between a gaseous nebula and a cluster too distant for existing telescopes to resolve into stars. It was not even known that gaseous clouds existed. One of Huggins' early triumphs came in 1864, when he looked at the spectrum of a small nebula and found to his astonishment that it was not at all like that of a star, but only a bright line, proving the object to be not an aggregation of stars, but a luminous gas.

Meeting Sir William and Lady Huggins in London nearly fifty years after this discovery, I was delighted to hear them recount the joys of being astronomers in the 1860s, when nobody knew what a star was made of. "Those were the days," said Sir William, "when there was something worthwhile to do in astronomy."

All honor to those pioneers who accomplished so much from their visual observations of stellar spectra. For the human eye is not sensitive to a large range of color, and much of the blue end of the spectrum is produced by rays of wavelengths too short to be seen visually. But another development was close at hand. Chemists were busy mixing bromides and gelatins that were destined to change the whole method of astronomical research. Celestial photography had been started at Harvard on daguerreotype plates as early as 1850, and by the wet collodion process in 1857, but had been abandoned because of the slowness of the films. In 1882, when dryplates were available, astronomers were quick to recognize their value. The successful impression of the Great Comet of 1882 on such a plate in South Africa caused Sir David Gill, Her Majesty's Astronomer at the Cape of Good Hope, to commence the photography of the southern stars. Henry Draper of New York succeeded in photographing the spectrum of Vega, showing the dark lines of hydrogen. Edward C. Pickering, then director of Harvard College Observatory, commenced to experiment with lenses and dryplates, so that by 1885 he had started in earnest the great Harvard photographic collection of celestial objects.

Excellent star spectra dating back to 1885 may now be seen on Harvard plates, films still unfaded. Professor Pickering's interest never faltered, and the photographic telescopes were never idle on good nights. His successor, Harlow Shapley, continued with the same zeal, so that the Harvard photographic collection now contains five hundred thousand negatives, which may be likened to a library of first and only editions, the whole forming the sole record of events occurring in the stellar universe for the last half century. . . .

With the success of the photographic method, the old science of astronomy became a daylight profession, for one may see more by examining a photographic plate with a magnifying glass than by sitting up all night with eye at the telescope. Thus, naturally, astronomical research has a greater appeal to women than ever before. There is hardly an observatory in these latter days without a corps of women assistants. . . .

The harvest of discovery of peculiar and interesting celestial objects began with the first inspection of Harvard photographs. Let us note a few of these early discoveries. First, on December 11, 1885, the spectrum of the famous variable star Mira showed the hydrogen lines to be bright, which gave the first knowledge of this characteristic of long-period variables, and led to the detection of hundreds of similar variable stars. It may be added that by various methods, more than ten thousand variable stars have been discovered by means of the Harvard photographs.

Again, on November 3, 1887, the first photographic nova, V Persei, appeared on a Harvard photograph, and since that time the plates have yielded forty-five more. Doubtless many others are yet undiscovered among the great star clouds of the Milky Way.

Just one other instance of an important early discovery. On September 8, 1887, when there was much skepticism as to photographic evidence, and differences in the width of spectral lines was considered improbable, the spectra of Deneb, having very narrow lines, and Altair, with wider hazy lines, were photographed on the same plate to show such an appearance to be real and not due to the "vagaries of a negative."

As soon as a sufficient number of photographs had been secured, a sorting and classification was begun by Willimina Paton Fleming, so that as early as 1890 a catalogue of more than ten thousand stellar spectra was published. It was attempted merely to place all similar spectra together in groups designated by letters of the alphabet, for little was known of stellar evolution. Thus the A stars were those in whose spectra the lines of hydrogen predominated, as, for instance, Sirius and Vega; the G stars were of the solar type, as Capella; while M stands for red stars, as Betelgeuse. Photographs of larger dispersion, showing greater detail, were used by Antonia C. Maury in her classical study of the brighter stars, with results published in 1897.

For some years, little interest was shown in the subject of the classification of spectra, but about 1905, astronomers generally began to realize that the class of a star's spectrum is a fundamental fact, closely linked with other physical properties of the stars, such as motion, temperature, effective age, and even distance. Rather suddenly, it seemed, the class of spectrum became fashionable in astronomical circles. Makers of any sort of star catalogue, even the *Nautical Almanacs*, decided that inclusion of the spectra would be of value. Hence requests for the spectra of various lists of stars were constantly being received at the Harvard Observatory, since such information was not available elsewhere.

It was thus decided to select the best plates over the whole sky and make a general survey, including all stars for which the class was clearly indicated. "A census of the ether," this plan was called by Professor Turner of Oxford, for just as in the Roman census each citizen was assigned to his proper class and tribe, so each citizen of the sky, sufficiently bright, was given its proper place in the archives of the heavens.

By the time the whole sky from the north to the south pole was covered, 225,300 stars were enrolled in about forty classes of spectra. The results filled nine large volumes of the Harvard Observatory *Annals*. The classifi-

FIG. 51. The Harvard spectral sequence. (Harvard College Observatory photograph)

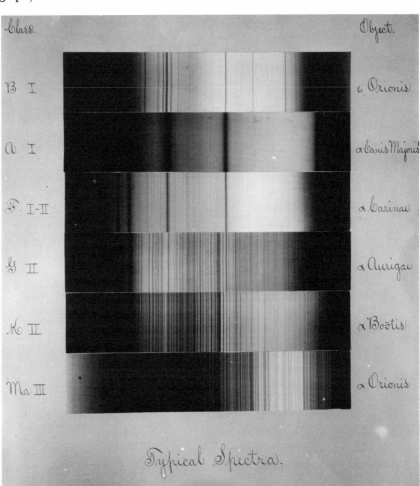

cation of such a large and varied assortment of stars "furnished proof," to quote from the minutes of the International Astronomical Union, "that the spectra of nearly all stars can be arranged in a continuous sequence differing almost imperceptibly from one another." The interest in the subject had become so great that many astronomers could not wait for publication, so that lists of spectra were made out from the copy and sent to other observatories or to isolated investigators.

Following the publication of the final volume of this catalogue in 1924, even fainter spectra were wanted by astronomers ever peering into more distant corners of the universe. Could we furnish them? Better instruments together with plates of more sensitive emulsions were proving successful in showing fainter spectra, so why not give them to those who could use them to increase human knowledge?

Astronomers form a true international brotherhood. Therefore, the Harvard photographs have been searched to furnish much information now incorporated in catalogues of several American observatories, as the United States Naval, the Yale, and the Dudley, as well as the Royal Observatory at the Cape of Good Hope. . . .

....

Miss Cannon and
Stellar Spectroscopy

CECILIA H. PAYNE-GAPOSCHKIN

(*The Telescope*, May–June 1941)

There is one book that is an essential component of the library of any observatory—whatever be the branch of astronomy to which the institution is devoted. Students of stellar motions, of galactic structure, of variable stars, all need to refer to the *Henry Draper Catalogue*.

The *Henry Draper Catalogue* is the greatest legacy that Miss Cannon has left to the scientific world. The system of the spectral classification of the stars that it contains represents a work comparable to the system of classification of living things that was made by Linnaeus. Almost a quarter of a million stars are contained in the catalogue, and they are arranged in about thirty stellar species, which are designated for convenience by the letters of the alphabet.

In the year 1884, when Miss Cannon graduated from Wellesley College, little indeed was known concerning the spectra of the stars. The pioneers of stellar spectroscopy had worked visually, but little progress was made until the methods of photography were applied to the study of stellar spectra. It was the eighties of the last century that saw the beginnings of the modern science in the work of Huggins and Lockyer in England, and the initiation of stellar photography under Edward C. Pickering at the Harvard Observatory. The succeeding ten years had seen the unfolding of new possibilities and the developing of new techniques, and when Miss Cannon joined the staff of the Harvard Observatory in 1896 it must have seemed to her that an unlimited area of uncharted country stretched before her; the spectra of hundreds of thousands of stars were accessible to classification. To her fell the pioneer's task of surveying the unknown territory; and at the end of a long and active life she has left it surveyed and mapped.

The first fruits of Miss Cannon's labor were contained in her description of the spectra of about sixteen hundred of the brighter stars. In the year 1901, after five years of research, she published her catalogue of these stars —a piece of work that is still a happy hunting ground for students of peculiar stars. But its chief value is the fact that this volume is the cornerstone on which her far greater catalogues were to be based—and securely based; for the foundations had been well laid.

Pickering, then the director of the Harvard Observatory, had long entertained the hope of producing a catalogue of the spectra of all the stars brighter than the ninth or tenth magnitude—a colossal enterprise, embracing almost a quarter of a million stars. When the telescopic equipment, in both the northern and southern hemispheres, was in readiness, he made his choice of the investigator who should carry out the work—and selected Miss Cannon. Her first catalogue (containing less than two thousand stars) had been the work of five years; the classifications that went into her second catalogue (which contained about two hundred and twenty-five thousand stars) were also carried out in the small span of five years, having been begun in 1911 and finished in 1915. The catalogue, which was named the *Henry Draper Catalogue* (in honor of the first man to photograph stellar spectra), was by no means completed when the classifications had been carried out from spectrum photographs [similar to that shown in Figure 51]. There remained the enormous task of collecting and arranging the material, preparing it for the printer, and seeing it through the press. That this task was by no means negligible in comparison with the actual scientific work may be concluded from the fact that the final volume was issued only in 1924. Miss Cannon bore much of the labor of supervising the publication, and carried the whole work after the death of Pickering in 1919.

The publication of the *Henry Draper Catalogue* did not see the end of

Miss Cannon's contributions to stellar spectroscopy. When its final volume was issued she was sixty years old and might well have felt that her life work had been completed. But, with the astonishing vitality that amazed and abashed her colleagues, she at once embarked on the heroic task of classifying the spectra of even fainter stars: an undertaking that was beyond the power of any human being to carry to completion. Until a few weeks before the end of her life, she continued the garnering of new material, and she leaves, unpublished, the spectra of a number of stars almost as great as that contained in the *Henry Draper Catalogue*. . . .

The continuous series of stellar spectra is a commonplace with astronomers of today. And yet it was only yesterday (cosmically speaking) that this same series of stellar spectra were shown to be the outward sign of stars very similar in general composition, but differing greatly in temperature and gravity at the surface. The spectral sequence is the foundation on which the science of modern astrophysics, the youngest and most vigorous child of the oldest of the sciences, has been founded. The astrophysicists of our own day, and of many a day to come, will build on the foundations of the *Henry Draper Catalogue*. Miss Cannon has mapped the field; and if the view that we see is distant and splendid, it is because we stand upon her shoulders.

....

Laboratory Exercises in Astronomy— Spectral Classification

OWEN GINGERICH

(*Sky and Telescope*, August 1964)

Auguste Comte, the French positivist philosopher, defined astronomy in 1835 as "the science by which we discover the laws of the geometrical and mechanical phenomena presented by the heavenly bodies." While the motions of the solar system could be analyzed and understood, the physical nature of the distant stars must be forever unknowable. "Men will never compass in their conceptions the whole of the stars," he stated.

Less than a quarter century later the German physicist Gustav Robert Kirchhoff laid down the laws of spectrum analysis, which opened a wholly new field for investigation. The study of the chemical and physical nature of the sun and stars, considered by Comte as hopelessly out of reach of the human intellect, became one of astronomy's most important branches.

After Kirchhoff's fundamental work, spectrum studies of the stars followed two different avenues. Astrophysicists such as William Huggins and Norman Lockyer combined laboratory experiments with detailed examinations of comparatively few stars in an attempt to discover their composition and physical conditions. On the other route, such pioneers as Angelo Secchi and E. C. Pickering undertook vast classifying schemes in order to understand better the diversity as well as the unity of the stellar populace. Ultimately both approaches were joined when Cecilia H. Payne (now Professor Payne-Gaposchkin) demonstrated that the apparent spectral differences arise primarily from variations in temperature or density, and that the overwhelming majority of stars in our galaxy must have quite similar chemical compositions.

Of all the great spectrum classification projects, none is more extensive than the famed *Henry Draper Catalogue,* a compendium of the spectral classes and magnitudes for 225,300 stars, prepared by Annie J. Cannon at Harvard Observatory. (The extensions to this catalogue, and other lists, brought the total of stars classified by Miss Cannon to nearly 400,000.)

Our laboratory exercise presents several score of stellar spectra in Figure 52. By a close examination of the numbered images, we can distinguish the salient features of the Harvard system, which forms the basis of most present classification schemes. This photograph, B9431, was taken with the 8-inch Bache doublet at Harvard's Arequipa, Peru, station in 1893. A thin prism covered the objective lens of the refractor, producing a spectrum for each star in the field.

This area of the sky, around Eta Carinae, exhibits a fascinating variety of spectral types. Nearly every major class is represented, as well as an unusual sprinkling of rarer kinds. Not only does this plate record a spectacular celestial region, but it is destined to be remembered in another way: B9431 was the first plate ever classified by Miss Cannon.

To begin your own classification of the stars on the portion of B9431 reproduced here, it is best to examine the enlarged samples in Figure 53. The narrow vertical lines provide the basis for the classification scheme. (Disregard the curvature of these lines, caused by aberrations in the optical system; they appear to curve in different ways because the samples have been selected from various parts of the plate.)

The stars in the key are placed in order of decreasing temperature. Violet is to the left, red toward the right, but since this is a blue-sensitive plate, the red, orange, and yellow have not been recorded. Note, however, that the hotter stars are generally much more intense in the violet than the cooler or "late-type" stars.

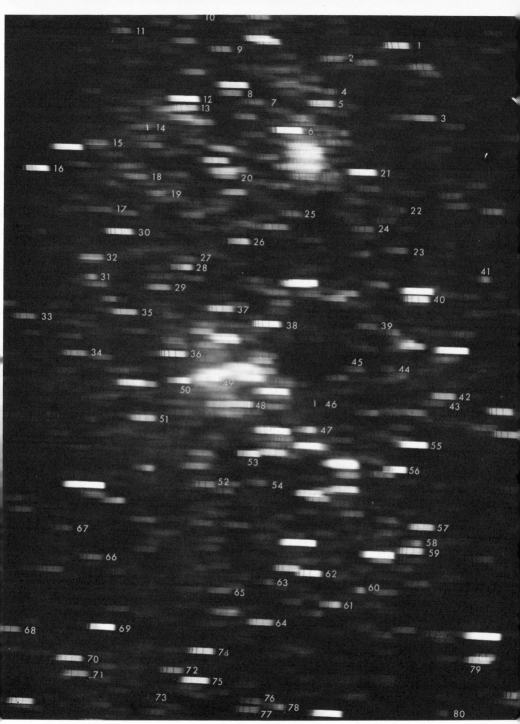

FIG. 52. An objective-prism spectrogram of the Eta Carinae region of the southern Milky Way, a 140-minute exposure on May 13, 1893, with the 8-inch Bache refractor. The violet ends of the spectra are to the left. (Harvard College Observatory photograph)

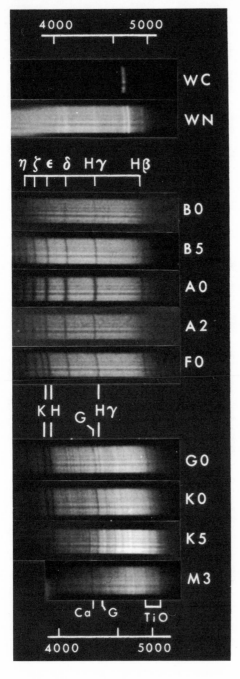

FIG. 53. Enlarged samples of spectra in Figure 52, placed in order (top to bottom) of decreasing temperature. Violet is to the left, red toward the right. WC = a Wolf-Rayet star, rich in carbon; WN = a Wolf-Rayet star, rich in nitrogen. (Harvard College Observatory photograph)

At the top of the key are shown two rare Wolf-Rayet objects, placed first because they are the hottest stars considered here. Since only about a hundred of them are known in the entire sky, the number shown on our plate is unusual. Note that bright (emission) lines appear in these hot stars. A first glance at the bottom of the key chart could suggest that emission lines are found there too, but this is simply an illusion caused by the crowded pattern of dark absorption lines, which predominate in K and M stars.

In the spectral types B, A, and F, the pattern of hydrogen lines (the so-called Balmer series) plays an important role. A wavelength scale and the Greek-letter designations of the hydrogen lines are marked above this group. The secret for classifying B, A, and F stars lies in the dominance of the hydrogen lines and in the relative strength of the K line of ionized calcium (Ca^+), marked below the group. Note that a decimal subdivision is used within the major letter types. For example, A-type stars can be divided into ten classes, A0, A1 . . . A9. Class B9 precedes A0, and A9 is followed by F0.

For the later spectral classes, G, K, and M, the strength of the G band with respect to $H\gamma$ (hydrogen-gamma) or the neutral calcium line at 4227 angstroms provides the best clue. In the M stars, the shaded molecular bands of titanium oxide (TiO) are conspicuous.

We can now investigate the smaller spectra on the photograph itself. For this purpose a small lens or magnifier will prove invaluable. As examples, examine the spectra numbered 30 to 32, and then 27. The hydrogen Balmer lines predominate in 30; clearly this is a late B- or A-type spectrum. Although the spectrum is well exposed, no trace of the K line is present, which indicates that the spectrum must be A0 or earlier. The hydrogen lines are conspicuous, though less so than in some comparably exposed spectra, such as 36. Therefore this star is classified B9.

Spectrum number 31 is much shorter than 30, which immediately suggests a late-type star. A comparison of the G band with the weakly visible 4227 line, plus the fading of the violet and consequent absence of H and K lines, indicates that a K5 classification could be defended. Above 31 lies the much longer spectrum of an early-type star, labeled 32. The hydrogen lines are barely visible. Miss Cannon lists it as B1 in the HD [*Henry Draper Catalogue*], but on the reproduction there is little to distinguish it from either B0 or B2. . . .

Beware of the unequal intensities of the spectra (caused by the differing magnitudes of the stars). Could 21 be an A-type star with some lines obliterated by the heavy exposure? Comparison with 38, another bright star, suggests that 21 actually has a B-type spectrum.

Armed with the key photograph and descriptions below, you should be able to work faster and more accurately than Miss Cannon could back in 1896. In her first three days she classified sixty-two A stars, eleven G stars, five M stars, and a K star, without numerical subclasses. . . .

The following descriptions are designed to supplement Figure 53:

Bo—On a long continuum the Balmer series of hydrogen is faintly visible; if the spectrum is well exposed, a few helium lines may be seen. Neutral helium is strongest at B2, and then fades rapidly toward Ao.

Ao—Hydrogen lines of the Balmer series are at their strongest; helium is no longer present, and the calcium H and K lines are not yet visible on this reproduction.

Fo—The Balmer lines are still conspicuous, although only half as strong as in Ao; the K line of ionized calcium is as strong as the blend of Hϵ (hydrogen-epsilon) and the H line of calcium.

Go—In this solar-type spectrum, the H and K lines are the strongest features. The Balmer lines are no longer conspicuous. The continuum spectrum shows through between the numerous metal lines that are just at the limit of visibility, sometimes giving a false impression of emission lines. This aspect is even more troublesome in the K stars.

Ko—The energy maximum of the spectrum lies so far to the red that the calcium H and K lines cannot be seen on a weak spectrum, even though they reach their greatest intensity in this class. Many metal lines are easily visible. The strongest is that of neutral calcium at 4227 angstroms. Even stronger is the G band 80 angstroms to the red of the calcium line.

Mo—The wide bands of TiO, shaded toward the violet, mark the spectra of the M class. The 4227 line of calcium is very strong, and the G band is also conspicuous.

Spectra were first observed by eye; then, as noted in the early parts of this chapter, photography was used to great advantage. For quantitative measure of the brightness at various wavelengths in a spectrum, however, the photographic plate or film introduces difficulties. The blackening produced by light can be measured accurately, but the amount of blackening depends on brightness in a complicated way; it also depends on the color of the light, on development, and on how the film was manufactured and stored. For many of the same reasons that photoelectric photometers are used instead of photographs to measure star brightnesses, new techniques are being introduced for direct electronic recording of spectra. —T L P

....

Electric
Spectrophotometry

(*Sky and Telescope*, April 1953)

An electric thermometer for taking a star's temperature was described by Donald A. MacRae, of the Warner and Swasey Observatory, Case Institute of Technology. The surface temperatures of most stars range up to four or five times that of the sun, which is close to 6000° centigrade. By combining a photoelectric cell and the objective prisms of the Schmidt telescope, small differences of temperature of the order of 2 per cent can readily be detected.

A hotter star will have a greater light intensity in the violet and a smaller intensity in the red when compared to a cooler star of the same apparent magnitude. This corresponds to the well-known fact that hot stars have a bluish hue, while cool stars like the sun are yellowish. The photoelectric cell, recently put to widespread use in astronomical problems of light measurement, makes it possible to measure these differences of intensity with great accuracy directly from the spectrum of each star.

Previously, the photoelectric colors of stars have been studied by the use of broad-band light filters. The present method is more advantageous because the range of wavelength admitted to the photocell at one time is much smaller, the part of the spectrum measured is accurately defined, and the heavy absorption lines which block off the star's continuous radiation can be avoided. The older methods of scanning photographic spectra in a similar manner also had these advantages; but the observations were tedious, only the brightest stars were generally accessible, and a single spectrogram was of low precision. The new instrumental combination can reach the seventh magnitude without serious loss of accuracy or telescope time. About five minutes are required for the tracing of one star's spectrum, with a result like that shown in Figure 54 for Vega.

MacRae showed how slight anomalies in the spectral distribution of a star's light intensity could be detected and how the color temperatures could be compared with temperatures found by other methods. The reddening of starlight by interstellar dust is clearly marked in some distant stars. The growth and decay of the stronger absorption lines along the spectral sequence can also be measured quantitatively from the observational data.

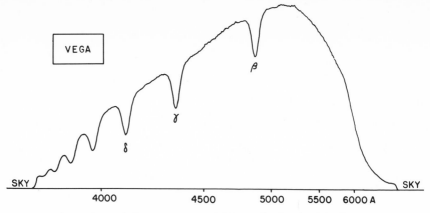

FIG. 54. A tracing of the spectrum of Vega obtained with the 6° objective prisms and the photoelectric photometer attached to the Schmidt telescope of the Case Institute of Technology.

The red end of the Vega photoelectric spectrogram is toward the right. The recurrent dips in intensity are the strong absorption lines of the Balmer series of hydrogen, beginning with Hβ in the green. The numbers along the bottom are wavelengths in angstrom units. The horizontal tracing gives the measured intensity of the sky background; the height of the trace above this reading is directly proportional to the light intensity in the star's spectrum. The intensity falls rather abruptly in the red because the photomultiplier tube ceases to be sensitive to radiation much beyond 6000 angstroms. The intensity falls slowly toward the blue because the analyzing slit admits a smaller range of wavelengths as it proceeds in this direction, on account of the increasing dispersion of the prism.

Although higher accuracy is possible, this photoelectric scanning of a spectrum is still limited to fairly bright stars. Notice, also, that only one spectrum can be observed at a time, while the objective prism photograph in Figure 52 records more than a hundred. In infrared wavelengths, photographic emulsion loses even this advantage, and new techniques have been developed during the past twenty years. First, during World War II, infrared detectors were invented, and these were used to scan the spectra of planets and stars. Most recently, the interferometer has been applied in an ingenious scheme to avoid wasting light from a faint source. — T L P

●●●

Infrared Spectroscopy with an Interferometer

PETER B. BOYCE AND WILLIAM M. SINTON

(*Sky and Telescope*, February 1965)

Astronomers have been studying the spectra of celestial objects in ever-increasing detail. In stellar spectroscopy, for instance, photographic techniques have long been used to determine the luminosities and temperatures of stars, and more recently for refined analyses of their chemical compositions.

To determine abundances, it is necessary that some characteristic line from each element be present in the observed spectrum. Especially in the case of molecules, which are abundant in cool stars, the characteristic spectral features may lie in the ultraviolet or infrared portions of the spectrum. Two of the most familiar molecules, water and carbon monoxide, can be detected in stellar spectra only by observations in the infrared.

Ultraviolet radiation from the stars is cut off by the earth's atmosphere, but the infrared spectrum can be studied in certain wavelength regions ("windows") where the atmosphere is quite transparent. In particular, the interval from 1.8 to 2.6 microns (one micron equals 10,000 angstroms) is relatively free from atmospheric absorption, and it is here that certain groups of lines of carbon monoxide and water vapor appear. The presence of these molecules, although predicted by the theory of molecular formation, has only recently been confirmed observationally for a few stars. Consequently, it is important to search spectroscopically for these molecules in a large number of stars of various spectral types and luminosities.

Unfortunately, stars radiate very little energy in the 1.8-to-2.6-micron region, and the sensitivity of the available detectors is quite low. Since no photographic film is sensitive enough to be useful for recording stellar spectra at wavelengths longer than one micron, the present practice is to scan the spectrum with a photoelectric detector [Fig. 55]. In this method, the starlight is dispersed into a spectrum by either a prism or a grating, as in a conventional spectrograph. Instead of the photographic plate, a second slit is used to isolate a small region of the spectrum. All of the light passing through this slit is made to fall on a photosensitive detector. A tracing of intensity versus wavelength is then produced by sweeping the

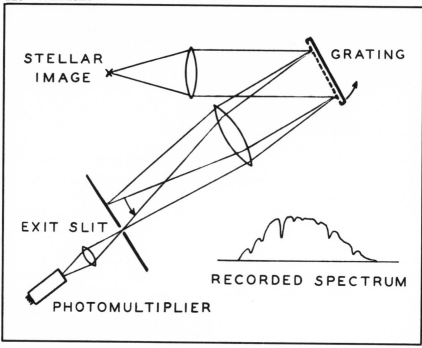

FIG. 55. Essential parts of a scanning spectrophotometer. As the grating turns, the photocell output traces the spectrum.

spectrum past the second slit. Unavoidably, only a small fraction of the total light falls on the detector; the rest does not pass through the exit slit and is wasted.

However, there is a way to obtain stellar spectra that is not so wasteful of light. This is the method of interferometry, in which the total light is split into two beams that travel different optical paths. If the source is monochromatic (one emission line), and if the path lengths are the same, the recombination produces a total intensity that is the sum of the intensities of the two beams. If, however, the paths differ in length by exactly one half the wavelength of the light, the two beams are exactly opposite in phase when they are recombined, and the resultant intensity is zero.

When we start with two equally long optical paths and gradually change one, the intensity of the combined light beam goes through a series of maxima and minima that are called *fringes*. In general, these fringes are recorded with a photosensitive detector. Fringes will be produced even if the light is not monochromatic, but the amplitude will decrease rapidly with increasing path length.

The importance of the fringes is that their pattern is directly related to the spectrum of the light source, whether this is monochromatic or not. The relationship is unique; one spectrum will produce only one set of fringes, this set being different from that produced by any other spectrum. Mathematically, the fringe pattern is said to be the "Fourier transform" of the spectrum. The practical problem is to record the fringes with some kind of digital data device, in such a manner that an electronic digital computer can process them. The computer can be programed to transform the fringe pattern into the spectrum of the light entering the interferometer.

From what has been said, it is obvious that all the light goes into the formation of the fringes that carry the spectral information, apart from a quite small wastage in the optics of the instrument. Thus the interferometric method of recording stellar spectra should give a large gain over conventional procedures.

The theoretical gain can be expressed as follows: Suppose we wish to observe conventionally a 1000-angstrom interval of spectrum by scanning it with a 10-angstrom slit. In this case, the spectral region of interest is split into 100 independent intervals. The interferometer gain will be the square root of the number of intervals, in this instance $(100)^{1/2}$, or 10. This gain can be realized with infrared detectors but not with photocells, where the noise increases with greater light.

Several spectral interferometers have been built for astronomical purposes. Hitherto these telescope accessories have not turned out to be as good for spectral work as had been hoped, because of the strong influence of atmospheric seeing fluctuations upon the resultant spectra. Most of the designs have been similar to the conventional Michelson interferometer, in which the light is split into two beams by a semitransparent mirror. Such an instrument is very hard to keep in alignment, particularly when it is fastened on the end of a telescope that may be pointed in various directions and is subject to large changes in temperature.

To overcome these drawbacks, we at Lowell Observatory use the birefringence of a crystal to produce the difference in path lengths. This design, originally suggested by Lawrence Mertz of Block Associates, uses a Wollaston prism to divide the light into two beams polarized at right angles to each other. Then the two beams traverse a birefringent crystal in which the path length for plane-polarized light in the direction of the optical axis is different from that of light polarized at right angles to it. Finally, the two beams are brought together in another Wollaston prism to produce the interference (Fig. 56). Our birefringent crystal is made of two titanium-dioxide prisms placed together. The thickness of this crystal, and hence the difference in path lengths, is changed by sliding one prism across the

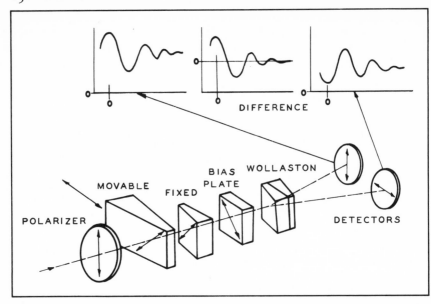

FIG. 56. A schematic diagram of Boyce and Sinton's interferometer. Starlight enters at lower left, passes through two rutile prisms and a rutile bias plate, then is split into two polarized beams by a Wollaston prism. The difference between the two fringe patterns is analyzed to find the spectrum.

other. The scheme is almost one hundred times less sensitive to errors of alignment than is the Michelson type of interferometer.

A serious problem in recording stellar spectra is the change in atmospheric "seeing." In addition, the sky radiates quite strongly at various wavelengths throughout the infrared. Thus it is very important to employ a comparison instrument that can remove the effects of sky radiation. This can be done by using two apertures and alternately recording the signal of the sky alone and of star plus sky. Subtracting the first signal from the second gives that of the star alone.

The Lowell Observatory interferometer also utilizes the fact that the beam coming out of the last Wollaston prism can be divided into two sets of fringes of opposite phase. The difference between these two gives another set of fringes that are relatively independent of intensity fluctuations due to the earth's atmosphere.

This seeing compensation has proved good enough to allow us to obtain for the first time with an interferometer good infrared stellar spectra. We have obtained spectra of fainter stars than has heretofore been possible in the wavelength range from two to four microns. At present, our limit is about magnitude 2 for Ko stars and 6 for M5 stars with a 69-inch telescope, and about 2.5 magnitudes fainter with a 200-inch telescope. However, by reworking the optics and employing different detectors, we should eventually be able to go another two or three magnitudes fainter, with a resolution of about eighty angstroms at two microns.

So far, we have observed more than forty stars with the Lowell interferometer, attached to the 69-inch Perkins Observatory reflector and the 200-inch telescope at Palomar Observatory. The fringe intensities are sampled at equal intervals of path difference, and the voltage output from the amplifiers is converted to numbers which are punched automatically into an IBM card. The digital recordings of the fringes are converted into a spectrum by an IBM 7094, all in about fifteen seconds for a full-length spectrum.

The spectra obtained in this way reveal several interesting features. Figure 57 shows our spectrum of Aldebaran; the dashed curve is for Sirius, plotted on the same scale. The bands at 2.01 and 2.06 microns, due to carbon dioxide (CO_2) in the earth's atmosphere, are common to both stars. But at 2.293 microns and continuing toward longer wavelengths,

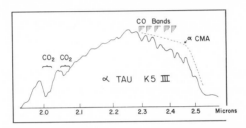

FIG. 57. Intensity tracings of the spectrum of Aldebaran and Sirius made with Boyce and Sinton's device. The CO bands originate in the star's atmosphere, the CO_2 in the earth's.

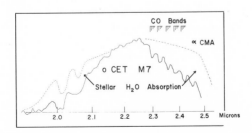

FIG. 58. Spectrum of a very cool star, Mira, reveals the existence of water vapor in its atmosphere. This is shown by the weakness of both ends of its spectrum relative to that of the hot star, Sirius (dashed line).

the Aldebaran spectrum is depressed by bands of carbon monoxide (CO) in that star's atmosphere. Since Sirius is much too hot for CO to form, it lacks these bands. Other observations show that with stars of advancing spectral type the strength of the CO bands increases.

Very red giant stars, of which Mira is a good example, not only show the CO bands very strongly, but their spectra are depressed at each end, compared to the spectrum of Sirius (Fig. 58). To understand this, it is important to realize that water vapor in the earth's atmosphere is limiting the wavelength region under study. These water-vapor bands become much broader at high temperatures. These wide absorptions in the spectra of very late-type stars are due to water vapor in the stellar atmospheres themselves. . . .

Characteristics

of Stars

Derived

from Spectra

Miss Cannon's spectral classes for the quarter million stars in the Henry Draper Catalogue showed a regularity in the spectra—the temperature sequence O, B, A, F, G, K, M—and provided a vast quantity of data for statistical analysis. For instance, these data raise the questions, Are there more B-stars than A-stars? (B-stars are stars with spectra of type B; A-stars have type A spectra.) Are all M-stars of the same luminosity? The same mass? Do stars form clusters according to spectral type? Are other observable characteristics, such as motions, rotations, and variability, correlated with spectral type?

One of the earliest of such statistical studies, and possibly the most significant, concerned the correlation between spectral type and luminosity as shown by a "Hertzsprung-Russell diagram," a plot of one against the other, as in Figure 59. For this purpose, and for many others, spectral type might have been replaced by color index, $B - V$, since both measure the surface temperature of the star. Much of the recent research is phrased in terms of "color-magnitude" diagrams rather than H-R diagrams. (Note, however, that spectral type is used in Figure 59 despite the word "color" in the title of the article.) — T L P

■■■

What Determines the
Color of a Star?

MARTIN SCHWARZSCHILD

(*The Telescope*, July–August 1940)

Why do stars look different? Why, for example, is Sirius so much bluer than Betelgeuse and Capella so much brighter than the sun? There seem to be two possible reasons for these differences among the stars, namely, differences in the masses and differences in the chemical compositions. Unfortunately, these data are not easily accessible to observation. The composition of a stellar atmosphere may be derived more or less accurately from analysis of the spectrum, but there is little reason to believe that the interior of a star is identical in composition with the atmospheric "skin." Stellar masses may be obtained only for the components of double stars, which are rather few in number.

There are two other quantities, however, that can be measured for a great number of stars: the luminosity (or absolute magnitude), and the color (or spectral type). Since one can expect these two quantities to be closely related to the masses and compositions, the study of the luminosities and colors of stars plays an important role in the theory of the stellar interior.

When the colors and luminosities of the stars are plotted on a diagram, several interesting features emerge. Such a diagram for the nearby stars, first constructed by Hertzsprung and Russell in 1913, is shown in Figure 59A. Each point represents a star; points in the upper part of the diagram represent intrinsically bright stars and in the lower part fainter stars; points at the left-hand side correspond to blue stars; those at the right to red stars. The sun, a yellow star, lies near the middle of the diagram at absolute magnitude +5 and spectral class G0.

We see that the diagram is not at all uniformly filled with points. On the contrary, the majority of points crowd toward a line running diagonally through the figure. This line is called the main sequence. The luminosities of the main-sequence stars are correlated with their colors; the most luminous stars are blue, and the fainter main-sequence stars, the *dwarfs*, are yellow or red. A few faint bluish stars are situated in the lower left-hand corner; these are the *white dwarfs*. A number of luminous, yellow or red stars, the so-called *giants* and *supergiants*, lie in the upper right-hand corner.

What can we now find out about the relation of the luminosities and

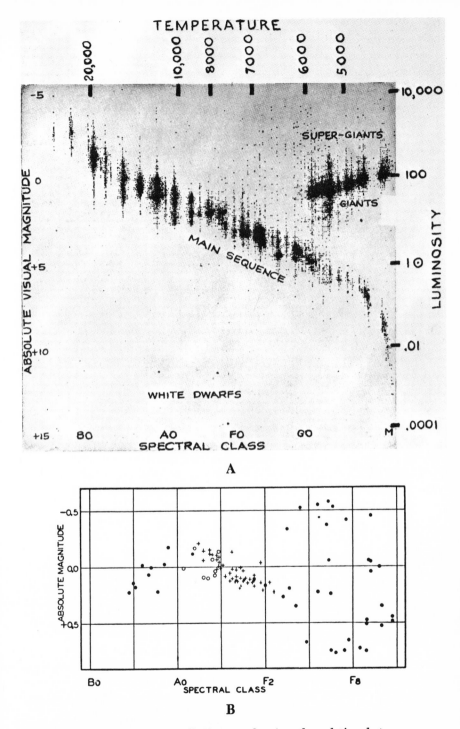

FIG. 59. A. Hertzsprung-Russell diagram showing the relation between spectrum (color) and absolute magnitude (luminosity) of stars in general. The points represent 6700 stars. (Diagram by W. Gyllenberg) B. A similar diagram for the Cepheid variables in Messier 3. Solid dots are nonvariable, comparison stars.

colors on the one hand and the masses and compositions on the other? From the determinations of the masses of double stars has emerged the discovery that stellar masses are closely correlated with luminosities in the sense that the most massive stars are the most luminous. Thus stars in the upper part of Figure 59A are highly massive, whereas those in the lower portions are relatively light.

We see, therefore, that the differences in luminosity are essentially produced by differences in mass. Should we not suspect, then, that differences in color may be produced by differences in chemical composition? In order to test this hypothesis, we should like to be able to compare the colors of stars of different chemical composition. The stars that make up the clusters, both open and globular, would seem to afford the best means for such a comparison. Since the stars in clusters are physically associated, it is reasonable to assume that they are built of the same "star stuff." We might therefore expect similarities in the compositions of all the stars in one cluster but considerable divergences in composition from one cluster to another. Observations show striking differences in the colors of stars in one cluster as compared with those in another cluster. In the Pleiades, for example, the brightest members are all blue main-sequence stars, whereas the brightest members of the globular cluster Messier 3 (Fig. 60) are red giants. The more luminous stars of one cluster are very similar in color to one another, but very dissimilar compared with the stars in another cluster. Hence we conclude that differences in composition are most likely responsible for differences in color among stars of the same mass. We have thus obtained at least a qualitative picture of the way in which the mass and the composition of a star determine its color and luminosity and therefore its position in the color-luminosity diagram.

Where are the variable stars in the Hertzsprung-Russell (H-R) diagram? The physical variables like the Mira stars, the Cepheids, and the short-

FIG. 60. Messier 3 photographed in red light. The bright images are giant red stars.

period variables lie with the giants on the diagram. A special investigation of the globular cluster Messier 3 has recently been concluded at Harvard Observatory for the purpose of studying in detail the locations of variables and nonvariable giants on the H-R diagram. The essential results are illustrated in Figure 59B, showing only a section of the diagram. Each dot represents a nonvariable star in Messier 3, and each cross or circle a variable. Notice, first, that the variables all fall in a very small region of the diagram; and, second, that no nonvariables occur in this region. (New measures indicate that the one star represented by a dot near the center of the variable region is also variable.)

Remembering that the position of a star in the diagram is determined by its mass and composition, we may conclude not only that a star must possess a specific mass and composition in order to vary, but also that if a star does possess this specific mass and composition, it *must* be variable.

There is much more about variable stars in Chapter 5. Cepheid variables pulsate periodically, and the period is longer for the more luminous Cepheids. That is, the average luminosity of a Cepheid can be calculated from its measured period of pulsation, and comparing the luminosity with the measured brightness (apparent magnitude) yields the star's distance (see p. 90). Hence Cepheid variables have been very useful for measuring astronomical distances.

In addition to the color and spectral type, both related to surface temperature, other details in a star's spectrum reveal such conditions as pressure, magnetic field, and motion—turbulence in hot gases near the surface, or rotation of the star, or motion of the star in an orbit around another star, or straight-line motion in space. Only the motions toward or away from the earth produce a "Doppler shift" in the spectrum. This shift is a change in the wavelength of each line from its normal λ to a new value, λ', and the size of the shift, λ'—λ, is proportional to the radial velocity, V. In fact, λ'—λ = λV/c, where c is the velocity of light, 186,000 miles per second.

If a star is moving toward us at 186 mi/sec, the green hydrogen line, Hγ is at λ' = 4336.13 A instead of its normal 4340.47 A wavelength, a Doppler shift of 4.34 A toward the blue. In the same spectrum, Hα at 6563 A is shifted 6.56 A, and the strong utraviolet line, Lyman α, normally at 1215.7 A is shifted 1.22 A. Turbulence and stellar rotation can produce a wide range of motions toward and away from us, giving a broadening of all lines in the spectrum.

The "Zeeman effect" is a more complicated shift of spectrum lines, caused by magnetic fields in the outer layers of a star, as described in Chapter 6. Pressure has an effect too—lines are broadened and some of them enhanced. This provides a simple way to distinguish between giant stars

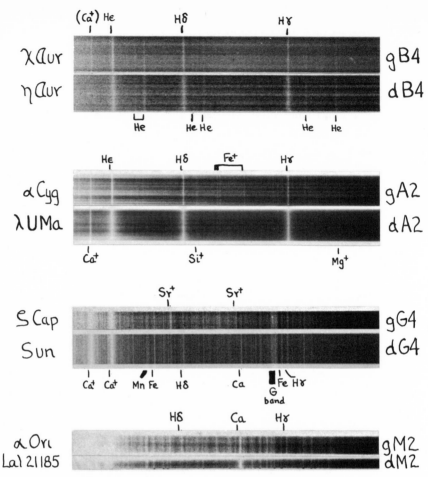

FIG. 61. The differences between the spectra of giant and dwarf stars are shown here. The upper spectrum of each pair is the giant. In χ Aurigae and α Cygni, the lines are sharper than in the dwarfs of the same spectral type. In ζ Capricorni, a giant, the lines of ionized strontium are much more conspicuous than in the dwarf sun (both are G-type stars). The line in χ Aurigae marked Ca+ is due to interstellar calcium, indicating the star's great distance compared with that of η Aurigae. (Spectra by W. W. Morgan of Yerkes Observatory, from *The Milky Way* by B. J. Bok and Priscilla Bok, Harvard University Press, Cambridge, Massachusetts, 1957)

and main-sequence dwarfs (see Fig. 61). In addition to the spectral type it is possible to rank stellar spectra by "luminosity classes": I for giants; II, III, IV, and V for dwarfs—a sequence first used for distance estimates by Walter S. Adams at Mount Wilson and later established by W. W. Morgan and Philip Keenan at the Yerkes Observatory during the 1930s. In white dwarf stars (see Fig. 108) the pressure effect is extreme and the lines so broadened that the spectral type is almost unrecognizable. Luckily, the white dwarfs (see Chapter 7) did not confuse Miss Cannon and the early work on spectral classification; the first spectrum of a white dwarf was photographed by Walter S. Adams at Mount Wilson in 1915. —TLP

A Master of Stellar Spectra

HARLOW SHAPLEY

(*Sky and Telescope*, July 1956)

The passing of Walter Sydney Adams at the age of eighty on May 11 has taken from us an American astronomer of the first rank, who was director of Mount Wilson Observatory from 1923 to 1946. . . .

Adams was a builder and a manager, but primarily an observer. Probably few men have devoted more hours at the eyepiece of a spectrum-measuring engine than he, and for this devotion the stars owe him much. His catalogues of high-quality radial velocities will stand as a quiet monument, for Adams measured extensively the ordinary stars whose characteristics are needed against which to judge the more exciting exotics.

FIG. 62. Walter S. Adams (1876–1956) (California Institute of Technology photograph)

Although he was catalogue minded, many spectroscopic highlights are his, for example, the difficult analysis of the spectrum of Sirius B, the most famous white dwarf. We probably have not had the last word on the red shift in the spectrum of that faint, exceedingly dense star, but Adams found that, in addition to its orbital motion, there is a line shift consistent with what we would expect from relativity theory.

The work of Adams, with G. E. Hale, C. E. St. John, and their colleagues, on the intricacies of the solar spectrum is historic. The rotation, eruptions, and other manifestations of that turbulent stellar surface were analyzed with increasing instrumental power. . . .

The name of W. S. Adams will always be associated with spectroscopic parallaxes [distances determined from luminosity class and measured brightness of each star]. He was the pioneer. He can rightly be called the father of that tremendously important extension of the Draper system of classifying stellar spectra by luminosity classes. But when Adams first published on this subject, in 1916, the criteria of absolute magnitude (luminosity) were not considered to require a second dimension in spectral classification. That concept was developed much later by W. W. Morgan and others. Forty years ago, however, it was nothing less than sensational to find that one could look at the dark lines of strontium in the spectrum of a distant star (for which the apparent magnitude had been measured) and announce its distance. Certainly the concept of spectroscopic parallax was one of the major early contributions from Mount Wilson Observatory. It took a keen eye and a keen mind to open that field.

Modesty was instinctive with Walter Adams. . . . I remember complimenting him once on his designing the series of powerful and tricky spectrographs that were used in the Mount Wilson stellar and solar work. "It is a very low form of cunning," he replied.

···

Stellar Rotation

OTTO STRUVE

(*Sky and Telescope*, November 1946)

My first task upon arrival at the Yerkes Observatory twenty-five years ago was to determine the radial velocities of several hundred helium and hydrogen stars[1] by measuring their Doppler displacements. I vividly recall

[1] Stars of spectral classes B and A are notable, respectively, for the lines of helium and hydrogen in their spectra.

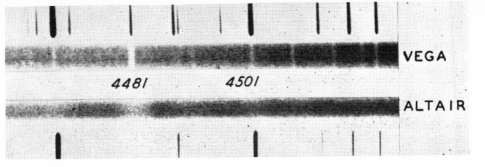

FIG. 63. Comparison of the spectra of Vega and Altair shows the widening of the lines in the latter star, due to its rapid rotation. The effect is particularly observable in the 4481 line. (Yerkes Observatory photograph)

the feeling of frustration which I experienced when I found that more than half of the stars on Professor Frost's program had such broad and ill-defined absorption lines that accurate settings with the wire of the microscope were difficult or even impossible. It is true that these diffuse lines agreed in position and pattern with the laboratory lines of such common substances as iron, magnesium, calcium, and so forth, so that there could be no doubt about their identifications. But whereas in the laboratory, under low or moderate pressure, the spectral lines are always sharp and narrow, in the stars these same lines may be either narrow, as in Vega, or broad, as in Altair. There is no conspicuous physical difference between these two stars: their temperatures, luminosities, diameters, and masses are roughly the same. Yet, when photographed with a spectrograph of moderate power, their spectra are strikingly different.

To an observer of radial velocities this phenomenon must have appeared as a threat: how can we be certain that the processes which tend to broaden the stellar absorption lines work in a symmetrical manner? Would a setting made upon the geometrical middle of a line, whose edges correspond to radial velocities of, perhaps, +310 and —290 kilometers per second, actually represent the motion in the line of sight of the star as a whole, which may be as small as 10 kilometers per second? Without a knowledge of the broadening mechanism, we could quite easily imagine processes at work whose effect would have been to vitiate the measured velocities. My first interest in the problem of diffuse absorption lines arose from a desire to clarify this question.

Several astronomers had already suggested that the broadening of the lines could be caused by the rotation of the stars around their axes. But the evidence was very confusing, and the opinions were divided. The prevailing view was to doubt the possibility of equatorial velocities of rotation which exceeded by a factor of 100 the velocity of rotation of the sun.

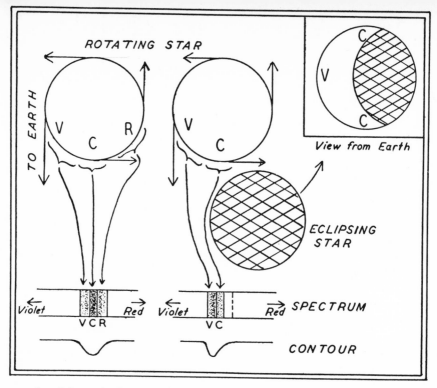

FIG. 64. Schematic diagram showing (left) the simple theory of how a star's rotation about an axis approximately perpendicular to the line of sight to the earth widens its spectral lines. The portions V, C, and R of the line come from the corresponding areas of the hemisphere of the star we see. If the star is eclipsed, its companion may cut off a portion of the light (right) and change the position and contour of a spectral line. The inset shows the "appearance" from the earth at the phase of the eclipse here illustrated.

In an eclipsing variable,[2] during the partial phases, the eclipsing component gradually obscures and then reveals the eclipsed component (Fig. 64); just before totality sets in and immediately after it only the opposite limbs of the eclipsed component remain visible. By observing the spectrum at these two times, we should be able to determine the radial velocities of the opposite limbs directly, and then derive the velocity of rotation. This procedure was applied by E. Rossiter and Dean B. McLaughlin independently, to the Michigan observations of Beta Lyrae and Algol respectively, and established beyond doubt the existence of large rotational velocities in close binaries.

The recognition that rotation accounts for the diffuse lines of *single* stars came gradually. For example, if we determine the velocity of rotation

[2] A double star in which first one star, then the other star comes between its companion and the earth.

of Algol from the diffuseness of its lines when the star's light is at maximum, we find exactly the same value as that determined from observations of the eclipsing effect. And furthermore, the shape (or contour) of the absorption lines of Algol outside of eclipse (see Fig. 65) is precisely the same as that of many single stars, so that there is no reason to doubt that the broadening mechanism is the same. C. T. Elvey has aptly described these lines as "dish shaped."

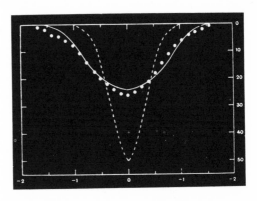

FIG. 65. The ionized magnesium line 4481 when Algol is out of eclipse. Abscissas are angstroms, and ordinates are percentages of absorption. The observations are shown by the dots. The broken curve represents the assumed contour of the line for a nonrotating star, and the continuous curve is the computed contour for a rotational velocity of 67 kilometers per second.

An interesting early confirmation of these ideas was obtained by G. Shajn, the present director of the Crimean Astrophysical Observatory in Russia. He photographed the spectrum of Jupiter with the 40-inch reflector at Simeis, and permitted the entire disk of the planet to trail uniformly over the slit of the spectrograph. The spectral lines were appreciably broadened, and since the rotation of Jupiter is known, Shajn was able to verify that the theory gave correct results. The results of Shajn's work, together with my own, were published in 1929 in a joint paper in the *Monthly Notices* of the Royal Astronomical Society.

Since then he and I, and many others, have worked on the problem of stellar rotation, and the principal results are fairly well known. There are, however, a number of unsolved riddles, and to some of these I should like to devote a few paragraphs.

What is the spectrum of a rapidly rotating star like when it is observed from the direction of the poles? Among the many stars whose real equatorial velocities of rotation are several hundred kilometers per second, there must be some which are oriented in such a way that we see them from the direction of their axes. The lines would then be narrow, and we might find it difficult to distinguish such stars from others whose real rotations are slow. . . .

About two years ago F. J. Neubauer, of Lick Observatory, and I observed the eclipsing binary RZ Scuti. During the partial phases the shift in radial velocities is very prominent. But we found that the rotational velocity measured in helium is about twice as large as that measured in hydrogen. Our conclusion is that the star has no sharp edge, and that its gases are stratified, with helium below and hydrogen on top. Presumably the inner, helium, atmosphere rotates with the star, but the upper, hydrogen, strata fail to keep up with this rapid rotation, and fall behind. This is somewhat like the conception held by some ancient astronomers, who denied the axial rotation of the earth because of the "wind" that would be produced by the stationary air. . . .

Another question of cosmogonical interest arises when we compare the rotational velocities of the components of close double stars. All systems thus far observed have rotations in the same sense, namely in that in which the orbital motion takes place. . . . Are there any systems in which the rotations are opposite in sense to the orbital motion, or in which at least one component rotates with a longer period than it revolves? We do not know. . . .

We are approaching the toughest question of all, How did stellar rotations originate? . . . There is a very remarkable relation between the physical characteristics of stars and their average rotations. Among the O, B, A, and early F stars we find some that rotate rapidly and some that rotate slowly, but all single stars of classes F_5 and later have relatively slow rotations. . . . The transition at about F_5 is quite sudden. Why? . . . Can it be that a large fraction of those late-type stars which would normally possess rapid rotations have, by some as yet unknown process, produced planetary systems and in this manner relieved themselves of a large fraction of their angular momenta? After all, the sun is also a late-type star; and computation shows that if the planets were combined with the sun, the velocity of rotation of the latter would be much more rapid than it is at present. It is only fair that I should warn the reader to accept this speculation with reserve. . . .

Struve's ideas about the links between stellar rotation, orbital motion in pairs, and planetary systems are still under study by many astronomers. (There is further discussion of the planetary systems in Volume 3 of this series, The Origin of the Solar System.)

The broader aspects of stellar spectroscopy applied to normal stars have shown that most stars seem to have the same chemical composition despite differences in spectra due to different temperature, surface gravity, and rotation. There has recently been a great deal of interest in the abundances of chemical elements in the stars. These abundances may reflect the way in which the elements themselves were formed by nuclear reactions like those deep within the sun (see Chapter 1).

The formation of helium from hydrogen, often called "hydrogen burning," is the first and simplest of these nuclear reactions. That is, it takes place at temperatures of 15 to 20 million degrees in the cores of stars, whereas other nuclear reactions will not start until the temperature reaches 100 million degrees or more. Then helium can combine to form carbon, oxygen, and heavier elements, with such a sudden release of energy that the star literally blows away its outer layers. The resulting cloud of gas, after cooling and mixing with other gas clouds, is expected to form new stars. The following article shows how far studies of these processes have been carried. — T L P

....

Helium and the
Galaxy's Age

(*Sky and Telescope*, April 1965)

Cosmologists usually assume that the original material from which our galaxy formed was pure hydrogen. They believe that all the other elements were produced by nuclear reactions inside stars, several stellar generations being required to attain the present observed abundance ratios. In support of this general picture is the fact that the most abundant heavy elements in nature are those being generated in stars.

But helium, the second lightest element, presents a special problem because there appears to be at least ten times too much of it. Our sun seems to have begun its evolutionary life with about 24 per cent helium, while the O and B stars—so young that their composition has had little time to change—contain about 35 per cent helium. To give these ratios in a galaxy initially composed of pure hydrogen, the material must have undergone lengthy processing in stellar interiors before the sun and the OB stars were born.

This helium problem has recently been explored by A. G. W. Cameron, of NASA's Institute for Space Studies, and Yale University graduate students J. W. Truran and C. J. Hansen. They have attempted a preliminary numerical evaluation of the changes in the composition of the stars and interstellar medium that result from stellar evolution and from interchange of material between stars and surrounding space.

These workers emphasize that large amounts of helium could not have been produced by a postulated multitude of O and B stars during the early history of the galaxy. Their main reason is that the Japanese astrophysicist C. Hayashi recently showed that a far-evolved, massive star has only a very thin layer of helium between its hydrogen-burning and helium-burning layers, most of the mass being in the helium-exhausted core. When such a star explodes as a supernova, only a small quantity of helium, comparable to the elements heavier than helium, can be ejected.

A more copious ejection of helium can be expected from stars of roughly solar mass, their long lifetimes more than compensating for the lower rate of escape. Eventually, they will enrich the interstellar medium sufficiently for later stars to be formed containing appreciable initial amounts of helium. A tentative calculation indicates that the observed helium content of the sun and of O and B stars can be obtained only if the galaxy is very old—about 20 billion years.

The age would be even greater if star formation began gradually. In all the models considered by Cameron and his collaborators, the heavy-element content of the interstellar gas grows rapidly and then changes little with time, whereas the helium content increases much more slowly. This behavior of the heavy elements is qualitatively confirmed by chemical abundances from the analysis of stellar spectra.

Throughout these calculations, the amounts of the principal long-lived radioactive elements were checked. The calculated ratios of uranium and thorium isotopes are consistent with those observed terrestrially and in meteorites, over a wide range of assumed values of the helium content of the interstellar medium. Hence it is evident that these radioactive elements give little information about cosmochronology.

Why are the massive, hot, blue O- and B-type stars so highly luminous, appearing in the upper left corner of the H-R diagram (Fig. 59A)? Roughly, this may be understood in terms of the energy radiated by a hot surface, which increases rapidly with temperature, T. In fact, the energy radiated per square centimeter, $E = \sigma T^4$, is such that doubling the temperature of a star multiplies the luminosity by sixteen if the star remains the same size. The energy radiated must be replaced at the same rate from within, if the star is not cooling off; therefore high luminosity is required to keep an O- or B-type star hot.

Also, the gases from which a star is formed are kept from expanding by gravity, which is itself dependent on the mass of the star. Hence, a star should be massive and luminous in order to have a high surface temperature that persists. How hot can a star be? — T L P

....

The Hottest Star

OTTO STRUVE

(*Sky and Telescope*, January–February 1952)

Nearly every astronomer knows that the infrared component of Epsilon Aurigae is the largest, and at the same time, the coolest star on record; that Plaskett's famous spectroscopic binary, HD 47129, has the greatest mass; and that in all probability Strand's faint companion of 61 Cygni is the least massive self-luminous star yet investigated. [See, however, p. 243.] But ask him which star is the hottest, and you will only embarrass him, for he has no satisfactory answer; and in this lack of knowledge there lies an interesting story.

Superficially, it would seem easy to find the surface temperatures of the stars. Even with the naked eye we distinguish the reddish color of Antares or Betelgeuse from the bluish light of Sirius or Rigel. If we could measure the colors of the stars, and calibrate them in terms of temperatures, our problem would appear to be solved. However, in this procedure the stars are assumed to radiate as *black bodies*. This assumption is necessary, but it is not easily understandable. Why, indeed, should the brilliant light of a star resemble the "blackness" of everyday experience? The difficulty is more or less removed when we realize that what we discern as "black" in the glare of the day is the property of a substance to absorb all radiation falling upon it, and to re-emit it as heat. We can easily convince ourselves of the re-emission if we touch a black piece of metal exposed to full sunlight!

The physicists have given a definition of "blackness," involving the absorption of all radiation, and they have combined it with Kirchhoff's law, which states that there is a relation between the absorbing power of any body and its emission of radiation: At a given temperature the emission divided by the absorption is the same for all bodies and is equal to the emissive power of a complete absorber, or black body, at the same temperature.

The emission of a black body is accurately known from the work of Max Planck. It can be demonstrated as a somewhat complicated formula, or it can be shown in a diagram which contains a family of curves labeled with the corresponding temperatures (Fig. 66). The abscissas are wavelengths

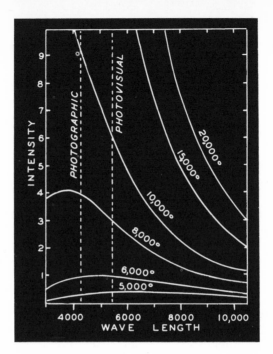

FIG. 66. Curves of relative energies radiated by a "black body." The dashed vertical lines mark the regions for which photographic and photovisual magnitudes are effectively measured.

and the ordinates are intensities of light or heat. The total amount of radiation is small for low temperatures and large for high temperatures; it varies as the fourth power of the absolute temperature, T, in degrees K.

The maxima of the curves are not all in the same place of the wavelength scale. They may be computed from the fact that the wavelength of maximum intensity is equal to $3 \times 10^7/T$ angstroms. For example, at room temperature, about 300°K, the maximum is at wavelength 10^5 angstroms or 0.01 millimeter. This is "invisible light" and belongs to the domain of microwaves. But if the temperature is 3000°, the maximum intensity is at 1μ (one micron), which is detectable with infrared photographic plates; and if $T = 30,000°$, then the maximum is at 1000 angstroms, in the invisible ultraviolet. For the sun, the observed maximum of the light intensity in the normal spectrum (corrected to outside the earth's atmosphere) is in the yellow—at about 6000 angstroms. Correspondingly, the formula gives the solar temperature as 5000°K.

Because the actual maxima of the Planck curves fall outside the observable range of the spectrum, except for a narrow range of temperatures, from 3000° to 10,000°, we rarely use this method to determine actual stellar temperatures. Most work has been based upon finding the ratios of the intensities at two specified wavelengths, say 4300 and 5400 angstroms, and then finding, by trial and error, which of the curves in Figure 66 agrees with the observations.

As an intermediate result, if the brightness of a star is observed separately through yellow and violet screens, the difference in the magnitudes thus obtained is called the *color index* of the star. We arbitrarily set the color index of an A-type star (like Vega) as zero. Then the sun has a color index of about +0.7 magnitude, and a really blue star, like Rigel, has one of about —0.2 magnitude [see Chapter 2].

The whole procedure is essentially the same as trying to find the appropriate curve in Figure 66. It turns out, from the Planck formula which describes these curves, that there is a simple expression:

$$T = \frac{7200}{\text{Color index} + 0.64}$$

Thus, Vega has a color index of zero, and $T = 7200/(0 + 0.64) = 11,250°$. A red star like Antares has a color index of 1.7, and $T = 7200/(1.7 + 0.64) = 3077°$.

When the color index is —0.64, the denominator in the expression is zero, and the corresponding temperature is infinite. There can be no color index bluer than —0.64, or the temperature would become negative, which is physically absurd. Until recently, this restriction upon the color indices conformed to the experience of the observers. The bluest stars, Tau Canis Majoris and Zeta Puppis, had observed color indices of —0.3 magnitude.

A recent issue of the *Astrophysical Journal* contains two short papers from the Warner and Swasey Observatory of the Case Institute of Technology—one by D. A. MacRae, R. Fleischer, and E. B. Weston; the other by D. L. Harris. They call attention to a faint star, BD +28°4211, which has a color index of —0.62 magnitude. This would correspond to a color temperature of over 350,000°! Together with a few other faint stars previously found by Humason and Zwicky, and by Schilt and Jackson, it is one of the bluest stars yet measured.

Not many years ago it would not have been considered out of place to ask whether such large temperatures have any reality whatsoever. I remember a distinguished astronomer once remarking that to him 100,000° or 1,000,000° represented so large an extrapolation of known facts that he refused to believe in them. By contrast, it is interesting to recall Eddington's quiet reassurance in his 1927 book, *Stars and Atoms*, that even the 40,000,000° then believed to occur in the interior of a star had a definite physical meaning, and a simple one at that. It represents the state of chaotic motions of the atoms and electrons in the gas. The atomic bomb, with its millions of degrees in temperature, has now relegated contrary arguments into the domain of history.

But the Case Institute authors have no confidence that the phenomenally high temperature is physically real. We had assumed that the stars were black bodies; but our only real evidence in support of this assumption was the superficial resemblance of the sun's energy distribution with one of the curves of Figure 66—and even that is correct only in a short interval of wavelengths.

It was always difficult to justify the assumption; the early workers used it because they had nothing better, and they realized its limitations. Then there came a period during which astronomers were trying to forget about the limitations, always hoping that in the end the black-body assumption would prove to be correct. But these hopes were not well founded. Instead of resembling a Planck curve, the energy distribution of a star may look entirely different, as shown by Figure 67. . . .

The spectrum of the Case Institute star is remarkable, principally because it shows hardly any lines. . . . A high-dispersion spectrogram of this interesting star has recently been obtained with the Mount Wilson coudé spectrograph, by J. L. Greenstein, and to him I am indebted for a "peek" at his plate. The absorption lines are indeed weak, as though they were

FIG. 67. The behavior of hydrogen in a star's atmosphere causes its energy emission to show serious discrepancies with the theoretical curve of a perfect radiator. The visible region of the spectrum is shown by the small, dotted curve. (Diagram by A. Pannekoek)

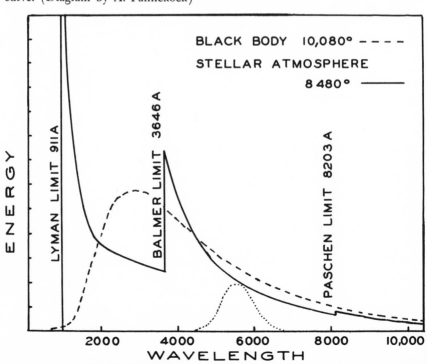

blurred out by some overlying continuous spectrum. One is reminded of Miss Annie J. Cannon's description of stars with pure continuous spectra —without either emission lines or absorption lines.

Whatever Greenstein's detailed study of his spectrogram may reveal, it is improbable, at this time, that we can accept the temperature of over 350,000° found from the color index. At such an enormous temperature the atoms of hydrogen and helium would be completely ionized, and no absorption lines of these elements should be visible, at least from the reversing layer of the star. There might be a higher layer of low density, something like a shell, in which the ionization is reduced. But we should ordinarily expect that such a shell would produce sharp absorption lines, and in addition there would be some strong emission lines. In reality, the absorption lines are diffuse, and there are no emission lines at all.

Before we can conclude consideration of the hottest stars, we must turn our attention to an entirely different group of celestial objects. These are the planetary nebulae, of which the best-known example is the Ring nebula in Lyra. When seen through small telescopes, these nebulae resemble the disks of planets, hence, their designation. In reality, each planetary is thousands of times larger than the solar system.

In many planetaries, and perhaps in all, there is a faint white-blue star near the center of the diffuse, nebulous disk. In some strange way, the central star seems to impart its light to the nebula. The latter shines not by reflection, but by a fluorescent process known as the Zanstra-Menzel mechanism. The central stars are hot and contain much light in the invisible ultraviolet portion of the spectrum. This stellar light passes through each nebula, whose atoms are voracious absorbers of all the ultraviolet light they can get. Thus, the hydrogen atoms swallow all, or nearly all, stellar light whose wavelength is shorter than 911 angstroms. But in doing so, they must lose their attendant electrons: they become ionized. The gas then consists of nuclei and free electrons, and also, of course, of normal neutral atoms—all rushing about hither and yon, with large and small velocities.

From time to time a free electron gets close enough to a hydrogen nucleus to "collide" with it and be captured. When that happens, the newly formed or, as we say, the recombined hydrogen atom spews out some or all of the energy it had originally absorbed from the stellar radiation. When the electron is captured into one of the possible outer orbits of the atom, the radiated energy is less than the energy originally absorbed from the star. An emission quantum of continuous Balmer, Paschen, or other radiation is formed, which is immediately (within one 100 millionths of a second) succeeded by one or more monochromatic line emissions as the electron "cascades" from one orbit to another, finally ending up in the innermost orbit, where it started from when the atom was first ionized.

This process seems complicated. But by an ingenious application of the principle of the conservation of energy, H. Zanstra realized that the total intensities of all the hydrogen emission lines must equal the intensity of the light of the star originally absorbed by the nebula. Thus, all we need to do is to measure the intensities of the hydrogen lines, allowing by computation for those we do not actually see; their total energy is the same as the central star's radiation of wavelengths shorter than 911 angstroms.

Then, by Planck's law, we find the temperature that the star must have to emit just the amount of ultraviolet light we have found. If the nebula is so tenuous that it does not absorb *all* the starlight short of 911 angstroms, then the intensities of the hydrogen lines register only a fraction of the true amount of ultraviolet starlight, and the real temperature of the star is higher than that we have just computed.

Zanstra has perfected this method and has extended it to other atoms, such as ionized helium. The results have in general indicated high temperatures for the central stars—of the order of 50,000°, or even more. . . .

Even more remarkable than the central stars of the normal planetaries is the hypothetical exciting star of a closely related object—the Crab nebula. This remarkable gaseous mass is the remnant of a supernova which exploded within our Milky Way system in the year 1054, as recorded in several Chinese and Japanese chronicles. This "guest star" reached an apparent magnitude brighter than Venus at her greatest brilliance, and it

FIG. 68. Photograph of the Crab nebula in Taurus by W. Baade with the 100-inch Mount Wilson telescope. (Mount Wilson and Palomar Observatories photograph)

remained visible for two years. The nebula, which started expanding in 1054, is still growing in diameter, and from the observed rate of the expansion, J. C. Duncan, and more recently, N. U. Mayall and J. H. Oort, as well as W. Baade have deduced a distance of 3000 to 5000 light years, with 3000 perhaps the best value.

Strangely, there is no conspicuous central star! Baade and especially R. Minkowski have carefully examined all suitable faint stars whose images fall within the nebula. Two sixteenth-magnitude stars are located near the geometrical center of the gaseous mass. One is quickly eliminated because of its very ordinary spectral type, G4, but the other resembles the spectrum of the Case Institute star, BD $+28°4211$, which we discussed above: it shows only a continuous spectrum, without any lines. Although this star is not strikingly blue, as is BD $+28°4211$, but rather imitates the energy distribution of a star with $T = 20,000°$, we have already seen that not much confidence can be placed upon such color temperatures.

The most remarkable thing about the Crab nebula is its large luminosity.[1] The photographic brightness of the exciting star must be seven or eight magnitudes fainter than the whole nebula. Both Minkowski and Baade have stressed this fact. It cannot be explained by absorption of starlight within the nebula because star counts in this region of the sky show that the nebular absorption is small.

Minkowski had already, in 1942, derived a temperature of 500,000° for the surface of the exciting star. Its radius is only 1/50 that of the sun, and its total luminosity is 30,000 solar units. . . .

The best we can do now is to point to the star that excites the Crab nebula to shine. That, at any rate, is the opinion of many astronomers. But a trace of doubt still lingers on. What about the black-body assumption? . . . We should be prepared to find that the light of the Crab nebula may not be caused by the conversion of ultraviolet starlight into visible nebular luminosity. The temperature of the exciting star should not be taken too literally.

Minkowski has recently emphasized the fact that the Crab is a strong source of radio waves. We do not definitely know whether the nebula or the central star is responsible for this effect of "cosmic static," but there is a possibility that the high intensity of this extremely longwave radiation will make it necessary to discard the assumption of a black-body distribution of energy in the source. . . .

---

[1] Most recently, the Crab nebula has been found to emit X rays. In July 1964 a group of scientists at the Naval Research Laboratory, led by Herbert Friedman, sent an X-ray telescope on a rocket outside the earth's atmosphere to record a lunar occultation of the Crab nebula. The X rays detected (as the moon covered up the nebula) varied in such a way that the source of X rays was shown to be an extended one, rather than a star. —T L P

....

Very Hot Stars

(*Sky and Telescope*, March 1950)

Planetary nebulae are known to receive their energy to shine from very hot stars located at their centers. Thornton Page, [then] of Yerkes Observatory, described how in the case of these stars, surrounded by vast spherical shells of glowing gas, we have a sensitive method of determining surface temperatures, using the far-ultraviolet light, which is converted to visible light in the nebulae by the well-known process of fluorescence. From the intensity of the *visible* light of the nebula we have a measure of the amount of *far-ultraviolet* energy emitted by the central star, and this, in turn, depends on the star's surface temperature. The visible light of the star is also directly related to its temperature.

Therefore, by measuring the intensity of the nebula's light and comparing it to the star's light we can determine the star's surface temperature. In the past, the emission lines of the nebula's spectrum have been used, first by the Dutch astrophysicist Zanstra, but the resultant values are theoretically much too low. A variation of the Zanstra method has recently been proposed by the German astrophysicist Karl Wurm, whereby the fainter continuous emission of the nebula is compared with the star's spectrum. Wurm's method has been applied by Page to three planetary nebulae, confirming the earlier temperatures of the central stars in two cases, and leading to the very high figure of over 150,000° for the third. This star is the nucleus of the well-known Ring nebula in Lyra and it has, therefore, one of the highest surface temperatures known in the universe.

....

The Origin of
Planetary Nebulae

OTTO STRUVE

(*Sky and Telescope*, August 1957)

Before much can be said about the origin of the rapidly evolving planetary nebulae, we must have some accurate information on their distances, in order to know the scale of the processes at work in them.

About twenty-five years ago at Mount Wilson Observatory, A. van Maanen measured the trigonometric parallaxes of twenty-seven planetary nebulae. Only for one object, the giant planetary NGC 7293 in Aquarius, was the resulting parallax appreciably greater than its probable error. The value was 0.038 ± 0.008 second of arc, meaning that there was a fifty-fifty chance the distance of NGC 7293 lay within the limits 71 and 109 light years. The other planetaries turned out to be too remote for the trigonometric method to give meaningful distances. . . .

According to H. Zanstra, the absolute magnitude of the central star in NGC 7293 is +5.6. It is easy to calculate the distance from the formula relating absolute and apparent magnitude: $M-m=5-5 \log D$. The result in this case is about 350 parsecs (about 1140 light years), more than ten times van Maanen's direct measurement of the distance. . . .

At 60 light years, or 26 parsecs, the angular radius of NGC 7293 (about 7 minutes of arc) implies a linear radius of about 1/20 parsec or 1.6×10^{17} centimeters. The total volume of the nebula, considered as a sphere, would then be 2×10^{52} cubic centimeters.

Such a planetary nebula consists almost entirely of hydrogen, which is certainly highly ionized, the protons and electrons being separated from each other at a density of about 10^3 electrons and 10^3 protons per cubic centimeter. Hence, the total number of protons in NGC 7293 is about 2×10^{55}, each with a mass of 1.7×10^{-24} gram. The electron is negligible in comparison. Therefore, the mass of the entire nebula is $1.7 \times 10^{-24} \times 2 \times 10^{55}$, which is 3.4×10^{31} grams. This is about 1/60 the sun's mass, consistent with our belief that the upper limit for mass of a typical planetary is about 1/10 that of the sun. . . .

These and similar considerations led I. S. Shklovsky, in the *Russian Astronomical Journal*, to propose a new method for determining the distances of individual planetaries. It applies only to those that are optically thin, containing too little gas to dim appreciably other objects shining through them. This is true for most planetaries, and certainly for all the large ones of relatively low surface brightness. . . .

Shklovsky reasons that the amount of light produced by each cubic centimeter of the nebula must be proportional to the number of protons and also to the number of free electrons in it. Since these numbers are equal, the emission from each cubic centimeter is proportional to the square of the density. Multiplying this by the volume and dividing by the surface area of the nebula, he deduces that the surface brightness is proportional to the square of the total mass divided by the fifth power of the linear radius, that is, to M^2/r^5.

If the distance of the nebula is D and its angular radius is s, then the linear radius is proportional to Ds, and we may express the surface brightness, I, as proportional to M^2/D^5s^5.

Next, Shklovsky suggests as a good approximation that we assume the masses of all planetaries are the same. This makes M a constant in the relation:

$$D \sim M^{2/5}/sI^{1/5}.$$

With this value of M, we can then compute the distances of all those optically thin nebulae for which s and I have been listed.

There seems little doubt that the distances Shklovsky found by this method are much better than any earlier ones. For NGC 7293 he finds 50 parsecs, in reasonably good agreement with van Maanen's direct measurements....

Of course, it is hardly likely that all planetaries actually do have identical masses. But the distance depends only upon the 2/5 power of the mass in Shklovsky's formula, and a tenfold error in the adopted mass would cause only a 50-per-cent error in the distance.

The Russian astronomer has used his distance determinations to draw some interesting conclusions. He estimates the density of the planetaries in space, finding the total number of these objects in our galaxy to be 60,000. Other studies show that the average lifetime of a planetary nebula is about 20,000 years. Hence, to maintain a uniform population of 60,000, about three new planetaries are somehow produced each year, and three old ones disappear, as they expand to large size and low density. Shklovsky thinks that this disintegration process may actually maintain the total mass of the gaseous substratum of the Milky Way.

Once we know the distance of a planetary nebula, we can compute the absolute magnitude of its central star directly from its apparent brightness. For example, we have noted that the central star of NGC 7293 has an apparent magnitude of +13.3; since it is 50 parsecs from us, according to Shklovsky, the absolute magnitude is +9.8. Other planetaries have much brighter central stars—for instance, absolute magnitude 0 for NGC 2392 and NGC 6578. Shklovsky concludes that, while planetary nebulae are all of approximately the same mass, their central stars have a very large range in absolute magnitude, between about −1 and +10. These central stars are all very hot, with surface temperatures between 30,000° and 100,000°....

Consider the central star of NGC 7293. In surface temperature it resembles an O-type star, whose absolute magnitude would be about −4. Both stars therefore emit about the same amount of energy per unit surface area. But the nucleus of NGC 7293 has an absolute magnitude of +9.8, making it 13.8 magnitudes fainter than an ordinary O star—a light ratio of 1 to about 330,000. Hence the central star of NGC 7293 must be much smaller than a normal O star, with only about 1/600 of its radius, or about 1/60 of the sun's radius.

While the masses of the central stars are not known, a reasonable guess is that they contain about as much material as the sun. If so, then the mean density of the central star of NGC 7293 comes out 300,000 grams per cubic centimeter! Even if we have overestimated somewhat the mass or surface temperature of this star, it is still probable that it resembles a white dwarf.

Shklovsky believes that as a planetary nebula evolves from a tiny starlike object to a large, turbulent gas shell of low surface brightness, the central nucleus also is changing from a fairly luminous hot O-type or Wolf-Rayet star to an exceedingly hot and faint white dwarf. If so, about three such degenerate stars are produced each year from planetaries, and in one billion years some 3×10^9 white dwarfs will have been added to our galaxy. Since this is close to the estimated total number of white dwarfs, it is not unreasonable to believe that all white dwarf stars are the descendants of former planetaries.

But what of the ancestors of the planetaries? These nebulae are expanding, and in their earliest stages they are small and dense, with high surface brightnesses. Such primitive nebulae are optically thick; they are opaque to the light of their central stars; and their outermost layers are essentially cold hydrogen gas. (This gas is neutral hydrogen because the ionizing ultraviolet radiation of the central stars does not reach it.)

According to Shklovsky's estimate, such a very young planetary may have only 1/100 or 1/1000 the radius of an old nebula like NGC 7293. The density of the primitive nebula would be about 10^9 to 10^{12} hydrogen atoms per cubic centimeter, and the temperature of the outer layers about 1000°.

These properties are like those of the outer parts of the extended, relatively cool atmospheres of the largest red supergiant stars, whose photospheres may be about 100 to 1000 times the sun's diameter, and whose tenuous atmospheres may extend ten or more times farther out.

The comparison is not spoiled by the fact that inside a young planetary there must be a very hot and small nucleus; all modern ideas on the evolution of red supergiant stars demand that they have just such nuclei.

Red supergiant stars that could qualify as the ancestors of planetary nebulae must meet two rather stringent conditions. First, their distribution in space and their space motions must resemble those of the planetaries and the white dwarfs. Also, the stars must not be excessively massive; the loss of mass during the planetary-nebula stage can hardly be much greater than the normal observed mass of the nebula itself—say 0.1 solar mass.

Shklovsky suggests that the RV Tauri variable stars (among other groups) may satisfy these conditions. Their distribution in space fits the hypothesis, and while their masses are not known, their radii and absolute magnitudes agree roughly with those of the youngest planetaries.

According to M. Schwarzschild and others who have worked on the theoretical problem of stellar evolution, a red giant represents a stage in the development of a star of moderate mass, in which the inner core is essentially devoid of hydrogen, consisting mainly of helium. This core contracts gravitationally at a fairly rapid rate. The resulting heating of the core affects the outer layers of the star and may, according to Shklovsky, trigger the observed expansion of the planetaries.

The simple question, How hot can a star be? has led to several difficulties with definitions of the terms temperature and surface, and to the speculation that very hot stars may not last very long (this being a difficulty with the definition of "star"). Since Struve wrote the article above, the significance of radio emission (p. 218) has been recognized, and a new class of extremely luminous radio sources discovered. These are the distant quasi-stellar objects ("quasars") far outside the Milky Way, each of them more luminous than 100 billion suns. They, too, are thought to be of limited duration, like a giant explosion, and only a few are blowing up at any one moment.

The planetary nebulae and their superhot, small, nuclear stars similarly are rare objects—60,000 of them in our Milky Way Galaxy of several hundred billion stars, the vast majority of which have temperatures between 2000° and 20,000°. However, the rare and transitory type of star may help fill in the full story of a star's life. In any case, the extreme conditions of high temperature and density test the theories of stellar structure and the underlying physics. The instability of the surface layers of stars had long been of concern. Calculations (confirmed by direct observations of the sun; see p. 54) showed that the cooling effect of radiating energy away would cause a "boiling" or turbulence that modifies the star's structure.
—TLP

....

Turbulent Stellar
Atmospheres

(*The Telescope,* January–February 1939)

It has for some time been recognized that the atmospheres of many stars are by no means quiescent and unperturbed. They exist in a state of ferment and agitation. Some unknown force or forces appear to be at work in continually stirring up the great gaseous masses which a stellar atmosphere comprises, and creating maelstroms of turbulent motion. The phenomenon is believed to occur mainly in the highly rarefied and greatly distended atmospheres of supergiant stars. The existence of turbulence in the atmosphere of the sun has been strikingly demonstrated by the brilliant motion pictures of the chromosphere achieved by the McMath-Hulbert Observatory at Lake Angelus, Michigan, and by B. Lyot in France.

Naturally, the method of direct photography cannot be applied to the distant stars. Fortunately, however, the phenomenon of turbulence can be detected also from studies of the absorption lines that are formed in the stellar envelope, and observed in the spectrum of a star. Such lines appear to be broadened, because of a number of different factors. One factor, *velocity broadening*, depends upon the average random speed of the atoms absorbing the line. In a normal, quiescent stellar atmosphere, this velocity, for a given element, is determined by the temperature of the atmosphere. When turbulence is present, however, the average atomic velocity is increased over the normal value, and consequently the absorption lines for a star of a given temperature are broader than one would normally expect them to be. From studies of the widths of absorption lines in stars of known temperature, one can therefore determine how great an increase in velocity due to the motion of the atmosphere would be required to produce the observed broadening of the spectral lines. In the sun the average turbulent velocity is about one kilometer per second.

A study of the widths of absorption lines of neutral helium and of ionized oxygen and nitrogen, in the spectra of the supergiant stars of class B, has recently been completed by Leo Goldberg at the Harvard Observatory. The B stars are massive and very bright, and the supergiants of this type possess highly rarefied and distended atmospheres. The results of the investigation indicate that the supergiant B stars possess very turbulent atmospheres. Furthermore, the turbulent velocities appear to be correlated with temperature, ranging from a few kilometers per second at a temperature of 13,000° centigrade to about forty kilometers per second at a temperature of 30,000°. This result suggests that radiation pressure may be the force responsible for the turbulent agitation in stellar atmospheres.

···

Stellar Atmospheres
Turbulent

(*The Sky*, March 1939)

Recent work has shown that the atmospheres of many stars are in violent turbulent motion. New evidence for this conclusion has been found by Lyman Spitzer, Jr., at Harvard College Observatory, on examination of Mount Wilson plates of the spectra of the red supergiant stars Betelgeuse, Antares, and Alpha Herculis. The widths of the strong iron and sodium absorption lines in these spectra are best explained by the assumption of turbulent velocities of some 15 km per sec. The distribution of these velocities indicates that they arise from violent atmospheric storms and currents rather than from ordinary thermal motion. Moreover, there is apparently no single temperature characterizing these atmospheres, since the total radiation, the number of excited atoms of different elements, and the observed velocities all point to quite different temperatures, ranging from 2000° to the 500,000° which would be necessary if the observed line widths were actually due to thermal motion. In other words, the rarefied turbulent atmospheres of these stars do not approximate even closely the conditions of matter in equilibrium.

···

Zeta Tauri—a Star
in Eruption

(*Sky and Telescope*, April 1965)

Until recently, Zeta Tauri has been a placid shell star, occasionally showing short intervals of activity. But, presently, remarkable changes are taking place in its spectrum. These changes were reported [at the December 1964 meeting of the American Astronomical Society] by Canadian astronomer Anne B. Underhill, now at Sonnenborgh Observatory, Utrecht, Netherlands.

For many years the unusual spectrum of this third-magnitude object has attracted attention. Although Zeta Tauri is a spectroscopic binary, with an orbital period of 133 days, the spectrum of the secondary component has never been detected. The primary's spectral type is about B2, and the width of its spectral lines indicates that it is rapidly rotating.

Superimposed on the B-type spectrum are absorption and emission lines formed in the extensive low-density atmosphere or shell that surrounds the primary star. The shell absorption lines are sharper than the stellar lines, but not very sharp. In the shell, the level of atomic excitation corresponds roughly to that found in an A-type supergiant, such as Deneb (Alpha Cygni).

The shell spectrum was found to be strong in 1914 and in 1950, and occasionally at other times. Since 1950, regular spectrographic observations have been maintained by Margherita Hack and her colleagues in Italy, and by R. Herman in France. They have shown that the shell lines weakened from 1950 to 1952, then strengthened until 1958–9. Since then the shell lines of the ionized metals have weakened again.

In 1961, a complex structure of emission and absorption components was seen at the hydrogen-beta line, and the French observers noted that the absorption features were asymmetrical at times. From 1961 to 1963, the hydrogen-line absorption cores showed large displacements to longer wavelengths. There was some indication that inflow and outflow velocities as large as 100 kilometers per second occurred for brief periods.

These indications of renewing spectral activity in Zeta Tauri were the prelude to more striking changes. On a spectrogram taken October 19, 1964, with the 48-inch reflector of Dominion Astrophysical Observatory in Canada, Miss Underhill found four special points of interest:

1. Simultaneously present were strong lines of both neutral sodium and ionized silicon, indicating low and high excitation, respectively. Contrast this with the B8 supergiant Rigel, in which these silicon lines are about as strong, but where the sodium lines are barely visible—the expected state of affairs for a B8 star.

2. The shell lines were strongly asymmetrical, showing a considerable range of velocity within the shell. . . .

3. The hydrogen-alpha emission is now about twice as intense as in 1953, although no broader (see Fig. 69). . . .

4. The shell lines, in particular the neutral helium lines, have intensified steadily since 1950. . . . Apparently the level of excitation in the shell, as well as the amount of material there, has been increasing in recent years. . . .

Even though the spectral changes that are observed for Zeta Tauri refer to only a small part of the star, their origin raises interesting questions. Are we observing a phenomenon similar to the heating of the solar chro-

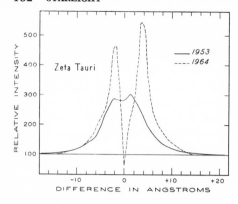

FIG. 69. Each curve is an observed profile of the hydrogen-alpha line in Zeta Tauri. The emission was much stronger in 1964, but had a deep central absorption.

mosphere and corona by mechanical energy? Although strong convection due to the ionization of hydrogen is not to be expected in B-star atmospheres, turbulence is known to exist. Such turbulence might arise from differences in the rotation rates of different parts of the extended atmosphere, or possibly from shock waves originating at an energy-generation instability beneath the surface of the star.

Pointing to the similarities between the spectra of shell stars and of early-type supergiants, Miss Underhill conjectures that the continuous ejection of a shell may be the means by which a main-sequence star evolves into a supergiant. . . .

Like planetary nebulae, shell stars may represent a brief phase in the life of a hot star. Unfortunately, the evidence is mostly indirect. Only recently has it become possible to observe the stars in far-ultraviolet light, which should show up hot stars (Fig. 66). This requires rockets to get outside the earth's atmosphere, which is opaque to ultraviolet light of wavelength shorter than about 2850A. (For more complete discussion of rocket astronomy and satellite astronomy see Volume 1 of this series, Wanderers in the Sky.) — T L P

....

Stellar Brightnesses in
the Far Ultraviolet

(*Sky and Telescope*, April 1964)

In November 1955, rocket astronomers at the Naval Research Laboratory made the first observations of far-ultraviolet radiation from celestial sources other than the sun. Then, a flight on March 28, 1957, with improved equipment seemed to indicate that many intrinsically hot stars were surrounded by extended nebulosities radiating in the ultraviolet. The best example appeared to be a diffuse patch 22½ ° in diameter, centered within a degree of Spica.

This discovery raised difficulties. Theoretical astrophysicists were puzzled by the intense short-wavelength radiation, and attempts to observe the Spica nebulosity from the earth's surface in visible light were unsuccessful.

Continuing its program of stellar photometry in the far ultraviolet, the NRL group, led by H. Friedman, succeeded in 1960 in establishing that the early-type stars radiate as point sources throughout the spectral range 1290 to 1550 angstroms, without detectable nebular glows associated with them. Several score individual stars could be identified on the photometer response records. The data permit plotting the stars' spectral types against their ultraviolet brightness relative to visible brightness at 5560 angstroms.

In general, the early-type stars seem about a magnitude less luminous in the wavelength regions 1290–1350 and 1350–1550 angstroms than predicted by stellar-atmosphere models. Nevertheless, the brighter observed sources match quite well the theoretical representation of the starry sky in the far ultraviolet compiled by Robert Davis at the Smithsonian Astrophysical Observatory in 1956.

Additional data were obtained in 1963, when the 1957 experiment was essentially repeated at 1225–1345 angstroms in a rocket flight on April 29. Spica itself was strongly recorded, and the upper limit to any nebular glow surrounding it was set at less than one tenth the flux reported in 1957.

Finally, the hydrogen Lyman-alpha line at 1216 angstroms and a broad band at shorter wavelengths were included in the coverage of four photometer-telescope combinations carried aloft on May 20, 1963. Except for mirror size and spectral-sensitivity bands, this experiment was identical with that of 1960.

The results indicate that accurate stellar photometry can be done by using photometers sensitive to the nighttime Lyman-alpha airglow and measuring the strength of the superimposed star signals, as illustrated above for Spica. There is no evidence for Lyman-alpha nebulosity brighter than 10 per cent of the ultraviolet airglow.

5

Variable
Stars and
Novae

There are many ways in which a star can vary: its brightness can shoot up suddenly and by an enormous amount in a one-shot explosion (a nova), or it can brighten and fade repeatedly in an irregular manner, or it can do so periodically. All of these brightness variations are accompanied by changes in the spectrum, most of them indicating changes in temperature (spectral type and color) and some indicating changes in radial velocity or magnetic field.

The periodic variables are of two types, one due to eclipses, where one star comes between us and its companion as they circle each other. Algol is one of these (see p. 169), and other eclipsing binaries are discussed in Chapter 7. The other type of periodic variable is a pulsating star, and the periods of pulsation range from fractions of a day to years. The Cepheid variables, pulsating with periods of several days, are best known for their use as distance indicators. They are very luminous, and the absolute magnitude, M, depends on the period; hence the distance to a Cepheid variable can be determined by measuring its average brightness or magnitude, m, and its period of pulsation, P. From P one gets M, and from $m - M = 5 \log D - 5$, one gets the distance, D.

The pulsating variables are not discussed fully in this volume; Volume 4 of this series, Telescopes, gives further details on light curves, and the

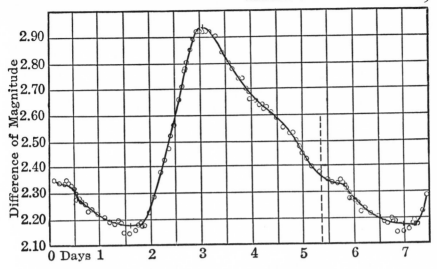

FIG. 70. The light curve of Delta Cephei, by Joel Stebbins.

theory of pulsation is reserved for a later volume. It may be helpful to mention two analogies that illustrate the relation between the period and the luminosity of a Cepheid: (1) air vibrating in an organ pipe has a longer period (lower pitched sound wave) for larger pipe volume, and (2) a vibrating tuning fork has longer period for greater mass. One therefore expects a larger, more massive star to have a longer period of pulsation. Large, massive stars are also the most luminous; hence high luminosity is expected for stars of long pulsation period.

Furthermore, gases are highly elastic; once a star starts pulsating, possibly due to some internal collapse, it is expected to keep on "bouncing" with constant period and amplitude. At maximum radius, R, the surface should be cooler than average; at minimum size, hotter. The maximum luminosity may occur between these two extremes, since L depends on R^2T^4. But these concepts are somewhat oversimplified, as the study of variable stars has shown.

Note that the variable stars are named by one or two capital letters before the Latin genitive case of the name of the constellation in which they appear. The first discovered in Taurus (the Bull) was called "R Tauri," the second "S Tauri," the third "T Tauri," etc. After the name "Z Tauri" was used, "RR Tauri" came next, then RS, RT, and so on. — T L P

....

What Is an Irregular
Variable?

(*The Telescope*, May–June 1939)

Those who are acquainted with variable stars through the medium of the printed page, rather than direct observation, may be tempted to think of variable stars as primarily regular. The eclipsing stars are pictured as running continually through the same smooth, symmetrical light curve, the Cepheids as repeating endlessly the same sharp rise and more gradual decline. The catalogues of variable stars give periods to within a millionth of a day. Actual contact with the variable stars tends to dispel these illusions.

The history of the heavens during the past fifty years lies at Harvard in the famous collection of astronomical photographs. During the past six months an astronomical expedition, financed by the Milton Fund of Harvard University, has made an excursion into the past and is measuring changes of the brightness of several thousand variable stars on these photographs. The measures will take years to complete and to compile. But already some interesting and unexpected results have been garnered. The regularities of the variable stars are not so great as might be supposed.

The eclipsing stars, which vary only for geometrical reasons, would be expected to be the strongholds of regularity. But those that are best observed are found to show deviations from the accurate performance of their schedules. The time of minimum (when one of the stars that make up the eclipsing system passes before the other) is not quite as regular as the simple geometry of the system would predict. For the star RS Canum Venaticorum, the time of passage swings to and fro, with apparent regularity, now early, now late, once in approximately fifty years. The eclipsing stars do not really "repeat themselves."

Even more obvious offenders are the Cepheid variables. The short-period cluster-type variables, which run through their cycles in less than a day, are not quite punctual in their behavior: TU Ursae Majoris falls more and more behind schedule as time goes on; BD $-29°8222$ runs ahead. Z Canum Venaticorum is so ill-behaved in this respect that it is difficult to obtain a clear picture of the real shape of its light curve; UY Bootis seems to be just as erratic.

The so-called Classical Cepheids are not too regular in their behavior. The well-known star SU Cassiopeiae, with a period of two days, has been changing both the form and amplitude of its light curve, as well as its period, during the interval that has been studied. Are these stars, then, irregular variables? They are not generally so regarded. Let us pass on to some stars that are even less dependable.

For a Cepheid, changes in the light curve are often considered unusual. But for long-period variables they are the rule. SX Librae has a range of two or three magnitudes in its brightness at maximum; whether it was a long-period variable at all was uncertain until the "Milton expedition" secured a continuous record of its brightness. Now it falls into line with other stars of the long-period group: the longer the period, the less regular is the light curve in shape and height.

But for real irregularity we must go further yet. All the stars so far mentioned, though irregular, are *periodic*. Not so the novae, which, so far as we know, rise in brightness but rarely (many perhaps only once), and if intermittently, then at irregular intervals. Not so the R Coronae Borealis stars, whose prototype seems to be quite irregular in the times of its precipitate drops in brightness. Have we here, perhaps, the truly irregular variable? R Coronae Borealis is, indeed, truly irregular as regards periodicity. But as regards variation of brightness, it can be depended upon to run true to type. When bright, it always is at the same brightness; when it grows faint, it grows faint suddenly, and usually recovers its brightness more slowly. The novae, too, usually brighten more rapidly than they fall. And their spectra usually follow the same general lines, though the range of detail is wonderful in its complexity. These stars are irregular, but not completely so.

For the truly irregular star we must turn to objects like T Tauri, R Coronae Austrinae, RU Lupi. These stars all share irregular and unpredictable behavior, nonperiodic, irregular, and nonrepeating, in the form and change of brightness. But they share another peculiarity—that of environment. All are situated in nebulosity. And it seems likely that the nebulosity lends the final touch of irrationality to the behavior of these stars. To them we must look to find the height of irregularity; and it is not their fault.

True irregularity of a repeating nature thus appears to be due to material outside the star—clouds of gas and dust through which it passes, suffering collisions or being obscured behind dark clouds or lighting up clouds on either side. In fact, the T Tauri variables are now thought to be stars in the process of formation—clouds of gas and dust falling together to produce a stable star.

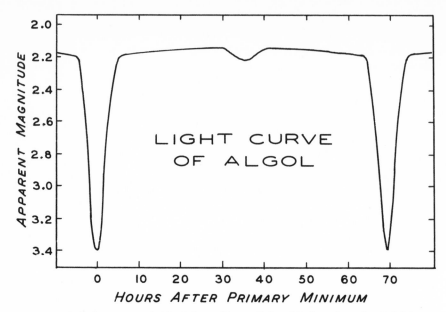

FIG. 71. A light curve of Algol in ordinary light. Notice that the brightness between minima is not entirely constant, increasing slightly toward the secondary minimum and decreasing later. The variation is due to the parasitic light "reflected" by the surface of the companion, which, illumined by its brilliant mate, exhibits phases like the moon's.

It is difficult to see how an isolated single star can vary in an irregular manner repeatedly. Similarly, just two stars should move in an accurately periodic way, and the ones with orbits lined up with the earth should produce periodic eclipses. But with three or more stars interacting there are many possible variations. Of course, the interactions are primarily gravitational, described by Newton's law for the force, F, between two masses, m_1 and m_2, distant r from each other: $F = G\, m_1 m_2/r^2$. Combined with Newton's law of motion, $F = m_1 a_1 = m_2 a_2$, where a_1 and a_2 are the accelerations, this leads to an elliptical orbit of one star about just one other, in the same way that planets move about the sun (see Volume 1, Wanderers in the Sky).

The best known eclipsing binary is the bright star Algol in the constellation Perseus called El Ghoul by the early Arabic astronomers. The star "winks" every seventy hours, as shown by the light curve in Figure 71. This periodic winking was explained in 1783 by a young Englishman, John Goodricke, who assumed that a large dark body is revolving around Algol. Later work by many other astronomers, including the Americans Pickering, Russell, Shapley, McLaughlin, and Hall, showed that the bright B8 star is about 70 per cent eclipsed by a much fainter companion that is about the same size (three times the size of the sun) but less massive. The two go around each other in nearly circular orbits less than ten million miles apart. A third companion had to be assumed to explain slight changes in period, and recently a fourth has been added. —T L P

. . . .

Algol—Still a Demon Star!

KYONG CHOL CHOU

(*Sky and Telescope*, January 1964)

One of the most famous of all variable stars is Beta Persei (Algol). It is the prototype of a group of eclipsing binary systems whose light curves are characterized by a deep primary eclipse and a shallow secondary one. . . .

FIG. 72. This chart demonstrates the accumulating effects of changes in Algol's period. The dots are annual means of the deviation of observed times of minimum from a uniform timetable. Each point represents one to sixty-six determinations, visual before 1932 and photoelectric thereafter. When Algol's period lengthens, the curve bends upward; a downward concavity means a shortening period.

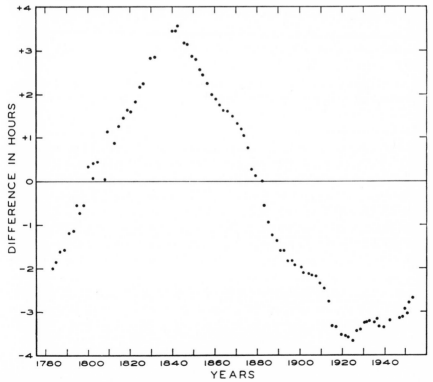

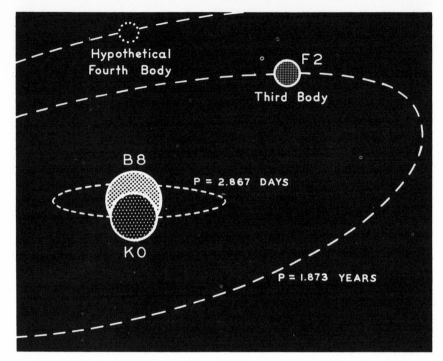

FIG. 73. Algol is actually a multiple-star system, containing at least four members, as indicated in this schematic bird's-eye view. Relative dimensions have not been preserved. The motions are shown relative to the brighter component of the eclipsing pair.

Inconstancy of the period was first announced by F. W. A. Argelander in 1855, who showed it had shortened by six seconds since John Goodricke's work in 1783. Such a change is by no means trivial; its effects accumulate, and after a few years minima run quite a few minutes ahead of or behind schedule. In the decades that followed, many astronomers recorded the times of minimum light, and it became increasingly apparent that the changes of period were very complex. Detailed analyses were made by S. C. Chandler (1888, 1901), J. Hellerich (1919), O. J. Eggen (1948), and Z. Kopal (1960). Algol, it turned out, was a system composed of at least four stars. The times of minima were advanced or retarded as the eclipsing pair was nearer or farther from us, during its slow orbital motion around the center of mass of the group.

Decisive confirmation that Algol was at least triple was made by the Russian astronomer A. Belopolsky in 1906, from his spectrographic observations. He reported that the radial velocity of the eclipsing system's center of mass oscillated in a cycle of 1.8 years. In other words, the eclipsing binary is in orbital motion relative to a third star known as "Algol C." Probably the most accurate determination of the cycle length is 1.873 years, by D. B. McLaughlin in 1924.

Already Chandler had suggested the existence of an additional, remoter component. Eggen confirmed that the times of minima indicated a slow underlying cycle, according to him 188.4 years long. This, he concluded, was due to a fourth star in the Algol system. He proposed that the new unseen companion was a white dwarf having a mass 3.8 times the sun's.

Very precise brightness measurements of an eclipsing binary are necessary if astronomers are to deduce the sizes, shapes, and other properties of the components from the shape of the light curve. Credit is due to Joel Stebbins for first applying photoelectric photometry to the study of Algol. He found that there is a minimum 0.06 magnitude deep, and the light curve is not quite flat between minima. Stebbins calculated the dimensions of the eclipsing components on the assumption that their disks were uniformly bright. . . .

In 1934, John Hall measured Algol's light curve in infrared light of 8660 angstroms wavelength and found a much deeper secondary minimum than is observed in yellow or blue light. Hence the fainter component is of considerably later spectral type than B8. . . .

In 1959, T. Herczeg made photoelectric measurements in three colors (ultraviolet at 3700 angstroms, blue at 4500, and red at 6000) which showed that the depth of the primary minimum varied from time to time. He also reported that the characteristic light-curve deformation produced by elliptical star disks was well recognizable in red light, but scarcely present in the other colors.

An important study of Algol was reported by A. S. Meltzer in 1957. On his spectrograms taken with the coudé spectrograph of the 100-inch Mount Wilson telescope, he noted certain faint, narrow lines evidently belonging to an F star. The radial velocities measured from these lines showed that they come from the third star, Algol C, previously unobserved directly and known only from its gravitational attraction on the eclipsing pair. From this study, Meltzer derived the specifications of individual components listed here in Table 6.

TABLE 6. THE ALGOL SYSTEM

Component	A	B	C	D
Spectral type	B8 V	K0 V	F2	?
Radius in solar units	3.0	3.2	1.2	?
Mass in solar units	5.0	1.0	1.3	3.8
Absolute visual mag.	−0.08	3.40	3.20	?

Since 1920, Algol has been photographed on many nights with the 24-inch refractor of Sproul Observatory, as part of that institute's parallax program. Up to 1951, 560 plates had been taken, and from them P. van de Kamp and his co-workers derived a parallax of 0.044 ± 0.003 second of

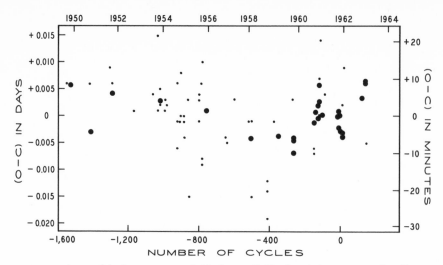

FIG. 74. A graphical summary of timings of Algol minima, 1949–63. Large dots represent photoelectric determinations; small dots are for visual minima. A positive value of $O-C$ [observed minus computed time] means that the variable was behind schedule; a negative value, ahead. If during these years the period of Algol had remained constant, the points would lie on a straight line, apart from observational errors. Instead, there is a strong suggestion of small, rapid changes in period.

arc for Algol. This corresponds to a distance of 22.7 parsecs or 74 light years from the earth. From these photographs could be measured the tiny 1.873-year oscillation in the position of Algol caused by the attraction of Algol C. . . .

Recent observations reveal that the period of the eclipsing pair undergoes unpredictable changes, probably of composite origin. Part may come from disturbances by additional companions, and part from . . . ejection of mass from one or both components. . . .

The recorded times of Algol minima since about 1950 are summarized in Figure 74. The vertical scale represents the difference between the observed time and that computed from

$$2,437,621.6152 + 2^{d}.8673331E,$$

where E increases by one each cycle, and the period of 2.8673331 days was chosen to give an approximate fit to the photoelectric minima, represented by large dots in Figure 74.

Actually, the times of photoelectric minima are more precise than this diagram might suggest. Part of their scatter is caused by the 1.873-year cycle, which can advance or retard a minimum by up to nearly 0.003 day, and which runs its full course as the epoch count, E, increases by 238. Nevertheless, we can clearly see a slight downward trend of the large dots until about 1959, followed by a tendency to rise. The small dots, representing visual minima, show a similar trend, but less distinctly. This trend and the large irregularity between 1960 and 1962 are not yet explained. . . . Although many hundreds of publications concerning the Algol system have appeared, this variable star presents many still unsolved problems. . . .

The complexities of combined periodic motions in multiple-star systems are a challenge to the astronomer's understanding of nature. Another famous case is worked out below. Note that it is only by good luck that these stars have orbits nearly edge-on to us. Without the eclipse information, neither system could have been analyzed so successfully. — T L P

●●

The Story of Beta Lyrae

GERARD P. KUIPER

(*Sky and Telescope*, March 1942)

Ever since 1784, when it was discovered that Beta Lyrae shows periodic variations of its brightness, astronomers have been interested in this star. The principal light variations are shown in the light curve in Figure 76. A comparison of this curve with that of Algol [Fig. 71] shows some striking differences. The minima are wider; this means that the stars are larger in

FIG. 75. In the familiar constellation of the Lyre, Beta is at a corner of the "parallelogram" (see arrow). Vega is the brightest star and Epsilon, the famous double, is to its left. (Harvard College Observatory photograph)

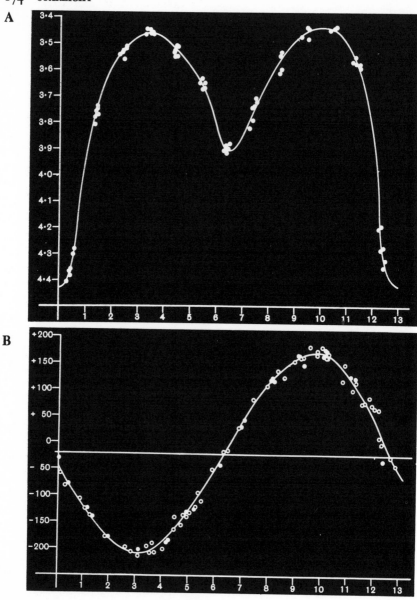

FIG. 76. The light curve (A) and the velocity curve (B) of Beta Lyrae. In graph A the horizontal scale is number of days; vertical scale is magnitude. In graph B the horizontal scale is number of days; vertical scale is kilometers per second. Note that the average velocity of the system is −20 km/sec, which is just the motion of the sun approaching the constellation Lyra. (From *The American Journal of Physics*)

terms of their mutual distance as compared to Algol, or, what is the same, they are closer together in terms of their sizes. In the second place, we find the maxima to be "round." This proves that the star (or the stars) responsible for the observed light cannot be spherical, because spherical stars outside eclipse show the same brightness in all directions. It is not so simple to get the precise value of the ellipticity of the star (or stars) from the shape of the light curve near the maxima, because if stars are ellipsoidal, their light intensity over the surface is not uniform. It is found from theoretical studies that the maxima are as bright as they are partly because at that time the largest side of each star shows, and partly because at the same time the brightest areas are visible.

This is all comparatively straightforward. But accurate photometric observations show the presence of two complications. First, the light variations are not the same for each cycle; differences of about 10 per cent in light are found between different cycles. This is certainly not true for Algol and hundreds of other eclipsing variables, which repeat themselves very strictly cycle after cycle. Second, it appears that the primary minimum is quite asymmetrical, and even the two maxima on either side are not always equally bright. We must conclude that the system is more complex than just a pair of stars.

Spectroscopic studies support this view. Again a comparison with Algol is useful. Algol shows a simple B8-type spectrum with the radial velocity varying in the same period as the light does (apart from a minor complication due to the third body, which causes a small superposed variation of long period). Algol's companion, which should give a secondary spectrum displaced in opposite sense with respect to the mean velocity, is not visible. The case of Beta Lyrae is much more complex. First, a B8-type spectrum is shown, belonging to a star of the same spectral type as Algol, but of higher luminosity; the star may be called a B8 giant. This star is moving at high speed (367 km/sec) in an orbit described in about thirteen days, the same period as found from the light curve (see Fig. 76). No secondary spectrum moving in the opposite sense is found. So far the analogy with Algol is close except that Beta Lyrae appears to be more massive and of greater dimensions.

However, the spectrum of Beta Lyrae shows much more than the B8 star. There is a set of strong, broad emission lines, the most prominent of which are due to hydrogen and helium. In addition, there are absorption lines which at first sight resemble somewhat those shown by a B5-type star; this spectrum is often called "the B5 spectrum of Beta Lyrae." But it is not a normal, complete stellar spectrum. Moreover, its intensity changes tremendously during the thirteen-day cycle; its strength is greatest (the absorption lines are deepest) shortly after the primary minimum of the light curve. The radial velocity shown by this absorption spectrum does not change very much, and is always one of approach, amounting to about 50 km/sec relative to the binary. From these facts, as well as from certain abnormal intensity ratios of lines, one may conclude that this "B5" spectrum arises from a nebula surrounding the components of Beta Lyrae; for some unknown reason this nebula is blown off from the system with a speed of about 50 km/sec.

A nebula of this kind should show two distinct spectra, just as the chromosphere and prominences on the sun do: those parts which are projected on the solar disk show an absorption spectrum, while the parts that stick out beyond the solar limb show emission spectra. Similarly, the part of the nebula in front of the B8 component of Beta Lyrae must show an absorption spectrum which is superposed on the B8-type stellar spectrum, while all the rest of the nebula, with exception of the parts hidden by the component stars, will show an emission spectrum. We mentioned already that such an emission spectrum is indeed present, but its lines are very broad. Since a nebula at rest would show sharp emission lines, it follows that the nebula is not at rest. Since, further, the centers of the emission lines are not much displaced, it follows that the nebula must be in rapid rotation *around* the binary. The rotational velocities will have to reach values up to 300–400 km/sec, as evidenced by the measured width of the emission lines.

Summing up, we have found that Beta Lyrae is a binary, with one component visible; the whole system is surrounded by a nebula that is expanding with a radial velocity of about 50 km/sec and rotating with velocities ranging up to 300–400 km/sec. The great change in intensity of the "B5" spectrum during the thirteen-day cycle further indicates that the amount of material in this nebula is by no means uniform over all angles, but that a very definite relation exists with respect to the line joining the components; in other words, these components in some way determine the density distribution in this nebula.

The observations reveal still more facts of importance; but before we consider them we shall examine whether or not the picture so far developed makes sense.

The nebula around the binary is expanding rapidly. It has been observed for fifty years now, and it is safe to assume that this process has been going on for a considerably longer time. The nebula must then be replenished by the binary, and the latter must in some way be unstable. We might have concluded this also from the lack of periodicity of the light curve, as well as from the asymmetry of the minimum.

The question then arises, how can a binary eject matter? A single star ejects matter if it is rotating so fast that gas is shed off at its equator. This process is very probably responsible for most of the Be stars (B stars with emission lines), which do not occur in binaries. If a binary consists of two components comparable in size, separated by a few stellar diameters, it is inconceivable that ejection of matter should take place. Because the rotation of the components will then tend to occur very nearly in the same period in which the double star revolves, under such conditions the stars are quite stable. But if the components get closer and closer, interesting things begin to take place in the binary system.

Instead of keeping the sizes of the stars fixed and their distance decreasing, we may consider the distance of the centers of the stars fixed, and the components increasing in size; then the different shapes are easily shown in one diagram, as is done in Figure 77. It has been assumed that the right-hand star has two thirds of the mass of the left-hand star. When the stars are small compared to their separation they are very nearly spherical. As they grow bigger (or closer, as we have seen) they will finally touch each other. When that happens their shape is given by the figure-eight curve passing through D, G, and K of Figure 77. The curves E-F and H-I show an earlier condition, in which the stars are still separated, though appreciably elongated. (It is noted that their shapes are not ellipsoidal, as is usually assumed for simplicity, but egg shaped, with the sharpest point directed at the other star.)

Suppose now that the stars get still closer, that is, bigger in Figure 77. They will then extend beyond the figure eight; this will go on until they reach the surface passing through C and L. This is the upper limit to the sizes of the components; if they were still bigger, a funnel would form

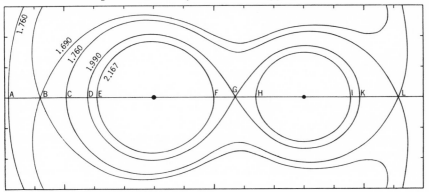

FIG. 77. Possible stellar shapes for the case in which the companion has two thirds the mass of the primary. The plane shown is that of the orbit.

near L through which matter would stream off into space. In the impossibly extreme case of the surface passing through B the funnel would be wide open, and a second funnel would be about to form near B. This second funnel would become of interest only if the two stars were of very nearly the same mass, so that symmetry in Figure 77 would almost prevail.

Are the components in Beta Lyrae close enough for these considerations to become of importance? This appears to be the case; while the precise dimensions are difficult to ascertain from the light curve because of many complications resulting from this closeness, it is practically certain that the two components have a common envelope. Once this result is adopted, a number of conclusions follow which are all in agreement with observation, while those same observations could not have been explained on the basis of separated components.

The fact that the spectrum of only one component is visible indicates that the masses are unequal; but the large orbital motion of the B8 component in connection with the fairly large period of thirteen days[1] shows that the companion cannot be very much less massive than the B8 star itself. So we have a condition as is represented in Figure 77, while the surface of the components may be assumed to be roughly that passing through C.

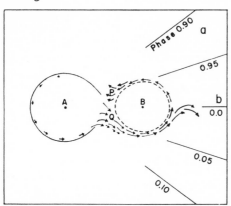

FIG. 78. Currents in a binary in which the components have a common envelope. The streams near P and O are actually observed spectroscopically.

Further investigation shows that if two unequal components have a common envelope, a system of currents will be set up as shown in Figure 78. Gas will stream from the bigger star to the smaller with great speed, but the stream is not symmetrical because the whole system is rotating. Part of this gas will fly off into space near the outside of the companion if the velocity is large enough or the envelope high enough. If the envelope

---

[1] The period, P, separation, S, and sum of the masses, $M_1 + M_2$, are related by Kepler's law: $S^3 = (M_1 + M_2)\ P^2$. — T L P

is as high as L in Figure 77, only a very small velocity is required for ejection. The inner part of the stream will swing around over the surface of the companion; its velocity will be less than that of the current leaving the primary. The net result is that the primary loses mass to the companion, and the latter ejects mass into space. It turns out that as a result the stars draw closer together, which speeds up the process. In fact, it can be said that if two sufficiently unequal stars have at first a small common envelope, this envelope will grow, the stars will get closer, and finally the envelope will be high enough for ejection to set in—a star like Beta Lyrae will result.

FIG. 79. Spectra of Beta Lyrae taken near the primary minimum. Note the satellite lines, especially of helium 4472, the conspicuous bright line near the left edge of the plate. Next to it is the emission line of magnesium 4481. (McDonald Observatory photograph)

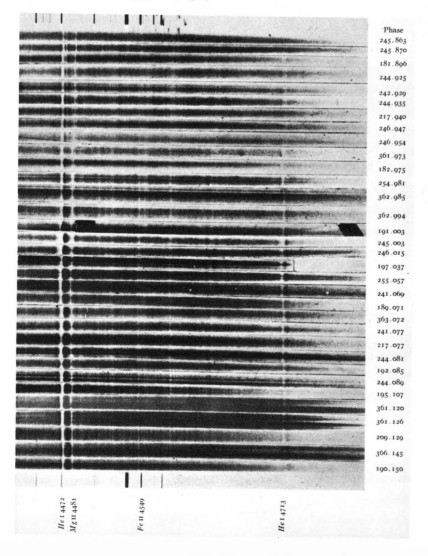

Phase
245.863
245.870
181.896
244.925
242.929
244.935
217.940
246.947
246.954
361.973
182.975
254.981
362.985
362.994
191.003
245.003
246.015
197.037
255.057
241.069
189.071
363.072
241.077
217.077
244.081
192.085
244.089
195.107
361.120
361.126
209.129
366.145
190.150

He I 4472   Mg II 4481   Fe II 4549   He I 4713

We indicated that some observational data were left unused so far. It is now possible to interpret them. About a day before primary minimum a set of extra absorption lines appears in the spectrum, shifted to the red by some 200 km/sec. At that time the position of the observer corresponds to the direction *a* in Figure 78. The observer sees the primary, A, but not the companion, B, which is too faint. The current near *P* will at this time be projected on part of A's visible disk, and we may consider this current responsible for these extra lines; the measures then indicate a velocity of recession of about 200 km/sec for that current.

As we approach primary minimum, the extra (or satellite) lines rather suddenly disappear, in a position roughly corresponding to *b*. We may explain this disappearance as a result of an eclipse by B. The appearance and disappearance is well shown by Figure 79, particularly by the helium line at 4472 angstroms.

After primary minimum, satellite lines appear on the violet side, indicating approach, but they are partly blended by the now very strong "B5" spectrum, which must be caused by the ejected gas. The velocity of the current near *Q* is thus found to be about 300 km/sec.

One point remains to be settled: what happens to the ejected matter? Computations show that the ejected gas will not return to the binary, but leaves the system in a roughly hyperbolic orbit. The properties of that orbit will, of course, depend on the velocity of ejection, but it appears possible to reconcile the velocities of the currents *P* and *Q* with the "velocity of expansion" measured in the "B5" spectrum, provided the currents experience a certain amount of friction while moving over B. A quantitative understanding of Beta Lyrae is therefore actually possible. While the gas is streaming out in a nearly radial direction away from the binary, the double star itself revolves untiringly with its thirteen-day period. The result is that it winds itself in its own streamer, very much like a giant pinwheel. The picture thus found on the basis of computations is shown in Figure 80.

It is really unfortunate that Beta Lyrae is not close enough to permit visual observation of its streamer. But if it were, we would see it only edge-on, of course. On the other hand, if our position were at right angles to the plane of the streamer, most of the characteristics now associated with Beta Lyrae would have disappeared. There would be no eclipse, and the light curve would be a horizontal line; the star would not show any variations of radial velocity, and we would not know it to be a binary; the "B5" spectrum would be absent; the emission spectrum would not be absent, but the lines would be narrow and constant in position and appearance; there would be no satellite lines at any time. What would we believe this remarkable system of Beta Lyrae to be? We would call it just another Be star!

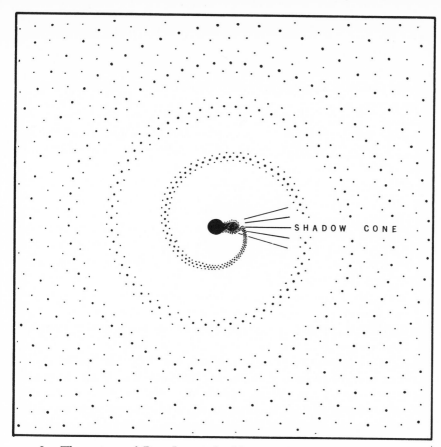

FIG. 80. The system of Beta Lyrae, the binary and streamer, as viewed from above its plane. (From *The American Journal of Physics*)

Perhaps this consideration should be a warning to us—the simplest explanation does not have to be correct. But our assumption of zero inclination is admittedly very special; and our erroneous picture of "just a Be star" is entirely due to it. Similarly, in the actual Beta Lyrae case we are unusually fortunate, because the inclination is very nearly 90°, so that the whole content of the complicated spiral and the currents P and Q pass over the B8 star, and show their colors (and speeds!). It is undoubtedly due to this circumstance that such a complete analysis and interpretation of Beta Lyrae has been possible.

The foregoing articles show the difficulties involved in fitting together a wide variety of observations and several basic laws of physics. When these can be fitted together consistently, they provide a confirmation of theory and observation that is the goal of all scientific inquiry.

The novae offer a similar challenge. As the name implies, it was long thought that they were "new stars," created suddenly where nothing existed before, contrary to the principle of conservation of matter, fundamental to chemistry and physics. One appeared in the constellation Hercules in December 1934. — T L P

A New Star Has Its Day

CECILIA H. PAYNE-GAPOSCHKIN

(*The Telescope*, March–April 1935)

The star that appeared in its spectacular rise to fame in the middle of December [1934] has reached the height of its brilliance and now has apparently started on the downward path to obscurity. . . . It reached its peak on December 22. Just two weeks before, the little world of science was roused by a telegraphic announcement that an English astronomer, J. P. M. Prentice, had seen a new star in the sky. Telescopes and spectroscopes were immediately turned to the western sky, where, an hour after sunset, a new star shone near Vega. . . . This new star, Nova Herculis, is happily placed for the astronomer—by the fortunate accident of its position in the sky, it can be studied all the year by astronomers in the United States; it will have no secrets from us. . . .

What is a new star? In recent years we have learned that "new star" is a misnomer, for a new star has not actually been created; a star already there has exploded with cataclysmic violence. We have no idea what causes the explosion, but with telescope and spectrograph it can be watched and described in detail. Nova Herculis must have once been a small, coolish star about the size of the sun. Then, for reasons connected with its internal economy, the little star began to swell. From patrol pictures made at the Harvard Observatory it seems that this happened at or soon after the first of November. At first the swelling was probably slow, but by the middle of December the star was blowing up at the rate of sixty miles a second in all directions, like an inflating balloon.

It was at this point that the brightening was first noticed and the spectrum photographed. Its light showed all the characteristics of the bright star Deneb (Alpha Cygni), and in addition, there were bright bands which told that the swelling nova was surrounded by an even greater atmosphere of glowing hydrogen, iron, magnesium, and other atoms less well known.

Most novae, such as the ones that appeared in Perseus in 1901 and in Aquila in 1918, have risen to "maximum brightness" with violent speed

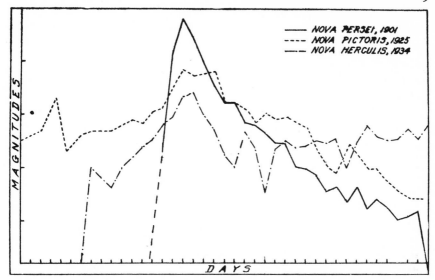

FIG. 81. Smoothed curves of the light variation near maximum of three novae. Maxima of light have purposely been made coincident. The curves have been shifted vertically to bring maximum light near coincidence.

within a day or two of discovery, but Nova Herculis, first seen as a third magnitude star on December 13, grew steadily and slowly brighter for nine more days, finally reaching magnitude 1.3. A few other novae have been slow in brightening and the slowness of Nova Herculis is not astonishing if we note that its speed of swelling up was unusually small for a new star. Roughly speaking, the faster a star swells, the faster it brightens.

As the star swelled, so it grew steadily brighter. The spectrum changed a little, the metallic elements becoming more prominent, and every day it seemed that the end must come. At last, on December 22, the bubble burst. That description is almost literally true; the swelling surface, which had given more and more light as it expanded, became too tenuous to give constant radiation, and the effect of the large surface disappeared. The hotter radiation from the deeper layers of the star began to pour through the still-expanding fragments of the bubble, and a real explosion may be said to have occurred.

Such a circumstantial description must be based on fact, and the observations have been quite explicit. The story can be read, provided one has the key to the cipher, in Figure 82. The spectra that compose it show absorption lines (dark lines crossing the spectrum) and emission (bright) lines, each characteristic of a particular kind of stuff. Hydrogen lines

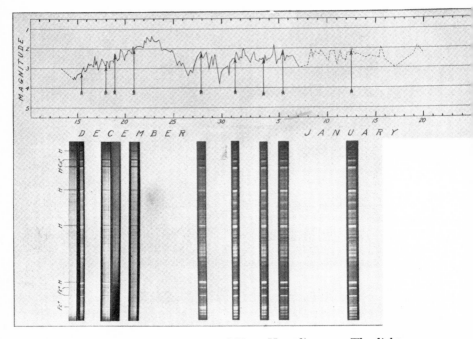

FIG. 82. Light curve and spectra of Nova Herculis 1934. The light curve was drawn from observations furnished by the American Association of Variable Star Observers. The dashes on its time-scale indicate the beginning of the day at Greenwich, England. The latter portion of the curve is dashed to indicate incomplete observations. The spectra were obtained at the times indicated by the arrows. The spectrum farthest to the left is that of Alpha Cygni (Deneb), a star whose spectrum includes most of the lines found in the nova's spectrum.

(labeled H), calcium lines (Ca), and iron lines (Fe) are conspicuous, though changing in form as the star undergoes its cataclysm.

The first nova spectrum, taken on December 15, shows a combination of bright and dark lines; the dark lines are like those of the star Deneb, whose spectrum is laid above for comparison, and they show that the nova is still in many ways like other stars. But the bright lines show that it differs from Deneb already in being surrounded by an enormous chromosphere—a stellar atmosphere of glowing gases rising thousands of miles above its surface. Most stars have chromospheres—our own sun has one—but only very few have, like the nova, one whose light can compete in brilliance with that of the star itself.

The star grew brighter for about a week, the interval covered by the next three spectra, and it is easy to see how its light began to overpower that of the chromosphere, which was not brightening, so that the bright lines faded away, and had nearly disappeared the day before maximum.

On December 22, when the star burst, it began at once to grow fainter, and the chromosphere flashed out with exaggerated brilliance, as may be seen in the spectrum taken on December 27. Figure 83 shows not only the fragments of the star's castoff skin that are flying in our direction, but also the fragments that are flying in all other directions; that is one of the reasons why the bright bands that show in the spectrum after maximum are so much wider and stronger than they were before the maximum, when the swelling body of the star hid everything that was happening on the back side of it.

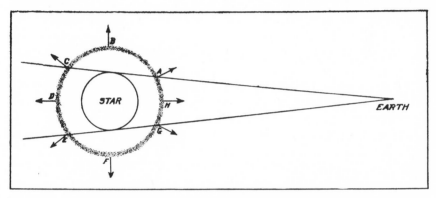

FIG. 83. An approximate diagram showing the nova's condition following maximum light. The portions of the expanding fragments of the star *ABC* and *EFG*, now clear of the star as seen from the earth, contribute the bright lines in the nova's spectrum; the portion *GHA*, seen superposed on the star, creates the absorptions appearing as dark lines in the nova's spectrum and displaced from normal position by an amount indicative of a high velocity of expansion; the portion *CDE* is invisible from the earth.

Now the star has become a tiny thing compared with the mighty cloud of gas pouring from it into space with a speed of several hundred miles a second. At first it grew suddenly faint, but after a few days it brightened once more, and for more than a month it fluctuated around the third magnitude, less than two magnitudes (one fifth) fainter than it was at the height of its glory. It seems as though it was profoundly shaken by the explosion, and still trembling and vibrating from the shock. This is not unusual; Figure 81 shows that Nova Persei and Nova Pictoris fluctuated violently for some weeks. . . .

What is to happen next? By analogy with other novae we can make a rough prediction. The star will fade slowly away, at first flickering as it fades, but later the flickering will become less and less, so that at last the star will grow steadily dim. Most novae have returned at least to their original brightness, so we may expect this one to sink once more to the fourteenth magnitude from which it rose.

[On March 31, 1935, the nova was at magnitude 4.4; during the next four days it decreased in brightness by one magnitude per day and then continued fading at a slower rate, reaching a minimum of 13.4 magnitude on May 3. From that date on, the star rose steadily in brightness to about seventh magnitude, where it remained until the beginning of 1936. By the end of that year it had dropped to eighth magnitude; by April 1938 it was at 8.5 magnitude, by November at ninth magnitude, by May of 1939, at 9.5 magnitude. Its slow decline took it to magnitude 13.2 by April 1946, and by June 1949 it had reached almost its present magnitude, about 14.2.]

As the star fades, its spectrum will show the exploding fragments of the old surface with increasing intensity. As the stellar gases move away and become more diffuse, they will shine with the light of the "forbidden lines," which cannot be produced in laboratories on the earth, but which are produced by isolated atoms in the Orion Nebula. . . . [Studies of the spectrum from 1935 to 1956 confirm this.]

Much can be told of the details of the catastrophe in Nova Herculis. We can identify the flying fragments, tell with what speeds they travel, and even watch their atoms readjusting themselves to a new environment. But we cannot tell the why and wherefore. These things happen to some stars; possibly a predisposition runs in certain families of stars. . . .

....

Novae in Sagittarius

(*The Telescope*, January–February 1938)

The richest field for the nova seeker is in the great star clouds of Sagittarius, where novae are discovered at the rate of about one every two or three years. Without the photographic plate, the discovery of some of these rare explosions would not be possible, for many of them pass like ships in the night, and are never seen visually.

From 1893 to the end of 1935 eighteen novae appeared in these clouds. During 1936 activity in the clouds was at a peak, for three novae occurring within that year have been found. One of these was discovered visually on October 4 by Okabayasi in Japan. The other two were discovered on spectrum photographs in the fall of 1937, more than a year after their appearance. One was found at Mount Wilson by Cora G. Burwell, the other at Harvard by Margaret L. Mayall.

Observations made on Harvard plates by Rebecca Jones show that the Mount Wilson nova was not brighter than 12.7 magnitude on March 31, and on April 2 it had increased to 7.5. On April 27 a maximum magnitude of 6.5 (about the limit of naked-eye visibility) was reached. The star remained near maximum until the middle of June, when it began to decrease in brightness as rapidly as it had increased.

Thus the visual and the photographic observers set a new record for the discovery of novae in the clouds of Sagittarius. An unusual feature is the occurrence of the spectra of Miss Burwell's and Mrs. Mayall's novae close together on the same Harvard spectrum-patrol plate. This rare occurrence is matched by another Harvard photograph, made in April 1937, which shows the spectra of the novae discovered by Okabayasi and by Miss Burwell. At that time Mrs. Mayall's star was too faint to be seen.

When two or more novae are found in the same region in one year, they are designated by the constellation in which they appear, followed by the year and the decimal of the year corresponding to the date of maximum brightness. The three novae of 1936, which reached maxima on April 27, May 13, and October 4 are known, respectively, as Nova Sagittarii 1936.32, 1936.37, and 1936.7.

::

What Becomes of
the Novae?

DEAN B. MCLAUGHLIN

(*Sky and Telescope*, May 1946)

... The outburst of a nova is an occasion for telegrams, minor headlines, major headaches, hurried preparation of charts and establishment of magnitude sequences, and general excitement on the part of all who are interested in observing it. The decline into obscurity carries no such excitement. At first you observe it every good night, but after it is down four magnitudes or so, you can skip a night or two with a clear conscience. Then you observe it once a week. Still later you put it off; it will be there next week. At last there comes a "next week" when it is beyond the reach of your instrument. . . .

A good deal of misinformation has been current at various times concerning the fate of novae. Most of this has resulted from too free speculation, jumping at conclusions, and failure to notice established, even if obscure, facts. For instance, it has been suggested that practically the whole star is dissipated in the explosion, so that what remains is a mere fragment, though the observed equality of brightness of the pre-nova and post-nova star in several cases should have suggested the error of such a view. When Nova Herculis appeared to be double, some conjectured that the actual fission of a star had been witnessed, ignoring the fact that the original star was simply engulfed in the intense light of two nebulous knots that were rushing away from it.

The most persistent of these notions is the supposition that every planetary nebula is the "wreck of an ancient nova"—a picturesque speculation, not without romantic appeal, but it is based only upon a superficial resemblance of the planetaries to the nebulae that expand around novae.

If we are to gain the clearest understanding of what happens, we must observe a nova with reasonable frequency all the way down its decline. This has been done adequately in only one case, Nova Aquilae 1918, but it is now being done for Nova Herculis 1934, which is still fading. . . .

There are fragmentary observations of several novae in the later stages of decline. For our knowledge of the spectra of novae some years after they have returned to minimum, we are chiefly indebted to Milton Humason, of Mount Wilson Observatory, who has observed a considerable number of them. The detailed record of Nova Aquilae correlates the observations of all the others, and the resulting picture is a consistent one.

When a nova has just passed maximum, its spectrum shows a characteristic pattern of broad bright bands with dark lines on their violetward edges (see Fig. 84). We have learned to interpret this structure in terms of the Doppler effect in a cloud of gases that is being erupted from the star in all directions. The various speeds of approach and recession of the gases, relative to the observer, shift the bright (emission) lines by different amounts to the violet and red, respectively, and this results in

FIG. 84. Spectra of Nova Herculis. The upper spectrum, photographed in January 1935, shortly after maximum light, shows broad bright bands with absorption in their violetward edges. The lower spectrum shows the nebular stage, ten months after the outburst. (University of Michigan Observatory photograph)

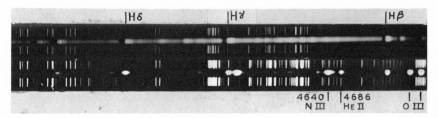

the broad bright band. But the nearest gases, approaching the observer, absorb light from the bright cloud behind them, and this makes the dark (absorption) lines strongly shifted toward the violet.

The cloud thins out as it rushes farther from the star, and the dark lines fade, but the wide bright bands remain to advertise the continuing expansion. With a knowledge of the speed (obtained from the Doppler shift) and the time interval since maximum light, we can calculate the size of the cloud. For example, the shell of gas around Nova Aquilae expanded at the rate of about 1000 miles per second. In one month its radius must have been 2.5 billion miles, nearly as large as the orbit of Neptune. No wonder that by that time its spectrum had changed so that it closely resembled that of a gaseous nebula, for it *was* a nebula so far as density was concerned [cf. Fig. 84].

In spite of its enormous dimensions, this cloud of gas around Nova Aquilae a month after the explosion still appeared as a point of light, like any other star, in the largest telescopes. But a few months later, Barnard discovered a tiny disk, or nebula, surrounding the star. Its diameter grew steadily, at the rate of two seconds of arc per year. In Figure 85 are shown four stages in this history.

The identity of this little nebulous disk with the cloud that produced the wide bands in the earlier stages was proven by spectra taken with the slit set along a diameter of the nebula and the star image held fixed at the center of the slit (instead of being allowed to trail the length of the slit). Then the bright nebular lines, instead of giving only broad bands of light, showed an elliptical form (see Fig. 86). The center of the nebula, near the star image, is partly between us and the star and partly beyond the star.

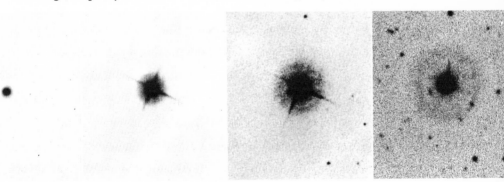

FIG. 85. The expanding nebula around Nova Aquilae 1918. The strong central spot is the greatly overexposed image of the star; the four rays are caused by light diffraction by the secondary-mirror supports of the telescope. (Negative photographs taken at the Mount Wilson Observatory)

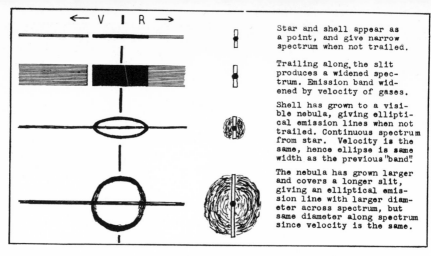

FIG. 86. The formation of elliptical patterns of nebular lines from expanding nova shells.

The portion between us and the star is rushing toward us, and gives a line displaced violetward. The portion beyond the star is receding from us, and its line is shifted redward. Thus, the center of the disk gives double lines. But out at the apparent edges of the nebula, the motion is all *across* the line of sight, so that there is no Doppler shift. Now the width of the ellipse *across* the spectrum was just the diameter of the nebula; the width *along* the spectrum was the same as that of the bright bands seen in the spectrum long before the nebula had grown to visible dimensions, showing the Doppler effect and hence the speed of expansion to be the same in both the early cloud and the later disk. Figure 87 shows the elliptical pattern of the nebular lines from the shell around Nova Aquilae 1918. . . .

Nova Persei 1901 must have had a very similar history. It was not followed closely through its later decline, but after the star had reached minimum its expanding nebula likewise showed the elliptical pattern in

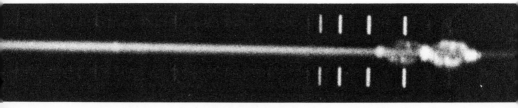

FIG. 87. The spectrum of Nova Aquilae and its expanding nebula shell, photographed with iron comparison lines in July 1920, with a much greater scale than in the direct photographs in Figure 85. The horizontal streak is the star's spectrum, continuous except for the emission of ionized helium at 4686 angstroms. At the right are two Doppler ellipses of doubly ionized oxygen, formed as explained in Figure 86. (Mount Wilson Observatory photograph)

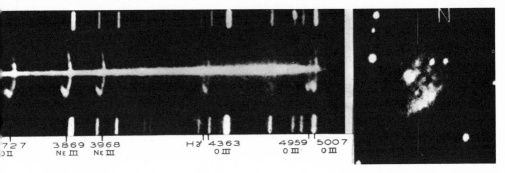

FIG. 88. At left is the spectrum of Nova Persei 1901 and its nebular shell, photographed in 1934 with helium comparison lines, by M. L. Humason. The horizontal bright strip is the continuous spectrum of the star. Each bright "fishhook" is about half a Doppler ellipse in the light of one of the lines emitted by the nebula. The nebula around Nova Persei in 1934 is shown in the photograph at the right, also by Humason. The fine line represents the position of the spectrograph slit when the spectrum at the left was taken. (Mount Wilson Observatory photograph)

the bright lines. But instead of a fairly uniform shell, this nova seems to have erupted a large mass of matter on one side, a smaller amount in a spherical cloud away from us, and very little directly toward us. The result is the peculiar fishhook form of the lines in Figure 88, which represent about half of a spherical shell, instead of a complete one as in Nova Aquilae. . . .

The apparent dimensions of these nebulae, combined with the expansion velocities, make possible a fairly accurate calculation of the distances of the novae. Thus it is found, for example, that Nova Aquilae 1918 is 1400 light years from the solar system. . . .

If the well-known planetary nebulae were the results of nova explosions, then they too should reveal similar rapid rates of expansion. A few do show very slow expansion—a few tens of miles per second—but most of them have fairly sharp lines. So they are not old novae of the typical violent kind. . . . To this categorical denial of nova origin of the planetary nebulae there is one known exception. The Crab nebula does show high velocities of expansion, and it occupies the position in Taurus in which Chinese astronomers recorded a brilliant nova in 1054. It was undoubtedly a super-nova. . . .

Let us look at what remains after a nova outburst. Nova Persei is now [1946] varying between the twelfth and fourteenth (visual) magnitudes in a quite irregular manner. If we had known it only since its outburst in 1901, we might say it has not yet quieted down. But Harvard photographs that preceded the explosion show the star was variable before 1901, and with about the same range. Apparently its violent experience has not changed its habits. Nova Aquilae varied through a small range for thirty years before its great explosion, and now that the show is over, it is actually quieter than before.

Owing to its recent [1946] second full-scale outburst, the behavior of T Coronae Borealis is of interest. For many years after it had faded to minimum following its outburst in 1866, it varied only slightly, if at all. . . . Between May 1936 and August 1938 it increased from the eleventh to the tenth photographic magnitude. The true increase was certainly much greater, for when the star appears of the eleventh magnitude, most of the observed light is that of the giant red companion. For several years it remained bright, with some fluctuations. Suddenly, in 1945, it faded to minimum again, only to "blow up" again in 1946. . . .

About half of the old novae are more or less variable, and the rest are nearly or quite constant in their light. . . . Nova Persei furnishes the most conspicuous example of continuing variation near minimum. Marked variations are shown also by Nova Ophiuchi 1848 and Nova Cygni 1876. But whether variable or constant, the old novae all seem much alike when their spectra are studied. Humason finds that all of them have continuous spectra very strong in the blue and violet, which indicates they are very hot stars. Some of them have nothing else, no absorption or emission lines. Others have bright lines of hydrogen and ionized helium. From their luminosities, which are similar to that of the sun on the average, we are forced to conclude that they are small superdense stars, somewhat like white dwarfs, but not so extreme. . . .

It is curious that several novalike variables, as well as two recurrent novae, T Coronae Borealis and RS Ophiuchi, have red giant stars for companions. Z Andromedae is a good example of this type of association. The more we know about novae and novalike stars, the more difficult it is to draw a line between them. Just what is the difference between T Coronae and Z Andromedae, except that we have *recorded* true nova outbursts of the one and not of the other? . . .

The recurrent nova, T Pyxidis, had observed outbursts in 1890, 1902, 1920, and 1944. At its maximum in 1920, its spectrum was indistinguishable from that of a typical nova. At its minimum between the outbursts, its spectrum was identical in appearance with any of several typical old novae. . . . And what, after all, are the SS Cygni stars, with their outbursts of three or four magnitudes every couple of months, if not just miniature repeating novae?

In the face of the tendency to repeat, it is difficult to find any justification for believing in theories of accidental cause of novae, such as collision with another star or a nebula. The cause must reside in the stars themselves. Since the post-nova stars are dense bodies, it has been suggested that collapse from low to high density accompanies the nova outburst. This would liberate enough energy to produce a supernova, and possibly supernovae do originate in such a way.

For a common nova, a very slight adjustment would suffice to produce all the energy involved in the outburst; the post-nova star would have almost exactly the same density and diameter as the pre-nova star. . . . The total mass of the star is almost negligibly altered by the ejection of a shell of gas, which is only about 1/10,000 of the sun's mass.

Some years ago it was argued that since novae occur at the rate of a score or so per year, in a few billion years every star would have been a nova. The fallacy here is obvious; what right have we to assume that a star can be a nova only once? It is distinctly possible that in the course of many centuries all novae repeat. "Once a nova, always a nova" is perhaps overstating the case, but a nova is a distinctive class of star long before and long after its great explosion. The novae of the future may include the old novae, the novalike stars, and some supposed white dwarfs, as well as many faint catalogued stars whose spectra are as yet unknown. . . .

It should be noted that other astronomers disagree with McLaughlin on the origin and expansion of planetary nebulae (see p. 154). Nevertheless, it is generally agreed that the novae form a special class of stars that blow off a small fraction of their masses at irregular intervals. These explosions are violent, but more violent ones are known.

The supernovae were first observed in external galaxies many millions of light years away. Each of these galaxies consists of hundreds of billions of stars and has a luminosity of several billion suns. When a small object

FIG. 89. The white line in the photograph on the left marks a supernova that flashed up in 1940 in the spiral galaxy NGC 4725 in the constellation Coma Berenices (photographed in May 1940). No star is visible in the corresponding place on the other picture, obtained in January 1941. (Mount Wilson and Palomar Observatories photographs)

(presumably a star) brightens up to stand out above this company, as in Figure 89, it must be 100 million times as luminous as the sun, or more. Over a hundred have been observed, many of them by Zwicky at Palomar Mountain in California.

It is easy to calculate that such an explosion within our Milky Way Galaxy would result in a star far more brilliant than the novae described in the preceding articles—except for those few like the one observed in A.D. 1054 at the place in the sky where the Crab nebula (Fig. 68) now is. Recent interest in this supernova of 1054 was stimulated by the fact that the Crab nebula is one of several hundred strong sources of radio emission discovered by the new radiotelescopes that focus and measure radio energy coming from outside the earth's atmosphere. These radio waves are like light waves—simply an extension of the spectrum beyond infrared rays— and are expected to be emitted by hot bodies in the relatively small amounts given by the Planck formula (see p. 148). However, the radiotelescope observations show that many of the strong radio sources are not thermal emitters. The flux (radio brightness) in the radio spectrum is not distributed as predicted by Planck's formula; the radio radiation arises from beams of moving charged particles that "spiral" around in a magnetic field. This "synchrotron radiation" is confirmed by other measurements in the case of the Crab nebula and is observed from other unusual objects, such as the QSO's (see p. 158), on which study is just starting.

Study of the Crab nebula and supernovae like the one that formed it may lead to explanations of these enormous rates of energy release.   —T L P

···

The Crab Nebula as a Supernova Remnant

OTTO STRUVE

(*Sky and Telescope*, February 1958)

. . . The Crab nebula lies in the same region of the sky as the bright supernova observed by Chinese and Japanese astronomers from July 4, 1054, to April 17, 1056. Moreover, John C. Duncan's measurements showed the Crab nebula to be expanding at approximately the rate which would have brought it to its present size if the expansion had begun some nine centuries ago. The evidence relating the nebula and the supernova was reviewed in several articles published in 1942, when N. U. Mayall

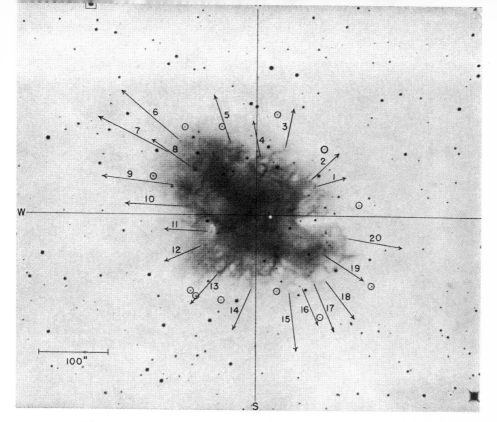

FIG. 90. The expansion of the Crab nebula, as indicated by measurements made by John C. Duncan. From his photographs with the 100-inch Mount Wilson telescope, he has plotted these arrows on a negative print to show motions during the next 500 years, if continued at their present rates. Circles mark comparison stars used. (Mount Wilson and Palomar Observatories photograph, from *The Astrophysical Journal*)

and J. H. Oort definitely identified the Crab with the remnants of the star of 1054, "which also probably was one of the brightest supernovae on record."

Modern observations show that the Crab nebula consists in part of luminous filaments with a bright-line spectrum. . . .

Much of the light of the Crab comes, however, from a relatively feature-less nebulosity that has a continuous spectrum. This amorphous substratum shines by strongly polarized light, as was discovered a few years ago by the Soviet astronomers M. A. Vashakidze and V. A. Dombrovsky. . . .

The polarized light of the Crab nebula is believed to be synchrotron radiation. Electrons moving at nearly the speed of light are compelled by the magnetic field of the nebula to spiral around and along the magnetic lines of force. This decelerates the electrons, which therefore emit completely polarized light of all wavelengths. Such radiation has been observed from fast-moving particles in laboratory synchrotrons.

There is great present interest among astrophysicists in the details of the processes by which the visible and radio radiations of the Crab nebula are produced. . . .

Oort and T. Walraven find that the mean value of the magnetic induction in the central part of the Crab nebula must be close to 1/1000 gauss. For comparison, the average interstellar magnetic field is around 10^{-5} or 10^{-6} gauss; the polar magnetic field of the earth is about 0.6 gauss; and the field of a magnetic star may be as large as 10,000 gauss.

The synchrotron theory of radiation by high-speed electrons fits very well with the fact that the Crab is a strong source of radio energy. Apparently, somewhat lower energies are involved than those required for the optical radiation. Thus, 10^9-volt electrons, when decelerated by a magnetic field of 1/1000 gauss, would produce radio waves with lengths between 10 centimeters and 7.5 meters. . . .

The supernova of 1054 was so brilliant that the Chinese saw it for twenty-three days by daylight. Its apparent magnitude may have been —6, corresponding to an absolute magnitude of —16 at the adopted distance of about 4000 light years. This is intrinsically some 350 million times as bright as the sun! . . .

Supernovae of type I, those that attain absolute magnitude —16, are exceedingly rare. Only one such object occurs each two hundred years in a galaxy like ours, according to W. Baade and R. Minkowski. In her new book, *The Galactic Novae*, Cecilia Payne-Gaposchkin states that the last object of this kind in our Milky Way Galaxy was Kepler's star of 1604. Only a faint, reddened, heavily obscured patch of nebulosity is visible as a remnant of that event. . . .

There are other supernovae, of type II, that differ radically in light curve and spectrum from those of type I. They are more frequent, and the question is still debated whether they are ordinary novae with extreme characteristics, rather than an independent species of star.

Although type-I supernovae are infrequent, our galaxy is so old that it must contain many post-supernovae. Dividing the age of the galaxy, say 6×10^9 years, by the average interval of 200 years between successive supernovae, tells us that there may be about 30 million stellar descendants of former supernovae now in existence. We have no idea what they are like—perhaps they are white dwarfs, but we really cannot tell.

A highly controversial question is the source of the enormous luminosity of a supernova at maximum brightness. It is believed that in an ordinary nova only the outermost layer of the star is blown off. As long as this layer

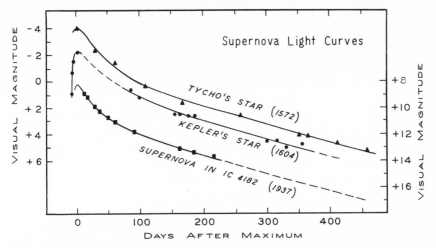

FIG. 91. All supernovae of type I have remarkably similar light curves. Walter Baade's diagram illustrates this for three supernovae. The first two were in our own Milky Way: one in Cassiopeia, observed by Tycho Brahe in 1572 to 1574; the other Kepler's star of 1604, in Ophiuchus. The third appeared in 1937 in the galaxy IC 4182. The magnitude scale at the left is for the two upper curves, at the right for the lowest curve. (Adapted from *The Astrophysical Journal*)

is dense enough to remain opaque, it shines like the photosphere of a star, and its rapidly increasing surface area satisfactorily explains the sudden rise in brightness of the nova. But for supernovae the problem is more intricate. Since most of the present light of the Crab nebula is of nonthermal origin (synchrotron radiation of fast electrons), perhaps the light of the supernova explosion itself was synchrotron radiation.

This viewpoint was urged by the Soviet astronomer Gordon, even before anything was known about how the Crab nebula shines. It has not been tested by direct observation, for no bright supernova in our galaxy has been observed by modern means during its outburst. Our information concerning the spectra and light curves of supernovae comes almost entirely from the fifty or so objects discovered during recent years in very distant galaxies.

A typical supernova of type I at maximum brightness has a spectrum containing very broad, as yet unidentified, emission features. Their widths suggest a velocity of expansion of the order of 10,000 kilometers per second. A few months later, while the supernova is fading, the spectrum shows emission lines of neutral oxygen, whose comparative narrowness indicates velocities of about 1000 kilometers per second. A deceleration from 10,000 to 1000 kilometers per second within a few months cannot be explained by the braking action of interstellar clouds, or by the star's own gravitation. It may have something to do with magnetic fields, such as are known from observation to exist in the Crab nebula.

The brightening of a supernova is exceedingly rapid, taking perhaps ten days, or 10^6 seconds. If we assume that the average velocity of expansion is 5000 kilometers per second, then the outward distance traveled by the shell would be 5×10^9 kilometers during the ten days. We know nothing definite about the radius of the pre-supernova, but perhaps it is roughly that of the sun, say a million kilometers. Thus during the explosion the radius of the star has increased 5000 times, and its surface area by 25 million times.

Now, if the blown-off shell continues to radiate as a black body with the star's initial temperature, the luminosity will have increased by this same factor of 25 million. In stellar magnitudes, this would be a brightening of 18.5. If the absolute magnitude of the supernova at maximum were −16, that of the star before the explosion would have been +2.5. While this may seem a little too luminous, we have no good reason for preferring some other specific number.

But Gordon has pointed out some rather disturbing facts. First, the shell ejected by the supernova contains a large fraction of the original material of the star. It must therefore have an average temperature far higher than that for any normal star—perhaps as much as one million degrees. If the surface temperature of the pre-supernova was 10,000 degrees, then the total radiation from each square centimeter of the shell would be 10^8 greater than from the same area on the original star. However, most of this would be of very high frequency, and in visible light the surface brightness of the shell would be only 100 times greater than for the star. Thus, in visual light the increase in brightness would be 100 times more than our previous calculation gave, corresponding to five magnitudes. The total brightness change would be 23.5 magnitudes.

This result is not unreasonable; it would require the absolute magnitude of the pre-supernova to be +7.5. But there are serious contradictions. How can we reconcile the million-degree temperature with the fact that supernovae at maximum have color indices matching those of A-type stars, whose temperatures are about 15,000 degrees? And why can we soon after maximum observe spectral lines of neutral oxygen, which require a relatively low temperature?

It seems to me that we cannot yet be certain which mechanism produces the light of a supernova, but Gordon's ideas have much to recommend them. Mrs. Gaposchkin believes that the visible radiation of type-I supernovae is not of thermal origin.

It is over 350 years since the last supernovae in our galaxy was recorded. The appearance of another one in our Milky Way system would enable the powerful observational tools of modern astrophysics to be applied to the problem of why and how they explode, and would also provide the most striking celestial spectacle in many years. . . .

···

Supernova in 1006

(*Sky and Telescope*, April 1965)

Convincing evidence that a bright supernova appeared in the southern constellation Lupus in the spring of A.D. 1006 has now been provided by a Yale University historian of science, Bernard R. Goldstein. It had long been known that a spectacular object, variously interpreted as a new star or comet, appeared that year, and the suggestion that it was a galactic supernova is not new. Goldstein has established its nature beyond reasonable doubt, from a critical analysis of medieval records from Europe, Africa, the Middle East, China, Korea, and Japan.

Particularly important is the long eyewitness account by the Muslim astrologer Ali ibn Ridwan of Cairo, who died in the year 1061. He gives the date of the first appearance as April 30 or May 1, 1006, and says that the object remained stationary (in celestial longitude 225°) with respect to the stars. This fixity rules out a comet. An ambiguously worded statement may mean that the new star was comparable in brightness to the quarter moon.

Another contemporary reference to the object of 1006 occurs in the annals of the monk Hepidannus, who lived at Saint-Gall, Switzerland. He speaks of it as visible for three months "in the extreme southern part of the sky." From this it may be inferred that the supernova was only a little north of declination −42½°, which is that of the south point of the true horizon at Saint-Gall.

The most satisfactory evidence as to the position of the supernova is found in the Far Eastern records. One Japanese and several Chinese sources say it was near the star Kappa Lupi, and another Chinese one places the star a degree west of Beta Lupi. Goldstein combines all the positional data to find that the supernova was within about three degrees of the tenth-magnitude planetary nebula NGC 5882. . . .

At the Yale-Columbia Southern Station in Argentina, Cyril Jackson reported finding a seventeenth-magnitude star surrounded by a ring 29 seconds in diameter, within a few degrees of NGC 5882. However, it would be premature to associate either the Jackson object or NGC 5882 with the supernova.

At the same time that he has verified one supernova, Goldstein has eliminated another. This is the supposed supernova of A.D. 827. D. M. Dunlop of Columbia University had succeeded in tracing all mentions of it to two early seventeenth-century books. The Yale historian demonstrated that both sources are actually misdated descriptions of the supernova of 1006.

··

Light Echoes from Ancient Supernovae

(*Sky and Telescope*, October 1965)

One of the most notable features of the famous Nova Persei in 1901 was its rapidly expanding halo of light, discovered by E. M. Antoniadi and C. Flammarion six months after the nova's outburst. It was a faint, diffuse cloud of light a few minutes of arc in radius, which grew noticeably from week to week. The Netherlands astronomer J. C. Kapteyn explained this halo as due to the illumination of interstellar material by the light front moving outward from the nova. This interpretation is universally accepted by astronomers.

Sidney van den Bergh, of David Dunlap Observatory, now suggests that it may be possible to detect analogous halos produced by supernovae that flashed up in our galaxy centuries ago. At maximum brightness, a supernova of type I shines at absolute magnitude −19, about 10,000 times brighter than Nova Persei at its peak. Hence such a supernova should be able to illuminate interstellar clouds to 100 times the distance that the nova could. He points out that the light halo of Nova Persei remained detectable for 20 months after the outburst, and the light echo from a supernova might be expected to last 100 times as long, or 167 years.

Actually the echo might remain observable much longer than this, perhaps 1000 years. A supernova fades less rapidly than an ordinary nova, and hence its light front is thicker and of greater surface brightness. Also, fast modern Schmidt telescopes can detect reflection nebulosity much fainter than could be recorded by the astronomical equipment of 1901 and 1902.

The Canadian astronomer's calculations indicate that it may be possible to record photographically light echoes near Tycho's supernova of 1572 in Cassiopeia and Kepler's of 1604 in Ophiuchus. On the other hand,

FIG. 92. Sidney van den Bergh suggests that supernovae may have light halos like this one that surrounded Nova Persei on September 20, 1901. (Yerkes Observatory photograph)

chances would be poor of finding the halo of the 1054 Taurus supernova associated with the Crab nebula. It would be a very faint nebulosity spread over a large area of the sky.

A fourth candidate considered by van den Bergh is the hypothetical supernova of about A.D. 1700, postulated by R. Minkowski as the origin of the radio source Cassiopeia A. Because of heavy interstellar absorption in that direction, light echoes from Cassiopeia A would be faint for even the 48-inch Schmidt telescope, but might be photographable in infrared light.

On a single photograph, it would be impossible to distinguish between a reflection nebula illuminated by an ordinary star and one illuminated by an old supernova. However, a second picture, exposed a few months later, should show significant change in the latter case [due to the outward velocity at the speed of light].

6

Magnetic Stars
and Flare
Stars

In discussion of the sun and of the extreme conditions of nova and super-nova outbursts, "magnetic fields" have been mentioned several times (p. 51, 195, and 196). The term can be loosely defined as the region around a magnet where a force would act on another magnet placed there. More precisely, the magnetic field is a vector quantity measuring the direction and amount of force that would be exerted on a standard magnetic north pole; the unit was originally called the "gauss," more recently the "oersted." Magnetic fields are produced by electrical currents as well as by iron magnets—more generally, by moving charged particles; and a moving charged particle is itself deflected by a magnetic field. The earth has a magnetic field that is about one gauss vertically downward over the north magnetic pole, and horizontally northward near the equator, accounting for the action of a magnetic compass. Cosmic rays and other charged particles coming at the earth from outside are deflected in a complicated way by this field, and the "Van Allen belts" around the earth consist of charged particles oscillating north-south along the field.

The sun also has a magnetic field, studied extensively at the Mount Wilson Observatory under the leadership of George E. Hale, its first director. —T L P

....

The Magnetism of the Sun

GEORGE E. HALE

(*The Telescope*, May–June 1936)

In 1908, after much previous study at the Kenwood, Yerkes, and Mount Wilson Observatories, a simple process of reasoning suggested that sunspots might be the centers of measurable magnetic fields. The spectroheliograph (see p. 66) had just recorded great vortices in the sun's atmosphere above the spots, resembling hurricanes or tornadoes in the atmosphere of the earth. If, as there was some reason to believe, the sunspots themselves were underlying vortices containing electrically charged particles, the whirling of these particles should set up magnetic fields. Rowland and others had shown that moving charged particles produced magnetic effects in the laboratory. The problem was whether similar phenomena actually existed and could be detected in the sun.

In 1896 Pieter Zeeman, the Dutch physicist, succeeded in obtaining a remarkable effect when the luminous vapor of an electric spark was observed between the poles of a powerful magnet: the lines of its spectrum were widened or split into several components. Moreover, the separate components, produced by a strong magnetic field, were polarized in a unique and completely characteristic manner. Faraday had sought for some such effect in his last recorded experiment, but his instruments were not powerful enough to show it.

Sunspots contain luminous metallic vapors, although they appear dark by contrast with the much brighter surface of the sun. Fortunately the 60-foot tower telescope on Mount Wilson, equipped with a spectroscope even more powerful than that of Zeeman, was available for the test. The polariscopic attachments were also at hand. All of the distinguishing features of the Zeeman effect were soon detected, and the presence of a magnetic field in every sunspot examined was established beyond question. The magnetic lines of force were found to be nearly at right angles to the solar surface at the center of the spot; near its outer boundary, however, they are approximately parallel to the surface.

After sufficient solar and laboratory results had been obtained to demonstrate the existence, strength, and general characteristics of the strong magnetic fields in several of the largest spots then visible, other phases of the problem were attacked. A bar magnet has two poles, north and south. In general, the magnetic fields of the sunspots observed north and south of the equator were found to be opposite in polarity. As some exceptions were noted, however, a general study of polarities was begun. This led to some curious results.

Anyone who will examine the early observations of Galileo, Scheiner, and their successors will notice the wide variety in the size and form of sunspots. They often appear at first as single spots but soon develop into elongated groups, containing large and small members. Many of these groups are double, comprising two large spots, with or without companions, or one large group, followed or (less often) preceded by a train of smaller spots. Such groups were found to be almost invariably bipolar, consisting of two spots or groups of spots having opposite magnetic poles. In the great majority of cases the preceding (western) spots of such pairs are opposite in polarity in the northern and southern hemispheres of the sun.

It was thus a comparatively simple matter to develop a scheme of magnetic classification, which has since been applied to the many thousands of sunspots observed at Mount Wilson. Nicholson, Ellerman, Joy, and many others have taken part in this long series of observations, which has now extended over more than two of the well-known frequency cycles of sunspots.

One of these cycles of approximately eleven years was near its height when the magnetic observations were begun. As time progressed, the succeeding spots broke out at lower and lower mean latitudes, preceding the sunspot minimum of 1912.

The first spots of a new frequency cycle appear in high latitudes, before the last low-latitude spots of the old eleven-year cycle have entirely ceased. We were surprised to find that the first spots following the minimum were reversed in magnetic polarity, as contrasted with the low-latitude spots of the old cycle. That is, the preceding spots of bipolar groups, south in the old cycle (for the northern hemisphere), were now of north polarity. A similar reversal, of opposite signs, occurred in the southern hemisphere.

FIG. 93. The largest group of sunspots ever recorded, photographed at the tower telescope of the Mount Wilson Observatory on April 7, 1947. The lower photograph is an enlargement of part of this photograph. The maximum area of the sunspot group, measured at Greenwich Observatory, was 6.3 billion square miles. Its maximum length was 200,000 miles. North is at the bottom of both photographs. (Mount Wilson Observatory photograph)

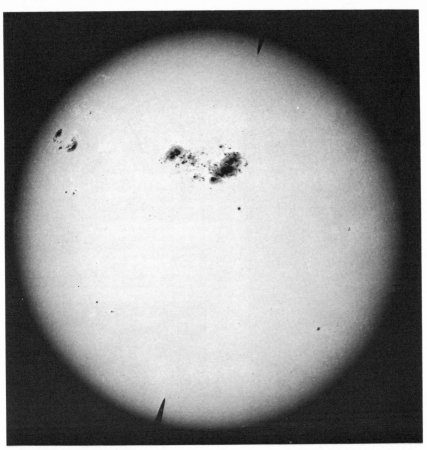

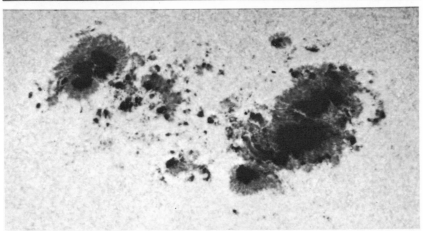

The Sunspot of April 7, 1947

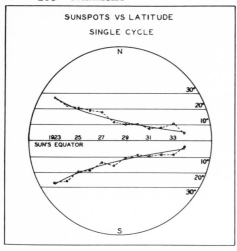

SUNSPOTS VS LATITUDE
SINGLE CYCLE

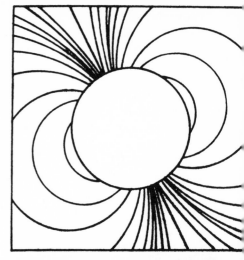

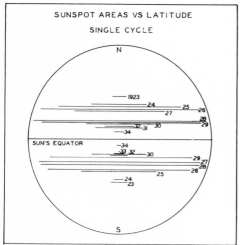

SUNSPOT AREAS VS LATITUDE
SINGLE CYCLE

FIG. 94. Two ways of indicating the characteristics of a sunspot-frequency cycle. The upper diagram shows the change in the average solar latitude of sunspots with the progress of a cycle; the lower one the variation in total spottedness, represented by the length of the horizontal line associated with a year, and the average solar latitude of the spots for that year.

FIG. 95. The solar corona. Compare the details of structure within it with the lines in the upper diagram, which show the directions of the lines of force of the magnetic fields surrounding a spherical magnet.

With only about 3 per cent of exceptions, the spots of the new frequency cycle continued to show these reversed polarities until after the next minimum in 1923. They had then reached a low mean latitude, not far from the equator. Then the first high-latitude spots of the next frequency cycle appeared. These again showed the characteristic reversal of polarity, which was observed for the third time in 1934.

The complete magnetic cycle thus lasts between twenty-two and twenty-three years and is about twice that of the better known sunspot-frequency cycle. It points toward some general solution, applying to the sun and doubtless to many other stars, but still not beyond the empirical stage.

The earth was shown to be a magnet by Gilbert in 1600. It remained for Schuster to ask in 1891 whether every rotating body is a magnet. Although the appearance of the corona suggested a similar condition for the sun, the question had not been settled in 1908, when the sunspot fields were discovered. It was evident that if any general magnetic field existed, it must be far weaker than that of the spots, as most of the lines of the solar spectrum are very narrow, even under high dispersion.

Finding that no sign of the Zeeman effect could be detected for the sun as a whole with the 60-foot tower telescope and 30-foot spectroscope, a better opportunity was awaited. This came with the completion of the 150-foot tower telescope and the 75-foot spectroscope in 1912.

It was obvious that regions away from sunspots must be observed by a differential method of great sensitivity. Moreover, every possible precaution must be taken to avoid instrumental errors and any effect of bias on the part of the measurers. Many members of the Mount Wilson staff joined in the work, and several different methods of measurement were employed. Those who took part included Anderson, Seares, Ellerman, van Maanen, while check measures were made by Walter Adams, H. D. Babcock, and others. The work was continued for several years, and the detailed results were published in a series of papers in *The Astrophysical Journal*. They seemed to leave no doubt as to the existence, polarity, and approximate intensity of a weak general magnetic field, rapidly decreasing in strength with altitude and having poles not far removed from the sun's poles of rotation.

The difficulties of measurement were so great, however, that some of the measurers could not detect the field, though all who succeeded were in agreement regarding its polarity and order of magnitude. . . .

Some years later, John Strong, using a Zeiss microphotometer, and R. Langer, using two forms of measuring machines, obtained results showing the same polarity as in the original work. J. Evershed, using his excellent method of measurement at his observatory in England, also

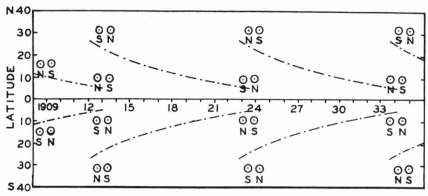

FIG. 96. Law of sunspot polarity. The curves represent the approximate variation in mean latitude and the corresponding magnetic polarities of sunspots observed at Mount Wilson from June 1908 until January 1935. In each pair of dots, the one to the right represents the preceding spot.

confirmed the original results on a number of the old plates. A statement regarding these measures was published in *Nature* for November 2, 1935. . . .

The overall probable error for all the measures obtained since last September is about one tenth of the maximum amplitude of the displacement. While the existence and polarity of the general magnetic field have thus been amply confirmed, its exact numerical value and the possibility of any variation in intensity must await further investigations by different observers. There is no indication of a change of polarity or magnitude in recent years.

The rapid rise of astrophysics, through the fusion of astronomy and physics, is illustrated in many researches of this type. While the results summarized in this paper are purely observational, a more intensive study of the underlying theory is still called for. The remarkable law of sunspot polarity could hardly have been predicted by theory, but it is hoped that astronomers, physicists, and geophysicists will be interested in the full interpretation of solar magnetic phenomena and their application in other branches of science.

Stars as Magnets

OTTO STRUVE

(*Sky and Telescope*, March 1950)

In 1947 Horace W. Babcock announced that the star 78 Virginis, observed by him at Mount Wilson, behaves as an enormous magnet, with an intensity of the magnetic force in its atmosphere far in excess of that of the earth and resembling that of the most powerful electromagnets produced, in minute volumes of space, in the laboratory. This discovery was the culmination of a long series of investigations which started early in 1908, when G. E. Hale recognized that the hydrogen flocculi of the sun frequently resemble the distribution of iron filings in the vicinity of a magnet. A few months later, on June 25, 1908, he succeeded in establishing that the spectral lines of the sun observed in and near a sunspot are, indeed, influenced by what is called the Zeeman effect: a single spectral line produced by an ordinary light source, such as an iron arc, is split up into several component lines, usually quite close together, when the emitting atoms are located between the poles of a strong magnet; this magnetic splitting of the lines is different, depending on whether we observe the light source at right angles to the direction joining the two magnetic poles or along this direction.

It is customary to describe the properties of magnetism by means of the concept of a magnetic field which is represented by a pattern of *force lines* indicating the direction of the magnetic force of attraction or repulsion. In the case of a bar magnet, in which the two poles are separated by a straight piece of iron, the field lines emerge radially from the north pole and curve around so as to enter the south pole.

If a magnetic needle capable of turning in all directions is placed in the field of a bar magnet, it assumes a direction given by the slant of the force lines. If an incandescent gas is located in the vicinity of a magnet, the splitting of a spectral line observed at right angles to the field lines produces three components, in the simplest cases. The central component is in the exact position of the undisturbed spectral line, while the two other components are shifted symmetrically toward the red and the

FIG. 97. The field of a bar magnet.

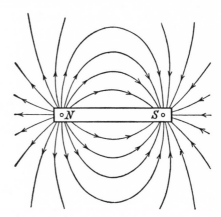

violet sides, the amount of the shift being proportional to the intensity of the field. All three components are plane polarized, but the direction of polarization of the two outer components is at right angles to that of the central component.

When we observe the gas along or parallel to the direction of the force lines, the central component is absent, and the two outer components show circular polarization. An ordinary piece of polaroid filter records no difference in the brightnesses of these two components when it is turned 90°. Nevertheless, the light is not of the usual unpolarized variety. . . .

We can, however, convert circular polarization into plane polarization by a simple trick: we insert into the beam of light a piece of doubly refracting crystal whose optical axis is perpendicular to the beam. . . . Such a plate, made of quartz or mica, is called a quarter-wave plate. In the Zeeman effect it is customary to employ a quarter-wave plate in front of the spectrograph. The two components then remain of the same intensity as before, but they become plane polarized in opposite planes and can be alternately extinguished by rotating a polaroid filter.

Now let us return to the problem of the stars. In 1913, Hale announced that he and his associates at Mount Wilson Observatory had detected a general magnetic field of the sun. According to this result, the sun must be regarded as a magnetized sphere, somewhat like the earth. We can imagine that in the center of the earth, or of the sun, there is something resembling a bar magnet, which we shall call a magnetic dipole. Its axis is inclined to the axis of rotation by about 6° for the sun and 11° for the earth. At the magnetic pole the field lines are straight, while near the equator they are greatly curved. . . .

The magnetic field of the earth is only a few tenths of an oersted [gauss]. The strongest magnetic fields of electromagnets which can be maintained for a considerable length of time are between 10,000 and 100,000 oersteds. Professor Peter Kapitza, a Russian physicist, obtained in the laboratory fields of the order of a million oersteds, for very short intervals of time. According to Hale, the magnetic field in the reversing layer of the sun's atmosphere, where the absorption lines in the solar spectrum are produced, is of the order of 50 oersteds.

Later investigations failed to confirm the existence of a constant field of the sun. In 1922 and 1923 the field strength was considerably less than 50 oersteds, and in 1933 no field strength could be detected. H. D. Babcock has summarized his measurements from 1940 to 1947. At times he recorded a general magnetic field ranging, in the direction given by Hale, between 6 and 60 oersteds. But at other times the field was practically zero. In Germany, G. Thiessen found in 1945 a magnetic

FIG. 98. The general magnetic field of the earth. The axis of rotation is dotted.

field of the same order as that announced by Hale in 1913. But in 1947 and 1948 he found no magnetic field greater than 5 oersteds in the expected direction, which, according to Hale, nearly coincided with the sun's axis of rotation.

It is thus possible that the magnetic field of the sun is undergoing variations. At any rate, it is either completely variable, or has a very small constant value. One of the difficulties in this work is the presence of the large magnetic fields connected with individual sunspots. . . . When a spot is near the limb of the sun, some of its force lines are parallel to those of the general field, and confusion may arise. It was for this reason that Hale and his associates always preferred to measure the general field during periods of minimum sunspot activity.

Horace W. Babcock reasoned that if the magnetism of rotating bodies is somehow related to their rotations—an idea which had been suggested by A. Schuster in 1892—there would be a strong possibility, even a probability, that rapidly rotating stars might show pronounced Zeeman patterns. The rotational velocity of the sun at the equator is two kilometers per second. That of a larger, hotter B-star or A-star may sometimes be as great as 500 kilometers a second. Therefore, we might expect in the spectra of such stars Zeeman splittings of spectral lines which are 100 or 1000 times greater than those measured by Hale in the general spectrum of the sun.

Because of the Doppler effect, however, rapidly rotating stars usually have very diffuse spectral lines. It is only when the axis of rotation happens to lie close to the line of sight that the Doppler effects from all parts of the stellar disk are the same and the spectral lines are sharp and therefore suitable for the test.

Babcock selected several stars of spectral class A [see p. 144] and found that the Zeeman effect is unmistakable in 78 Virginis, but is absent in

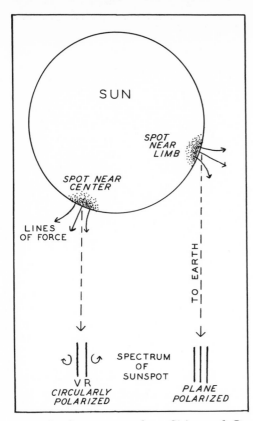

FIG. 99. This diagram shows the positions in which sunspots produce the two simple kinds of Zeeman effect in the sunspot spectrum. The reader is looking down at the polar regions of the sun, and the paper is the plane of the ecliptic.

several other stars, such as Sirius and Gamma Geminorum. The intensity of the magnetic field of 78 Virginis is about 1500 oersteds at the pole. (The quantity actually measured is an average value of the field strength integrated over the apparent disk of the star.) . . .

Since 1947 Babcock has measured a number of other stars, and, strangely, all of those which show large magnetic fields have unusually strong absorption lines of ionized silicon or of other elements, and other peculiar spectral features. Several are known to belong to a class of objects described as *spectrum variables*, in which the intensities of certain spectral lines change periodically. For example, in the star BD −18°3789 the lines of ionized chromium and ionized europium vary in a period of nine days, but with opposite phases; the europium lines are strong when the chromium lines are weak.

Babcock found that the magnetic field of this star varies between about +8000 oersteds when the Eu II lines are strong and −6000 oersteds when the Eu II lines are weak. In an ordinary electromagnet such a reversal of polarity can be obtained when the electric current is reversed. In a permanent bar magnet a reversal of polarity would suggest a rotation of the whole magnet around an axis that is perpendicular to the long side of the

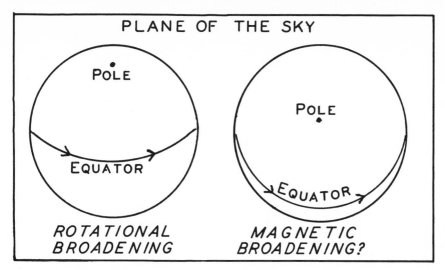

FIG. 100. Stars oriented as drawn at the left (in any position angle) can show strong Doppler broadening of their spectral lines if they are in sufficiently rapid rotation; but for stars oriented as at the right, with their poles pointing toward us, the rotational broadening will be negligible, and other effects, such as the magnetic broadening suggested by H. W. Babcock, should be observable.

bar. Perhaps the effect observed by Babcock is simply due to the rotation of the star around an axis which is at a considerable angle from the magnetic axis. In the case of BD −18°3789 the period of nine days would be the rotational period of the star, and this is not inconsistent with the appearance of the spectral lines. But this would mean that the rotation is rather slow, and that there is no simple relation between the star's spin and its magnetic field, as suggested by Schuster [and later by P. M. S. Blackett].

If this interpretation is correct, then the variation of the spectrum-line intensities must also be due to the rotation of the star around its axis. A. J. Deutsch points out that this would mean a tendency of the atoms of Eu II and Cr II to be concentrated at opposite magnetic poles. A hint as to the possible reason for a migration of different atoms toward the north magnetic pole or toward the south magnetic pole of a star has been made by Babcock. He suggested that chromium ions in stellar atmospheres are paramagnetic, while the europium ions may be diamagnetic. The paramagnetic materials tend to arrange themselves in a magnetic field as do the iron filings in the well-known experiment of Faraday. The diamagnetic substances, on the contrary, tend to assume directions which are at right angles to the lines of force. . . .

More recently Babcock has found three additional stars in which the magnetic field is variable, the most interesting among them being Alpha Canes Venatici. The magnetic field intensity reaches values of plus or minus several thousand oersteds. This star is the best known representative of the class of spectrum variables. Its period is 5.5 days, and the variations in the absorption lines have been analyzed by P. Swings and the writer. . . .

It now appears that stars with large magnetic fields are probably rotating less rapidly than such well-known broad-lined stars as Altair (whose period of rotation is about six hours), and that there may be large angles—up to 90°—between rotational and magnetic axes. When the angle is large and the axis of rotation is perpendicular (or nearly so) to the line of sight we observe a spectrum variable. When the magnetic axis and the rotational axis both roughly coincide with the line of sight we observe a star with constant magnetic field and permanent spectroscopic peculiarity. . . .

An entirely different explanation has been proposed by M. Schwarzschild. From the analogy of an electromagnet with alternating current in the coil, he attempts to show that if the star does not rotate around an axis which differs from the magnetic axis, then large-scale magnetohydrodynamic oscillations are needed to obtain the observed results.

It is premature to try to decide between these two remarkable hypotheses. On the former (Babcock's) we should perhaps think of a pair of large, diametrically opposite "starspots," permanent in location and exhibiting magnetic fields similar to that of a normal, large sunspot, but having opposite polarities. If these spots are on or near the star's equator, we have a spectrum variable. . . .

....

Intense Magnetic Field

(*Sky and Telescope*, March 1961)

A faint star in the constellation Lacerta has the strongest magnetic field known in nature, according to recent observations by Horace W. Babcock at Mount Wilson and Palomar Observatories. His discovery was made with high-dispersion polarized-light spectrograms taken with the 200-inch telescope. These show a pronounced Zeeman effect—a splitting of spectrum lines that occurs when light originates in a magnetic field.

The star is No. 215,441 in the *Henry Draper Catalogue*, where its visual magnitude is given as 8.6 and spectral class as AOp. The last letter indicates that the spectrum is peculiar, which led Babcock to examine it for the magnetic effect. He procured twenty spectrograms between July 14, 1959, and June 13, 1960, all showing evidence for an unusually strong magnetic field of positive polarity.

Several of the metallic lines, such as those of ionized titanium and chromium at 4163 and 4558 angstroms, respectively, were resolved into the fine components of the Zeeman pattern, permitting accurate measurement of the magnetic field strength involved. On four plates taken on successive nights from October 23 to 26, in 1959, a value of 34,400 gauss was obtained for the magnetic field.

Measurements on other spectra indicate that the field changes markedly in an irregular fashion, sometimes being as low as about 12,000 gauss. The polarity remains positive, and Babcock believes that the star's rotation and magnetic axes lie nearly in the line of sight.

The radial velocity varies erratically, and the brightness alters by 0.15 magnitude in a 9.5-day cycle, neither phenomenon being synchronized with the magnetic field variation. The H and K lines of ionized calcium appear to originate in a slowly expanding shell, located about 1.2 stellar radii above its surface.

Inside a normal star the weight of each layer is supported by gas pressure and radiation pressure. In HD 215,441, however, the magnetic forces are so great that they furnish the chief support for the outer layers. In fact, the strong, fluctuating magnetic field may cause the ejection of much material from the star. The amount of internal magnetic energy is probably at least equal to that of the total radiant energy it sends into space each thirty-seven days.

Another group of peculiar stars has been established by the study of magnetic fields in sunspots started by Hale sixty years ago. Recently, Babcock has developed a theory of sunspots linking them with the general magnetic field and the peculiar rotation of the sun, which is faster at the equator than near the poles (see p. 50). This and the theoretical explanation of magnetic variables are complex aspects of "magnetohydrodynamics," the study of motions of charged particles in a magnetic field. Such a conducting medium tends to drag the magnetic lines of force with it. Babcock reasons that the more rapid rotation near the sun's equator wraps the magnetic field round and round, just under the surface of the hot ionized gases. This would increase the field strength in the mid-latitudes, and sunspots would pop up in pairs where the "ropes" of magnetic lines of force come out of the surface (N polarity) and go in again (S polarity). Rising motions of material over the sunspots would carry lines of force outward, slowly decrease the field under the surface, and reverse it after eleven years, when the process would start again with opposite polarity. Babcock's theory thus qualitatively explains the sunspot cycle and the reversal of the sun's general magnetic field, but the complex effects of turbulent motion cannot yet be calculated with precision.

It has already been noted (p. 194) that radiotelescopes detect radio emission from many extraterrestrial sources, one of these being the sun (see p. 55). It is, in fact, the solar corona that accounts for most of the radio emission, and turns out to radiate radio waves as if its temperature were several million degrees (see Volume 2, Neighbors of the Earth). Superimposed on this radio emission in wavelengths around 1 meter (300 megacycles frequency) are bursts that appear to come from bright optical flares near the photosphere surface.   —T L P

....

Solar Radio Bursts

(*Sky and Telescope*, August 1959)

The recording of intense short-lived bursts of radio energy from active areas on the sun at the Harvard Radio Astronomy Station, Fort Davis, Texas, started in 1958. The original range of the equipment, 580 to 100 megacycles radio frequency, has now been extended to much lower frequencies, 100 to 25 megacycles, providing records of radio noise from high in the solar corona. [Because the corona is opaque to low-frequency radio waves, they must come from higher levels.] A. R. Thompson and A. Maxwell have reported on the program.

The additional equipment makes use of a fixed antenna that does not track the sun, but that has a broad beam directed along the meridian at the celestial equator, so the sun can be monitored for the greater part of the day. Two narrow-band tunable receivers of high sensitivity, made by Airborne Instruments Laboratory, sweep repeatedly, one over the 25-to-50-megacycle octave, the other from 50 to 100 megacycles. Their outputs are displayed on cathode-ray tubes and photographed with a camera in which film is moving continuously. . . .

Sample fast-drift bursts of February 20, 1959, are shown in Figure 101. The duration of a burst is only about 1 second at 500 megacycles, low in the sun's atmosphere, but it is of the order of 20 seconds at 25 megacycles. The leading edge of a fast burst is well defined, resulting from a disturbance moving unchecked outward with a speed of 60,000 miles a second. The new channels also record a much greater number of bursts with reverse drifts (increase of frequency with time), indicating that the disturbances are moving downward from high in the sun's atmosphere. . . .

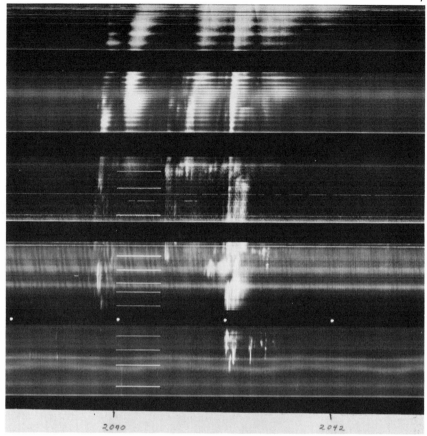

FIG. 101. These fast-drift bursts of solar radio noise were recorded during a four-minute interval on February 20, 1959. Time increases from left to right, and the top of the record corresponds to a frequency of 25 megacycles per second, the bottom to 580. The bursts are caused by disturbances in the sun's atmosphere traveling generally outward at enormous velocities. According to one theory, fast-drift bursts are cosmic rays moving at 0.3 the velocity of light; alternatively, they may be fast-moving shock waves. (Harvard College Observatory photograph)

The flares are short lived, and the bursts last only a few seconds, during which the radio frequency changes, probably as a shock wave races through the sun's atmosphere.

Other stars, usually of much lower temperature, show similar flare activity. — T L P

....

Visual and Radio
Observations of
Flare Stars

O. B. SLEE, C. S. HIGGINS, AND G. E. PATSTON

(*Sky and Telescope*, February 1963)

Astronomers have been interested for several years in the possibility of detecting radio emission from flare stars. These are variable stars that show occasional large increases in brightness, lasting for minutes. Such stars are red dwarfs of spectral class *M* [see Chapter 3], usually with strong emission lines of hydrogen and ionized calcium. A number of authors consider that the brightenings are caused by solar-type flares, which, in the case of the sun, often produce very intense radio bursts.

Since the energy liberated in the continuous spectrum of a flare star during an outburst is several hundred times greater than the continuum energy emitted from a solar flare, it is possible that the radio-frequency energy is correspondingly greater. If so, stellar radio bursts should be detectable with the large radiotelescopes now in use, even though flare stars are so much farther away than the sun.

Detection of radio emission from flare stars might lead to several important new fields of research. For example, although probably 80 per cent of all main-sequence stars are *M* dwarfs, we know little about the physical conditions in their atmospheres. Radio bursts might be generated in the coronas of some of these stars, if indeed they have extensive ionized atmospheres like the sun's.

Again, statistics of flare-star bursts may tell whether stars in general possess "starspot" cycles analogous to the eleven-year sunspot cycle. Finally, radio studies could show whether flare stars eject high-energy particles in sufficient amount to contribute appreciably to cosmic rays and, indirectly, to the radio emission of the Milky Way Galaxy.

Since September 1960, Australian radioastronomers and members of Australian amateur astronomical societies have been engaged in joint radio and optical observations of certain d*M*e [dwarf *M*-stars with emission lines in their spectra] flare stars. The radio monitoring has been performed by the Division of Radiophysics, Commonwealth Scientific and

Industrial Research Organization (CSIRO), Sydney. We used wavelengths of 15, 3.5, 0.75, and 0.20 meters, but most of our observations were obtained at 3.5 meters. . . .

Two records obtained simultaneously, the fringe pattern of one shifted by a known amount from the pattern of the other, allowed separation of man-made and natural interference.

It was possible to record a star for up to three hours per night near the time of meridian transit. We observed only at night, to eliminate the effects of solar radio bursts.

The sensitivity of the 3.5-meter equipment was determined from radio sources of known flux density. It turned out that when we used a smoothing time constant of about 5 seconds, radio bursts with peak flux densities exceeding 2×10^{-25} watt per square meter per cycle per second could be detected in regions of the sky with low background temperatures. . . .

For two weeks during last April and May, fifty-two hours of high-sensitivity records were taken with the 210-foot steerable reflector, at wavelengths of 0.75 and 0.20 meter. The minimum detectable signals were 1.5×10^{-26} unit at 0.75 meter, and 5×10^{-27} unit at 0.20 meter.

Each night, amateur astronomers attempted to catch any brightness changes of a flare star during the interval it was under radio observation. Since some of the stars are fainter than visual magnitude 11, observers near Sydney needed 10-inch reflectors for satisfactory results, but in the country 6-inch reflectors were found adequate for the brighter objects. For the first eighteen months, optical monitoring was confined to the environs of Sydney, where seven teams of observers and four 10-inch telescopes were available. During the last four months of the program, country observing stations were set up in New South Wales, Victoria, and Queensland. . . .

Three flare stars—UV Ceti, Proxima Centauri, and V1216 Sagittarii—were examined by radio for a total of 928 hours, with 403 hours of concurrent optical monitoring. In addition, radio observations alone were carried out for eighty hours on V371 Orionis.

Visual observers reported two "certain" flares, seen from different sites, and eleven "possible" ones, seen by single teams. The brightness increases ranged from 0.3 to 1.5 magnitudes, but the smaller ones should be regarded with caution because they were near the limit of detection. In two cases, as the star brightened it seemed yellower—probably good additional evidence for the reality of the events.

The optical brightenings differed greatly in duration; one was as short as three minutes, while the longest was about two hours. In two protracted cases, the light curves showed several maxima, each lasting about ten minutes.

TABLE 7. CORRELATION BETWEEN OPTICAL AND RADIO EVENTS

	Optical flare Vis. mag. rise	Minutes duration	Radio flux* 3.5 meters (J units)	Additional data
UV CETI				
Sept. 24, 1960	1.2	8	—	Radio observations incomplete
Oct. 22, 1960	1.2	4	<4	
Nov. 9, 1961	0.4	10	<2	Color change to yellow; <1000 flux units at 15 meters
Nov. 12, 1961	0.5	3	<2	
Nov. 13, 1961	0.3	60	3	4-min. radio burst; 50,000 flux units at 15 meters; erratic brightness changes began a few minutes earlier
PROXIMA CENTAURI				
April 27, 1961	1.5	40	<8	Certain optical flare
May 9, 1961	1.2	30	—	Radio observations incomplete
May 14, 1961	1.0	60	16	5-min. radio burst recorded near maximum light
June 19, 1961	0.6	120	<8	
March 29, 1962	1.0	8	<8	
April 3, 1962	0.3	30	<8	Color change to yellow
April 14, 1962	0.3	40	16	5-min. radio burst coincident with sudden brightening
May 3, 1962	1.2	14	<8	Certain optical flare; color change to yellow; radio flux <0.15 unit at 0.75 meter, and <0.05 unit at 0.20 meter

* The unit of radio flux (here J for Jansky) is 10^{-26} watt per square meter per cycle per second.

The radio results were disappointing in the sense that the two certain flares were not accompanied by detectable bursts. During the May 3, 1962, flare of Proxima Centauri, high-sensitivity observations were in progress with the 210-foot reflector, in addition to the lower-sensitivity 3.5-meter recordings, but showed nothing. However, at or within a few minutes of the times of three of the possible flares seen by the amateur astronomers, radio deflections were recorded consistent with an origin at the flare star.

In all three cases that we observed, the 3.5-meter bursts were small, but during the possible flare of UV Ceti on November 13, 1961, concurrent observations at 15 meters revealed an extremely intense group of bursts, about four minutes after a similar but much weaker group on 3.5 meters. Such time delays occur during the type II bursts which accompany some intense solar flares. . . .

To summarize, we have not yet obtained conclusive evidence for the detection of radio bursts from flare stars, despite several suggestive occur-

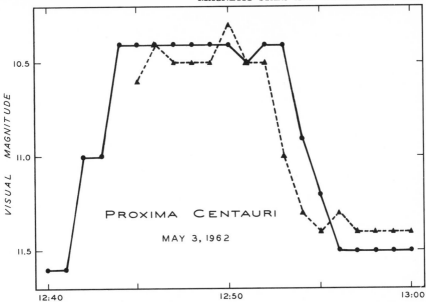

FIG. 102. Light curves for the May 3, 1962, flare of Proxima Centauri derived from simultaneous but independent observations in New South Wales. The solid curve represents magnitude estimates made at Belfield, the dashed one those made at Lakemba. For ten minutes or so the star was about three times brighter than normal.

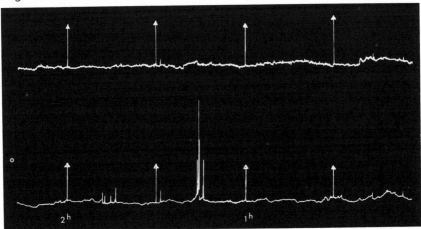

FIG. 103. At lower center are a group of 3.5-meter bursts that may have been emitted by UV Ceti at about 1^h15^m (local sidereal time) on November 15, 1960. Compare this trace, made with the antenna beamed directly at the star, with the upper one, for which the pointing direction was 3° away.

rences. Of the eleven optical events noted during radio observations, only three were accompanied by radio deflections consistent with an origin in the flare stars, and even for these cases the reality of the optical events is somewhat uncertain. . . .

The one definite result is our failure to detect radio emission from the two certain flares. It is well known that not all important solar flares are accompanied by intense radio bursts. Our sample of flares is as yet too small for any general conclusions about the radio luminosities of red-dwarf flares.

This work should be continued with the higher sensitivity afforded by large steerable radio reflectors. Also, visual observations of brightness should be supplemented by photographic or photoelectric methods.

TABLE 8.   SHORT LIST OF KNOWN AND SUSPECTED SOUTHERN FLARE STARS

Star	R.A. (1950)		Dec.		Spectrum	Vis. mag. at min.	Visual range
	h	m					
LPM 63	01	09.9	−17	16	dM5e	11.6	—
L726-8A	01	36.4	−18	13	dM6e	12.5	—
UV Cet	01	36.4	−18	13	dM5.5e	12.9	2.7
ADS 2894B	03	54.9	−01	18	dM3e	11.2	—
o² Eri C	04	13.0	−07	44	dM4.5e	11.1	—
Wolf 1539	04	49.4	+06	24	dM4e	11.8	—
Ross 42	05	29.4	+09	47	dM4e	11.8	—
V371 Ori	05	31.2	+01	55	dM3e	11.0	1.2
Ross 614A	06	26.8	−02	47	dM4.5e	11.3	—
YZ CMi	07	42.1	+03	41	dM4.5e	11.6	1.3
Wolf 359	10	54.2	+07	20	dM6e	13.5	1.0
Wolf 424A	12	30.9	+09	18	dM5.5e	12.7	2.0
Wolf 424B	12	30.9	+09	18	dM5.5e	12.7	—
Wolf 461	12	58.1	+05	57	dM5e	13.2	—
Ross 845	14	09.2	−11	47	dM5.5e	13.5	—
Proxima Cen	14	26.7	−62	29	dM5e	11.3	1.0
L1130-30A	16	04.0	+08	30	dM3e	12.0	—
L1113-55	16	33.5	+05	23	dM4e	12.2	—
GC 22805A	16	52.8	−08	15	dM3e	10.0	0.5
GC 22805B	16	52.8	−08	15	dM3e	10.0	—
Ross 154	18	46.7	−23	53	dM4.5e	10.5	0.5
β468B	19	43.5	+04	08	dM2e	11.4	—
HD 196982A	20	38.7	−32	36	dM4.5e	10.9	—
HD 196982B	20	38.7	−32	36	dM4.5e	11.1	—
20C1225	20	42.0	−31	31	dM2e	8.7	—
Wolf 922	21	28.6	−10	01	dM4.5e	11.5	—
Wolf 1561A	22	14.7	−09	03	dM4.5e	13.5	—
Wolf 1561B	22	14.7	−09	03	dM5e	14.5	—
BD −21°6267B	22	35.7	−20	52	dM4.5e	10.2	?
L789-6	22	35.7	−15	37	dM5.5e	12.6	—

We recommend flare star observations to all amateur astronomers, for they can do valuable work by preselecting stars for later joint optical and radio investigation. Table 8 is a list of known and suspected southern flare stars, the majority visible to observers in mid-northern latitudes. In many cases the magnitude ranges are based upon only one or two flares. Objects for which no ranges are given have been included because they have spectra similar to those of the known flare stars, but only extensive observing—perhaps over hundreds of hours for each star—can establish whether, in fact, they are flare stars. Any amateur with a 6-inch telescope or larger can improve this list from his own observations of suspected flare stars.

Many Australian amateur astronomers contributed to this work. Most were members of the Astronomical Society of New South Wales, but valuable support came from the Latrobe Valley Society, Victoria, and from the astronomical societies of Victoria and Queensland. A. R. Hogg of Mount Stromlo Observatory and Harley W. Wood, the New South Wales government astronomer, helped in the identification of flare star fields.

■■■

New Observations of
AE Aquarii

MERLE F. WALKER

(*Sky and Telescope*, January 1965)

Any up-to-date list of the hundred most important variable stars would contain AE Aquarii, a relatively inconspicuous object of about 12.5 photographic magnitude at minimum. Found by A. H. Joy in 1954 to be a spectroscopic binary, its light variations are extraordinary: erratic outbursts follow one another every few minutes or hours, producing a chaotic light curve like the sample in Figure 104. So rapid are the changes in brightness and spectrum of AE Aquarii that it is difficult to observe them. Indeed, even with the largest telescopes, it is not possible to follow them spectroscopically with even moderate dispersion using conventional photography. Consequently, a program was begun in 1960 of spectroscopic observation with a Lallemand electronic camera[1] attached to the coudé spectrograph of the 120-inch Lick reflector. . . .

[1] A photoelectric image tube of very high sensitivity designed by the French astrophysicist P. Lallemand. — T L P

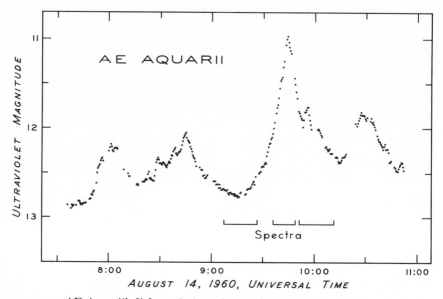

FIG. 104. AE Aquarii's light variations during an active interval. At such times, the fairly constant minimum is interrupted by complex bursts lasting a few minutes to a few hours.

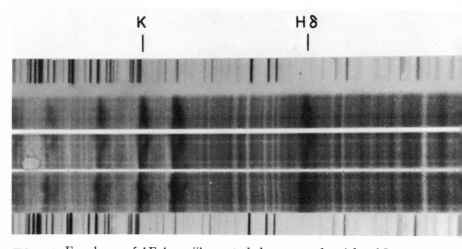

FIG. 105. Four hours of AE Aquarii's spectral changes on the night of June 30–July 1, 1964, as recorded by the author with the Lallemand electronic camera (photograph slightly retouched). At the top and bottom are two laboratory comparison spectra, added for calibration. The two horizontal white strips represent times when plates were changed, and the letters K and Hδ indicate positions of the K line of ionized calcium and of the hydrogen-delta line, respectively. Because this is a negative reproduction, emission (bright) lines register dark. The star image was allowed to trail once along the spectrograph slit. Three such "single-trail" exposures were made and combined here in such a way that time increases uniformly from 7:19 Universal time at the top of the star spectrum to 11:16 at the bottom. (Lick Observatory photograph)

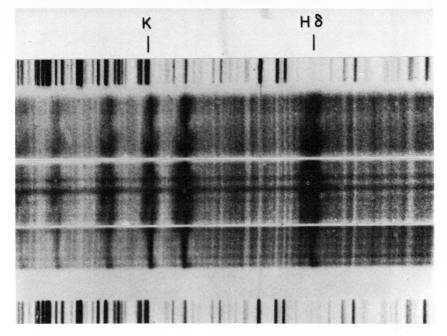

K   H δ

FIG. 106. On July 1–2, 1964, the night following the recordings in Figure 105, Walker obtained this second four-hour record of AE Aquarii in exactly the same manner. The star exposure began at 7:14 UT and ended at 11:16. The two dark horizontal streaks represent temporary brightenings of the star. (Lick Observatory photograph)

In new observations made this past summer, the star image was allowed to trail down a long spectrograph slit at a uniform rate. Thus, a continuous record was obtained, without risk of missing important events.

With the seeing conditions that prevailed at the time of observing, the rate of trailing and the size of the stellar image on the slit gave a time resolution of about five minutes.

At Lick Observatory the Lallemand electronic camera was used with the 20-inch Schmidt system of the 120-inch coudé spectrograph. The spectra in Figures 105 and 106 show no detectable background fog even in 80-minute exposures. This means that exposures of ten or twelve hours are now entirely feasible with the Lallemand equipment.

The information gain of the Lallemand camera is about fifteen times that of a baked Kodak IIa-O plate at a wavelength of 4000 angstroms. The dispersion on the photocathode was 48 angstroms per millimeter, and while the scale is reduced to 65 angstroms per millimeter on the nuclear track plates, the high resolving power of the electron optics and the fine grain of the nuclear emulsion give a final picture that is at least equivalent to that on a baked IIa-O plate at 48 angstroms per millimeter.

Figure 105 is a record of the spectral changes of AE Aquarii during a four-hour interval on the night of June 30–July 1, 1964. The direction of trailing of the star along the slit was such that time progresses downward. Actually, three plates were taken in succession; the horizontal breaks represent the intervals when the plates in the electronic camera were being changed. Simultaneous photoelectric observations were obtained by John Oliver using the observatory's new 24-inch photometric reflector. Preliminary analysis indicates that the events visible in the spectra correlate nicely with changes in light. Figure 106 is a second series of spectrograms, taken in exactly the same manner as the first, on the following night.

Several interesting effects can be noticed in the spectroscopic records. The wavelength shift caused by the orbital motion of AE Aquarii is clearly seen in the curvature of the absorption lines of the late-type component of the system, a dwarf K star. These lines appear white and are curved to the violet (leftward) in the June 30 spectrum (Fig. 105). It is evident that this star approached us most rapidly about midway during the four-hour interval of the observation.

On the following night (see Fig. 106), the lines are again curved, but this time toward the red (rightward), indicating that the late-type component was receding from us and on the other side of its companion. It is evident that on these plates all of the absorption features belong only to the late-type component. A study of these observations indicates that the orbital period is about 10 hours, instead of 16 hours 49 minutes as found by Joy in 1954.

Now let us consider the broad emission lines in the spectra, which appear dark on these negative prints. They are the Balmer series of hydrogen and the H and K lines of ionized calcium. Note that within the latter (and perhaps some of the Balmer lines) a very dark narrow emission component is visible. This shows the same velocity changes as the absorption lines, and evidently originates on or near the surface of the K star.

But the broad hydrogen and calcium emissions vary erratically both in velocity and intensity during the four-hour intervals of observation; these changes are related to the star's unpredictable flareups.

There is a general tendency for this broad emission to be shifted in wavelength opposite to the velocity shifts of the absorption lines. Joy, who used a lower dispersion and long exposures, interpreted this separation of the lines as indicating visibility of the second component. But the June 30–July 1 spectrogram shows clearly how the broad emission of the H and K lines was displaced to longer wavelengths, then shortward, and longward again, all within about two hours. Clearly it cannot originate in the other star. We now see that no spectral features of this second star are detectable, so that we have no idea of its spectroscopic nature.

The irregular velocity shifts of the broad emissions again demonstrate—as my earlier image-tube spectrograms had revealed—that these features originate in localized outbursts, not general explosions involving one or both stars. It might be better to refer to these events as giant flares. There is evidence that at least some of them originate on the K component; others may originate on the invisible star or between the two stars.

In Figure 106, note about midway during the four-hour record the two heavy dark streaks that run the entire breadth of the picture. These were caused by stronger than average outbursts of the system. In small explosions, only the emission lines are affected, and only the blue and ultraviolet light curves show a brightness increase in AE Aquarii. In large explosions, the white-light continuum is affected, and the yellow-light curve also indicates a brightening. . . .

The intent of the last two chapters is to show some of the ways in which stars can vary, or deviate from normal stable behavior. Not all the stars are constant, but a remarkably large percentage of them are. It is this fact that makes the few peculiar stars of such interest to the astronomer.
—T L P

Double Stars

and

Their Masses

Previous chapters have shown how the astronomer measures distances to the stars, how brightness is measured and the luminosities of stars are derived, how colors and spectral types are determined, and how widely these quantities vary from one star to another. In Chapter 4 it was implied that there may be some pattern, or norm, to be expected and that this pattern shows on the H-R diagram in the form of a "main sequence," a region on the plot of luminosity against spectral type in which most stars fall (Fig. 59). The hot blue ones are generally much more luminous than the cool red ones.

The clustering of stars on the H-R diagram implies that there are only a few ways in which a stable star can be put together. Clearly, the mass of material has something to do with this, and it has been noted that the luminosities are much larger for the more massive stars. Mass also entered the discussion of pulsating stars and novae.

How can we measure the mass—"weigh" a star as large as the sun and so far from us? —T L P

••

How Heavy Are the Stars?

SERGEI GAPOSCHKIN

(*The Telescope*, January–February 1937)

We understand the properties of bodies in our external world only through some kind of measurements. Everyone knows the heavy property of matter from visiting a shop to buy something for his earthly needs and observing the pointer of the scale which measures the pull of the earth upon the object. Thus we actually identify the heavy property of an object with its content of matter, expressed in the unit of weight, and we form the conception of *mass*. If we say, for example, that a leg of lamb weighs six pounds, we express the scientific fact that the leg of lamb has as much mass as about three quarters of a gallon of water. . . .

Everyone who drives a car knows that if he is driving along the highway with a speed of 35 miles an hour, he must, in the interest of safety, not be nearer than 35 feet behind the preceding car, because if he is compelled to stop suddenly, the car will continue to slide about 35 feet, in spite of all the power of the brakes. A heavy car requires more distance than a light car. If, by misfortune, a car has stuck in the snow, the driver may help himself by pushing it out if the car is a light one, but it is a hopeless expenditure of energy if the car is a heavy one. Thus we are able to judge the weight of bodies, both in motion and in repose, if we can observe their tendency to remain in motion or their possibility of being set in motion. Both these properties are called *inertia*. But is the weight obtained by a scale—the "gravity mass"—equal to the weight obtained by observation of motions—the "inertia mass"? If they are equal, their ratio will be equal to unity. This question is more or less academic. In practice, we express all earthly weights by the first method and assume that they are equal. . . .

Newton crowned a century of scientific work by showing how the method could be extended to the heavenly bodies.

We can measure the earth's speed in its orbit around the sun and thus are able to determine the ratio of the masses of the sun and the earth from the pull that the sun exerts on the earth. The actual mass of the sun can then be determined from terrestrial determinations of the mass of the earth, as in the famous "Cavendish[1] experiment." The motions of moons

[1] In 1798 the English physicist Cavendish measured the tiny force between two lead spheres of known mass. — T L P

around the other planets, and their effects on one another, allow us in turn to determine their masses.

Among the stars there are many which are double, two stars moving around a common center of balance, much as the planets move around the sun. Thus we are able to determine their motions in respect to each other, and accordingly their masses, all expressed in our earthly units of grams or pounds. . . . The stars are found to display just as great a variety in mass as they do in size: the lightest weigh about half as much as the sun; the heaviest, perhaps a hundred times as much.[2]

About ten years ago a discovery was made that was a great surprise for most astronomers, a discovery that led to another method for measuring the masses of the stars—the determination of the mass from the luminosity. . . . There are about a hundred double stars whose masses can be measured, and also their luminosities. A plot of these luminosities versus the masses gives a single curve, so that we can safely use the luminosities of the stars in estimating their masses. On the occasion of the Harvard tercentenary [in 1937] Professor Russell of Princeton reported on a survey of these results and concluded that the mass-luminosity plot can always be trusted to give a reliable measure of the mass. It reveals just as great a variety in mass as the first method indicated. . . .

From this simple beginning we can extend the notion of mass determination, showing what observations are required and what difficulties may be involved. As noted on p. 168, Newton's law of gravitation predicts elliptical orbits for one massive body moving around another. The size and period of each elliptical orbit are related to the masses of the two stars: $a^3 = (m_1 + m_2) P^2$, where 2a is the full length of the ellipse and P is the period. If P is measured in years, and a in astronomical units (1 A.U. = 93,000,000 mi), the masses are given in units of the sun's mass.

When two stars can be watched as one goes around the other, the two always being separable in the telescope, it is a simple matter to measure their relative positions in the sky ("distance" apart and angle of the line of centers, for instance), but a moment's reflection shows that the "distances" in the sky are angular. A linear distance in light years or parsecs from us to the pair of stars must be given, before a 5-second-of-arc separation can be converted to astronomical units. What's worse, the orbit is inclined at some unknown angle, i, which foreshortens the ellipse. However, a little trigonometry helps to estimate this angle, using the fact that the true orbit of star "A" about star "B" must have "B" at its focus. If the

---

[2] The range from 1/20 to 90 is now considered closer. — T L P

measurements are made relative to the "fixed" background of very distant stars, both star "A" and star "B" are found to move about the "center of mass" between them, and this allows m_1 and m_2 to be determined separately.

Observations like these can be made for well-separated "visual binaries," but because they are far apart, P is long, and weighing the stars takes many years. Closer binaries with shorter periods are generally eclipsing binaries like Algol (p. 169) or spectroscopic binaries without any eclipse. In the latter type the two star images merge—only one image can be seen or photographed in the telescope, and both spectra are superimposed. However, star "A" approaches us while "B" recedes for half the period, and vice versa for the other half. Hence it is possible to distinguish "A's" spectrum lines from "B's" and to measure Doppler shifts for two separate velocity curves. Again, the inclination of the orbit, i, is unknown (except in the case of eclipse when i is about 90°), and the distances across the elliptical orbit obtained from the velocity curve are foreshortened by an unknown amount.

Finally, it is often the case that only one spectrum can be measured because the other star is faint. Then the mass can only be roughly estimated. Fortunately, there are about a hundred double stars now measured from which accurate masses can be derived—distance known, both stars measured, and inclination determined. Henry Norris Russell, at Princeton, found that a plot of these masses against the absolute magnitudes (luminosities) gave a single line, the "mass-luminosity relation" predicted by the theory of stellar interiors. Within a factor of two, a star with luminosity 1 has mass 1; with luminosity 1000 has mass 10; and with luminosity 0.0005 has mass 0.1 suns. There are some notable exceptions, however, in the nuclei of planetary nebulae (p. 152), and in the white dwarfs, which show the Einstein red shift in their spectra.   — T L P

....

Sirius and Its Companion

ROBERT G. AITKEN

(*Sky and Telescope*, September 1942)

. . . Sirius has been of exceptional interest to me ever since 1896, when I had the quite unexpected opportunity to write a short paragraph of its history. . . .

In the years 1891–95, I was teaching mathematics and astronomy at the College of the Pacific, and had the privilege of taking my astronomy class to the Lick Observatory on special nights once or twice a year. I became well acquainted with Edward S. Holden . . . who offered me a position as assistant astronomer for the year beginning July 1, 1896. . . .

My duties in my temporary position were to be participation in the routine work of the observatory, and the reduction of some meridian-circle observations to which Holden had pledged himself. I was to spend three hours a day on the latter job, from 9 A.M. to 12 noon. Aside from that, my time was my own, and I could use any of the instruments freely. . . .

On October 23, 1896, after a heavy day's work, I went up to the 12-inch telescope, planning to work only till midnight. But I found the seeing so extraordinarily good that I continued work until toward morning. Then before going home I went across to the 36-inch dome. The dome was open, and Sirius, near the meridian, was shining directly in through the slit. It was the work of a few minutes to turn the telescope on the star. There stood the tiny companion as sharply and clearly defined as I have ever seen it, and both star images were perfectly steady. Without waiting to get my notebook, I recorded a complete set of measures on the back of an envelope, determined my constants, and then turned up the telescope and went home happy in the thought that I, too, had seen the tiny companion on the first night of its emergence from the rays of its bright primary.

Next morning I found that . . . my observation of the companion of Sirius was the first to be made since Burnham lost it in the rays of Sirius itself in 1892. . . . This was verified by a more experienced observer on the following night.

But why all this excitement about the observation of a double star? The answer lies in the history of the star, to which we now turn.

Since it is the brightest star in the firmament as viewed from the earth, Sirius must have attracted the attention of the very earliest stargazers. . . . Accurate records of the times of its rising were kept from about 300 B.C. Those who are interested in early star lore will find full references to the literature on Sirius in Lockyer's *Dawn of Astronomy* and Allen's *Star Names and Their Meanings*.

Whether the star has changed color since classical times is a question which has been hotly debated. . . . Astronomers generally attributed the apparent red color noted by the ancients to the strong scintillations of the brilliant star shining through the disturbed atmosphere over ocean and desert.

But if the star has not changed in color, it has changed its position in the sky with respect to other stars, as Edmond Halley discovered in 1718. He was the first to note that Arcturus, Sirius, and a few other stars had changed their positions in the sky relative to the other stars.

Prior to Halley's discovery, the stars were regarded as fixed bodies in space, every one holding the position assigned to it at the Creation. After Halley, that view was impossible; for, if a few stars were in motion, all might be, and man's entire outlook upon the nature and origin of the universe had to undergo radical revision.

Halley detected the proper motion of Sirius, but he did not note that its motion was not at a uniform rate, but described a wavy line. This discovery was reserved for Bessel, who, about a hundred years ago, showed that Sirius moved as though it had a companion massive enough to swing the bright star with it in an elliptic orbit about a common center of gravity in a period of fifty years. . . .

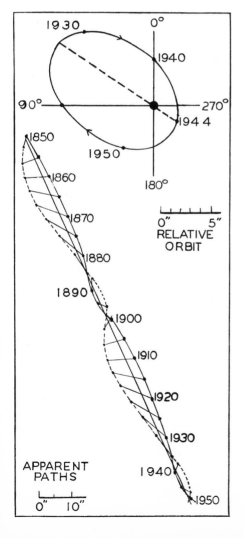

FIG. 107. The apparent relative orbit of Sirius' companion and the apparent paths of the two stars across the sky. The wavy motion of Sirius indicated to Bessel the presence of the companion. The mass ratio of five to two is found from the relative deviation of the two stars from the straight-line path of the center of gravity. (Upper diagram from *Astronomy*, by R. H. Baker, D. Van Nostrand, Princeton, New Jersey, 1964; lower diagram from *Astronomy*, by H. N. Russell, R. S. Dugan, and J. Q. Stewart, Ginn and Company, Boston, 1945)

Then, in 1862, Alvan G. Clark discovered a tiny companion to Sirius, while testing the 18½-inch telescope now at the Dearborn Observatory. . . . The tiny companion was followed by double-star observers as it gradually approached its primary, and the last measure before its disappearance was secured by Burnham with the Lick 36-inch telescope in 1892. Then it was lost in the rays of the bright star. The arc observed in the years 1862–92 was not long enough to permit the computation of a good orbit. It was necessary to *assume* the identity of Clark's companion with the one predicted by Bessel, and the consequent revolution period of fifty years. The question to be decided was whether this assumption was correct, which could be answered if, when the companion again became visible, it appeared in the position predicted upon that assumption. The measures I secured in 1896 settled that point; the companion star was close to its predicted position.

But now new questions arose. By the end of the century the distance of Sirius (8.8 light years), as well as its radial velocity and proper motion, had been well determined. Now a thoroughly reliable orbit could be computed for the system, and from the proper combination of the data, the mass of the system and of each component separately could be derived. The masses were found to be 2.44 and 0.88 times the sun's mass, for Sirius and its companion, respectively.

The spectrum of the faint star was somewhat more uncertain because of the presence of the brilliant white primary, but it was possible to say that the companion was of spectral type earlier than Fo (now known to be A5), while Sirius itself is of type Ao. Thus, they are both stars of comparatively high surface temperatures, and therefore of nearly the same radiation per unit area of their surfaces. But Sirius is of apparent magnitude −1.6, and its companion is 8.4, so the former radiates 10,000 times more light than its companion, which must consequently be a very small star.

It is impossible to measure the diameters of the two stars directly,[1] but by this and other indirect methods that have given fairly reliable results, it is safe to conclude that their ratio is about fifty to one. It follows, since Sirius has been found to be in all respects an ordinary star, owing its brilliancy chiefly to the fact that it is so near to us, that its companion must be extraordinarily dense. It became the first known *white dwarf*, of which other examples are being found constantly.

The questions are, How can we have matter so exceedingly dense which retains the properties of a gas? and in the second place, How can we explain the coexistence of such a body in conjunction with a normal star?

---

[1] Very recently the diameter of Sirius *has* been measured (see p. 78). The angle, 0.0068 seconds of arc, corresponds to a size twice the sun's.   — T L P

Eddington suggested a relief from the first difficulty by his theory that the atoms in such dense stars as white dwarfs have become completely ionized —the outer electrons and the nuclei can then be packed far more closely together, and the body attain the extraordinary density of 50,000 times that of water and still retain its gaseous properties.

A little later came Einstein with his theory of general relativity, one consequence of which is that light emanating from a strong gravitational field will be, as it were, "slowed up"—that is, the spectral lines will be shifted toward the red end of the spectrum. In a single star this shift cannot be separated from the radial-velocity shift due to motion away from us, but in a double star like Sirius, this latter shift can be accurately calculated from the constants of the orbit. The spectral lines of the faint companion of Sirius are very difficult to measure because of the blending with the lines from the bright star, but Walter S. Adams accomplished this with the 100-inch telescope at Mount Wilson, and his result was verified a little later by J. H. Moore at the Lick 36-inch. Einstein's predicted shift amounted to 17 kilometers per second; Adams observationally found 19 kilometers per second, and Moore's result was but little greater.

These observations are strong evidence supporting the extraordinary density of the star and the correctness of Einstein's theory. There are still doubters who hope that some other explanation for this density may be found, and in any event, the association of these two stars into a single double-star system has found no explanation.

The companion of Sirius is now in about the position it held when Burnham observed it in 1892. I hope to live long enough to learn, after its emergence in about 1946, following periastron passage [past the place in its orbit where it is closest to its companion] whether or not it will again be found in its predicted place.

Double-star Studies in Indonesia

(Sky and Telescope, November 1957)

At the Bosscha Observatory, near Bandung, Java, photographic observations of double stars form the main program of the 23½-inch refractor. In his report for the years 1955 and 1956, Director G. B. van Albada tells of special studies of several well-known double stars, including Sirius, Antares, Albireo, and Alpha Centauri.

FIG. 108. In this photograph of Sirius taken with the 23½-inch refractor at Bosscha Observatory, the famous white-dwarf companion appears above and to the left of the overexposed image of the primary star, which is flanked by diffraction images that can be measured for position. The enlargement from the original negative is about thirteen times. (From Bosscha Observatory *Contributions*, No. 3)

In a recent paper concerning photographic observation of binary systems with very large magnitude differences, van Albada describes the special techniques he has developed to obtain measurable photographs of such difficult pairs as Sirius, with results like that pictured in Figure 108. The companion is seen above and to the left of the overexposed central image of Sirius. From the astrometric viewpoint, the faint diffraction images on either side of the central one are especially important.

It is standard procedure in double-star photography, if the primary star is several magnitudes brighter than the secondary, to produce such fainter images by means of a coarse wire diffraction grating placed in front of the telescope objective. Because one pair of them are of about the same size and density as the image of the companion, the latter's position with reference to them may be measured much more accurately than with respect to the overexposed central image of the primary.

Van Albada has found that a grating of only five or six parallel wires, widely but *unequally* spaced, produces the desired result. The spiked appearance of the central image is caused by a hexagonal diaphragm in front of the objective, which produces a strong diffraction of light but reduces the intensity of the image in the spaces between the spikes. The diaphragm is oriented so the image of the companion falls in one of the clear spaces. . . .

The famous "dark companion" is undoubtedly there, close to Sirius, and its superdensity is confirmed by the measured orbit and period. Several other dark-companion white dwarfs like Sirius-B are known, and many other stars with white-dwarf spectra have been found. — T L P

....

White-dwarf Binary Stars

(Sky and Telescope, March 1957)

Thirty-two double stars are now known to contain white-dwarf components, according to W. J. Luyten, University of Minnesota. Binaries among such systems provide our sole direct means for determining the masses of white-dwarf stars. But so far the necessary information about orbital motion and distances is sufficient in just three cases—the companions of Sirius, Procyon, and Omicron² Eridani.

Of the other twenty-nine pairs, fourteen already show orbital motion, but another five may be merely chance optical doubles instead of binary systems. Only one double star is listed in which both members are white dwarfs. This is LDS 275 in the constellation Antlia; it consists of two fifteenth-magnitude stars 3.7 seconds of arc apart. Luyten suspects that their period of orbital motion is about 700 years.

Only one spectroscopic binary star is known that has a white-dwarf member. This system is a fourteenth-magnitude member of the Hyades cluster. Known as HZ 9, its binary nature was detected by Jesse L. Greenstein at the Palomar Observatory. Should HZ 9 turn out to be an eclipsing system as well, it would provide an unprecedented opportunity to measure directly the diameter of a white-dwarf star. . . .

....

The Star of Smallest Known Mass

SARAH LEE LIPPINCOTT

(Sky and Telescope, July 1955)

During the nineteenth century, the discovery of companion stars to both Sirius and Procyon was an outstanding event in positional astronomy. . . .

Later, a number of other stars were discovered to have variable proper motions, but until the case described in this article none of their companions had actually been seen or photographed.

Since 1937 the Sproul Observatory has been determining very accurately the proper motions and parallaxes of a selection of nearby stars, with the hope of discovering small deviations from straight-line proper motion for some of these stars.

The inconspicuous eleventh-magnitude red-dwarf star Ross 614, only thirteen light years away, had showed a perturbation in its proper-motion path, from measures on a series of parallax photographs taken some two decades ago at the McCormick Observatory; obviously the star was not moving alone. The period and amplitude of this apparent oscillation were not well known, due to lack of observations over a sufficiently long interval; no conclusive statements could be made about the unseen companion at that time, except that it must be a stellar lightweight.

But by 1950 the time was ripe to make use of the McCormick observations from 1932 to 1937 and Sproul photographs of 1938–50. The positions of the image of Ross 614 were measured, and referred to the images of four distant background stars appearing in the field. It was found that more than one revolution had been completed, so that a definitive orbit could now be derived. The image midpoint, or photocenter, of the Ross 614 system revolves with a period of 16.5 years about a point that marks the center of mass of the double-star system. The semimajor axis of this photocentric orbit is 0.31 second of arc, or 1.22 astronomical units, at a distance of thirteen light years from the sun.

The photographic image of Ross 614 taken with the Sproul refractor has an average diameter of 2.5 seconds of arc (2″.5). This diffusion disk has nothing to do with the true dimensions of the star itself, but primarily with the chemical process of building up an image on the photographic emulsion. If star B contributed no light to the photographic image, the orbit of the photocenter would be strictly that of star A about the center of mass. But if B is bright enough to build up an image of its own, the separation of the two components must be less than about two seconds of arc, since the B component is not observed separately on the Sproul photographs. In this case, we are observing a combination of two light sources, and the composite image is displaced from the position of the brighter star, A, toward B (and therefore toward the center of mass) by an amount depending on the relative brightnesses of A and B and the distance between them. This means that until the difference in magnitude of the components of Ross 614 became known, we could not tell whether the photographic image represented the light from the A image only, or some combination of A and B.

If the companion star contributes some light, then the photocentric orbit, which is the orbital path of the combined light of the two stars, is smaller than the orbit of star A about the center of mass. It follows

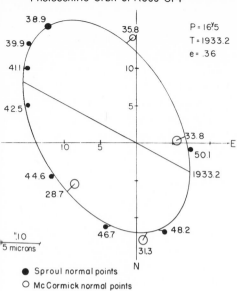

P = 16ᵞ5
T = 1933.2
e = .36

● Sproul normal points
○ McCormick normal points
The radius indicates the p.e.

FIG. 109. The photocentric orbit of Ross 614. The period is 16.5 years, periastron passage 1933.2, and orbital eccentricity 0.36. The year is given for each point, with century prefix omitted; i.e., 1938.9 appears as 38.9. The dots represent Sproul normal points, the open circles are McCormick normal points; the radius in each case indicates the probable error. (From *The Astronomical Journal*)

FIG. 110. Three successive 5-second exposures of Ross 614, taken by W. Baade with the 200-inch telescope, March 23, 1955. The faint companion is visible at position angle 36°, at the time of its greatest elongation. This is a 20X enlargement from the original negative, on which the scale was 11.12 seconds of arc to 1 millimeter. (Mount Wilson and Palomar Observatories photograph)

geometrically that the three orbits, of star A, star B, and the photocenter, are similar, differing only in size and in their phases.

A number of attempts to see the elusive companion with the 24-inch Sproul refractor have failed. From the photocentric orbit (Fig. 109) we predicted 1955 as the most favorable time for visual detection, because the separation of the two stars would then be greatest. We wrote Walter Baade, at Mount Wilson and Palomar Observatories, who said he would endeavor to observe the unseen star with the Hale telescope. . . .

Conditions on the night of March 23, 1955, were favorable, and Baade saw the companion of Ross 614. It was at the position angle we had predicted, and thus became the third such object finally seen, fifty-nine years after the visual discovery of the companion of Procyon.

Baade succeeded in obtaining some photographs of the two stars, exposures ranging from 2.5 to 10 seconds (Fig. 110); since Ross 614B does not appear on exposures of only 1 second, he estimates the apparent magnitude to be 14.8, 3.5 magnitudes fainter than the A component. The absolute magnitude is 16.8, with a probable error of half a magnitude, which gives this star second place in order of faintness. The five faintest stars known to date are listed in Table 9, in order of absolute visual magnitude.

TABLE 9. THE FIVE FAINTEST STARS

Van Biesbroeck's star	19.3
Ross 614B	16.8
Wolf 359	16.6
Luyten 726-8B	16.1
Luyten 726-8A	15.6

The measured separations of the centers of the two stars photographed by Baade were averaged, and the value of $1''.2$ was adopted for further use. On the Palomar plates the radius of the image of Ross 614A averages $0''.9$, and the components are not well separated even at greatest elongation. But when a Sproul refractor photograph is exposed long enough to bring out a fifteenth-magnitude star, the image diameter of Ross 614A grows to $7''$, which completely envelops the fainter star. Star B is so faint that the image of the photocenter always appears circular.

On March 23, 1955, the stars were measured as $1''.2$ apart on Palomar photographs. From the photocentric orbit, we know that the distance of the photocenter to the center of mass was then $0''.37$. The ratio of these two numbers, 3.2, is therefore the ratio of the scales of the relative to the photocentric orbits. Applying this scale factor to the photocentric semimajor axis, known to be 1.22 astronomical units, we find the relative orbit of the system to have a semimajor axis of 3.9 astronomical units. The Ross 614 system would fit quite easily within the orbit of Jupiter. From the relative orbit and the period, the sum of the masses of the two components comes out as 0.22 that of the sun.

How can we find the individual masses of the two stars? We must make use of the magnitude difference and the distance between A and B found by Baade. Since the B component is 3.5 magnitudes fainter than the primary, it can be calculated that the resulting photographic image on the Sproul plates has been pulled from the A toward the B component by 0.04 of their total separation. We can now relate the distances of the stars and the photocenter to the center of mass. Adopting the relative orbit scale as a unit, we find 0.35 and 0.65 for the scales of the orbits of A and B, respectively, around the center of mass which is their common focus.

The ratio of the distances of the A and B positions to the center of mass is inversely proportional to their masses, and we already know that the total mass is 0.22 that of the sun. The mass of Ross 614A is 0.14 sun, that of Ross 614B 0.08 sun. The latter has by far the smallest mass yet found for a visible star, and even Ross 614A is less massive than Krüger 60B, which was previously the star of smallest known mass, 0.16 sun. Ross 614B has only half this value.

Evidently Ross 614B is a star, not a planet. Although its visual luminosity is only 1/63,000 of the sun's, it would appear much fainter if it were shining only by reflected light from its primary. Although only 1/12 the sun's mass, it is still 80 times as massive as Jupiter, our largest planet. The information concerning Ross 614 yields a substantial extension of the mass-luminosity relation for stars of low mass. . . .

....

Barnard's Star as an Astrometric Binary

PETER VAN DE KAMP

(*Sky and Telescope*, July 1963)

In 1916, E. E. Barnard discovered that an inconspicuous star in Ophiuchus has the exceptionally large proper motion of 10.3 seconds of arc per year, which is still the record. This 9.5-magnitude star is drifting northward by a moon's diameter [half a degree] in about 180 years. It has the further distinction of being closer to the sun than any other known star, except the triple system of Alpha Centauri.

Physically, Barnard's star is a red dwarf of spectral type dM5, having only about one sixth the diameter of our sun. Very recently, an intensive astrometric study at Sproul Observatory has revealed that Barnard's star has an invisible companion which is in some ways even more remarkable.

As early as 1916–19, in order to determine the distance of Barnard's star, two dozen photographic plates were obtained with the Sproul 24-inch refractor. Then, in 1938, we began to take large numbers of plates, as this is a very important subject in our overall program of studying the motions of nearby stars. Our purpose was to improve the parallax of Barnard's star, to measure the progressive change in the rate of its apparent motion across the sky, but primarily to test that motion for periodic waviness that might indicate the gravitational influence of an unseen companion.

During the past twenty-five years, our systematic photography of Barnard's star has continued at an average of nearly a hundred plates a year.

All told, 2413 plates were obtained on 609 nights by fifty different observers. Outstanding was Roy W. Delaplaine, who in 1938–47 observed on 162 nights, while in 1951–59 Laurence W. Fredrick photographed this star on seventy-five dates.

The 24-inch telescope has a focal length of 36 feet, so its plates have the generous scale of 18.9 seconds of arc per millimeter. Thus the proper motion of Barnard's star corresponds to an annual 0.546-millimeter change in position on the photographs. So accurately can the star's place be measured relative to background stars that we may recognize its proper motion by comparing two plates taken only a few days apart. All the measurements are referred to the same three background stars, which may be used for the remainder of the twentieth century.

The plates have been measured principally by Sarah Lee Lippincott, assisted by Mary Jackson, Dorothy B. Allen, and nine other persons. About three fourths of the material was measured twice, and our error checks indicate a generally satisfactory small degree of personal equation, as well as reasonable constancy of the Gaertner measuring machine over two decades. But other effects had to be taken into account.

From the plates covering nearly half a century, we could derive a very accurate value for the proper motion of Barnard's star. . . .

By 1956, oscillatory motion with a period of sixteen years or more was suspected. This led us to use yearly mean positions, averaging ninety-six plates. The resulting yearly means clearly exhibit a long-period systematic run, mainly in right ascension but also in declination.

FIG. 111. After all known causes of position change have been allowed for, these drift curves of Barnard's star show 24-year oscillations in right ascension and declination—evidence for an unseen companion. Each dot is an annual mean, its size indicating the relative number of Sproul Observatory plates. Circles are early means transferred 24 years forward. The scale of the star displacements is shown both in terms of 0.01 second of arc on the sky and of one micron (1μ = 0.001 millimeter) on Sproul plates.

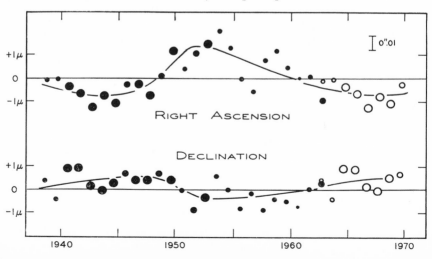

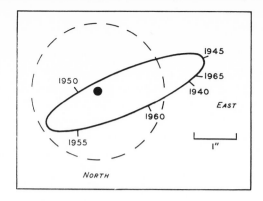

FIG. 112. The inferred orbit of the invisible companion relative to the visible component of Barnard's star. The dashed circle indicates the greatest size of the latter's image on the plates taken at Swarthmore's Observatory with the 24-inch refractor.

This can be seen in the time-displacement curves of Figure 111, which indicate that Barnard's star is shifted by the gravitational attraction of an unseen companion. The visible star's path through the sky shows a wave of 24-year period and a semiamplitude of 0.0245 second of arc—0.0013 millimeter on the photographs. The invisible body is moving in an elliptical orbit (eccentricity 0.6), which is inclined 77° to the plane of the sky. Minimum distance between the two stars (for a plan view of the orbit) occurred in 1950. Our measurements on fifty-two additional plates of Barnard's star from Leander McCormick Observatory are in agreement with our adopted 24-year period, and we expect to make a further test on eighty-two plates lent by Van Vleck Observatory.

The exceptional character of this binary system becomes clear when we consider the masses of its components. Barnard's star itself closely resembles Ross 614A and Krüger 60B in both absolute magnitude and color. Their masses are 0.14 and 0.16 sun, respectively, so 0.15 sun can be adopted for the mass of Barnard's star. This means that a small companion with a 24-year period will travel in an orbit whose semimajor axis is 4.4 astronomical units, or 2.4 seconds of arc. But as we have just seen, the semimajor axis of Barnard's star itself, as it moves around the center of gravity of the system, is about 100 times smaller. From this it follows that the mass of the unseen companion is only about 0.0015 sun—a mere 1½ times as massive as Jupiter!

Such an object must be regarded as a planet rather than a star. A gaseous sphere having less than about 0.07 solar mass cannot maintain a central temperature high enough to generate energy by the nuclear conversion of hydrogen into helium. Therefore the newly found body is not self-luminous, but shines only by reflected light, as do the earth and Jupiter. However, the companion can hardly appear brighter than about thirtieth magnitude —far too dim for us to detect it by any current techniques. No wonder its image is not found on our 1937–46 plates, when the apparent separation of Barnard's star and its companion was more than two seconds of arc!

The only other discoveries of planets outside our own solar system have been made at Sproul Observatory by the same method. An unseen component of 61 Cygni was recognized by K. A. Strand in 1943, and that of Lalande 21185 by Miss Lippincott in 1960. But both those companions have masses about 0.01 that of the sun, several times greater than the companion to Barnard's star. In many respects, the Barnard system forms a close analogy to Jupiter and the sun.

....

Mu Cassiopeiae as a Double Star

(*Sky and Telescope*, November 1964)

The fifth-magnitude star Mu Cassiopeiae has long been noted for its exceptionally large proper motion. It is drifting southeastward among its neighbors at 3.76 seconds of arc per year—a moon's diameter every five centuries.

In 1961, N. E. Wagman of Allegheny Observatory announced that this rapid motion is not uniform, but affected by a small oscillation with a period of about twenty-three years. The phenomenon was just that to be expected if an unseen companion formed a binary system with the visible star. The center of gravity of the pair would move along a straight line, but the bright star would describe a small orbit around the center of gravity.

At Sproul Observatory, Sarah Lee Lippincott and Susan Wyckoff have now confirmed this, from their measurements of the positions of Mu on 216 photographs taken in 1937–63 with the 24-inch Sproul refractor. They find that Mu is moving in an 18.5-year orbit that takes it as far as 0.22 second of arc from the center of gravity.

The mass of the unseen companion is estimated as between 0.2 and 0.7 the sun's, while the brighter star is 0.85. It is possible that in 1964 or 1965 Mu may be recognized visually in large telescopes as a very close and unequal pair.

Another result from the Sproul study is a precise value for the parallax of this nearby star, 0.127 second of arc. It corresponds to a distance of 7.9 parsecs, or 25.7 light years.

....

Many Planetary Systems?

(*Sky and Telescope*, November 1964)

Virtually every one of the 10^{11} stars in our Milky Way Galaxy may have its own retinue of planets, suggests Harrison Brown, California Institute of Technology.

His argument stems from a recent calculation by S. S. Kumar that a "star" of 0.01 the sun's mass, being unable to support thermonuclear reactions, would cool to invisibility in only 20 million years after formation. Such cold "black dwarfs" may be very numerous. In fact, Brown expects about sixty unseen bodies of planetary size for every visible star, from an extrapolation of the statistics of star masses.

The Caltech geophysicist next considers the fact that about half of the visible stars in the solar neighborhood are members of binary or multiple systems. And even though invisible planetary companions of stars are extremely difficult to detect, six and possibly seven cases have been revealed by the waves they cause in the motions of visible stars. All these cases are among the hundred nearest stars. Adding the sun-Jupiter system, it would appear that about 8 per cent of the visible stars have planets as large as Jupiter. The number of unobservable stellar companions as small as Mars must be considerably greater.

"If it develops that planetary systems are indeed as abundant as this discussion indicates, the search for intelligent extraterrestrial life is placed in a somewhat new perspective," comments Brown in *Science* for September 11, 1964.

Although this evidence strongly indicates that planets are in orbit around many stars, the studies of rotating stars (p. 140) make it unlikely that all stars have planetary companions. Most blue and white stars of spectral types O, B, and A are in rapid rotation, unlike our sun and other stars of spectral types G, K, and M. The manner in which planetary systems were formed is covered in Volume 3 of this series, The Origin of the Solar System, where it is shown that the angular momentum of a "protostar" goes into the forming planets, leaving a star that rotates very slowly, as the sun does.

From the small, cool stars, many of which are double or accompanied by planets, we now turn to studies of the large, hot stars. — T L P

··

A Massive Double Star

(*Sky and Telescope*, February 1949)

In the early 1930s, R. J. Trumpler of Lick Observatory found certain stars in the sky which showed an abnormal red shift in the lines of their spectra. These were all very hot stars of class O, and it was proposed that the red shifts were caused by an Einstein shift—the effect of gravity retarding the

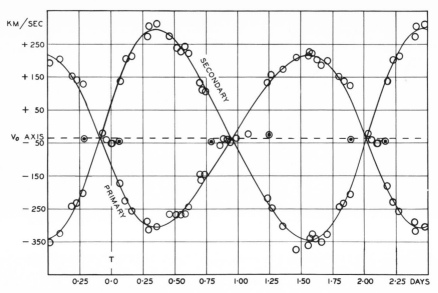

FIG. 113. The radial-velocity curves of the massive binary (HD 215835) found at the Dominion Astrophysical Observatory. The dotted circles represent R. J. Trumpler's early observations.

escape of light from the surfaces of very dense stars. Such an effect has long been confirmed for the companion of Sirius, but it is a white dwarf star, whereas the so-called Trumpler stars are all giants in luminosity and not expected to be of such high density. But the determination of their masses by other means than the proposed Einstein shift has only recently been tried.

At the Dominion Astrophysical Observatory, J. A. Pearce has made a detailed spectroscopic analysis of HD 215835, a ninth-magnitude star in the galactic cluster NGC 7380, in the constellation of Cepheus. Thirty-six single-prism spectra having a dispersion of 51 angstroms per millimeter at the hydrogen-gamma line were secured between January 8 and October 19, 1948. In the second plate taken in January, Pearce found double lines, indicating that the star is really double, each component contributing a set of spectral lines. He points out that Trumpler has also independently discovered the duplicity of this star.

As a spectroscopic binary, therefore, the period of revolution, 2.111 days, the eccentricity, 0.127, and other characteristics of the double-star orbit have been derived. From the strong interstellar lines, Pearce estimates the distance of the star as 2100 parsecs, or about 6800 light years. This agrees as well as can be expected with Trumpler's adopted value of 1840 parsecs for the cluster NGC 7380.

The components of HD 215835 have the earliest spectral types of all spectrographic binaries. They are normal absorption-type O5 stars, one

0.3 magnitude brighter than the other. From their distance and their apparent magnitudes, Pearce finds their absolute magnitudes to be —4.2 and —3.9, respectively. Applying these magnitudes to the normal mass-luminosity relation, the masses of the stars come out 33.8 and 28.2 times the sun's mass, respectively. Application of this result to the spectrographic orbit indicates the orbital inclination to the sky plane to be 62°, and as the stars are very near together in proportion to their sizes, Pearce predicts that they should partially eclipse each other, the change in light at maximum obscuration amounting to 10 per cent of the total light of the system.

Here, then, is a star which has a combined mass of about 62 suns, making it the third most massive system known. Each star's surface temperature is about 36,000° absolute. One has a diameter of 9.7 suns, or 8,380,000 miles; the other is somewhat smaller. Their densities are about 0.04 that of the sun. . . .

....

The Most Massive
Stars Known

OTTO STRUVE

(Sky and Telescope, November 1957)

A vital part of modern astrophysics had its beginning about 150 years ago, when it was realized that many visual double stars were not mere chance pairs but actual binary systems, often with conspicuous orbital motion. This motion was the visible effect of the gravitational attraction of one star upon the other. Since that time, astronomers have succeeded in determining the masses of the component stars of many binaries.

Data on star masses is fundamental to our newly gained understanding of stellar structure and stellar evolution, yet, even today, the only sure basis of this data is the orbital motion of the visual and spectroscopic binaries. We cannot measure the mass of an isolated star—except the sun, which has planetary companions. We are forced to assume, as a first approximation, that the masses of single stars resemble those of double-star components having similar luminosities, diameters, and surface temperatures.

Popular writers usually avoid explaining how the masses of double stars are computed because the problem involves a fair amount of algebra if all

FIG. 114. Plaskett's star is named for the Canadian astronomer J. S. Plaskett, director of the Dominion Astrophysical Observatory in British Columbia from 1917 to 1935.

kinds of binaries are included in the discussion. But the basic ideas are quite simple, and the masses of the heaviest known stars can be found from elementary considerations.

Large stellar masses are of particular interest. What is the heaviest star or pair of stars now known? Is there a physical limit to the amount of matter a star can accumulate? And what are the properties of the heaviest stars?

We choose for our example Plaskett's star, a very massive binary system just visible to the naked eye, located in the constellation of Monoceros about midway between Procyon and Betelgeuse. Also known as HD 47129, this object is of visual magnitude 6.1, and its spectrum is of type O8. In 1922 the Canadian astronomer J. S. Plaskett discovered it to be a spectroscopic binary, from spectrograms taken with the 72-inch reflector of the Dominion Astrophysical Observatory at Victoria, British Columbia. The period of orbital motion is 14.4 days.

In Figure 115 are plotted observations of the radial velocities of the two stars that constitute this system. The velocity curve of the primary star—the one with the stronger absorption lines—is represented by the dots. The symmetry of the curve shows that the orbit of this star relative to the other is very nearly circular.

What we measure on the spectrograms are the Doppler displacements of the absorption lines at different times (see Fig. 117). This gives us the star's radial velocity, that is, the component of the true velocity that lies along the line of sight, at each phase. At phase 0 days, the primary star

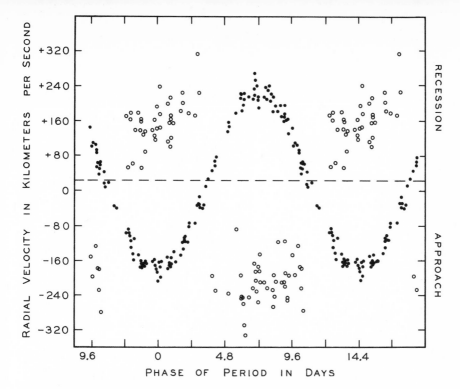

FIG. 115. K. D. Abhyankar plotted, at Leuschner Observatory, radial-velocity observations of HD 47129, using dots for the primary star and circles for the secondary, from spectrograms taken at Victoria, McDonald, and Lick observatories.

is approaching us with a velocity of 190 kilometers per second, and at phase 7.2 days it is receding at 240 kilometers per second.

A part of the velocity is due to the motion of the system as a whole relative to the sun. Were this motion zero, the circular orbit of the primary star around the center of gravity would produce equal values for the maximum observed velocities of recession and approach. The fact that these two velocities are unequal shows that this is not the case—the center of gravity is receding from us with a constant velocity of ½ (240 − 190) = 25 kilometers per second. The dashed line in Figure 115 indicates this motion of the center of gravity.

Thus, with respect to the center of gravity, the primary star is moving 190 + 25, or 215 kilometers per second when its velocity of approach is greatest, and 240 − 25, or 215 kilometers per second at maximum velocity of recession. This would be the orbital velocity of the primary star with respect to the center of gravity, provided the orbital plane were in the line of sight, that is, if the orbit were presented to us edgewise.

But since HD 47129 is not an eclipsing variable star, we infer that the orbit is not edge-on; there appear to be no rhythmic light variations caused by one star eclipsing the other at each revolution. The true orbital velocity must be larger than 215 kilometers per second, being diminished by foreshortening. Exactly how much larger is not known, but we shall probably not be far from the truth in assuming that the real, unforeshortened velocity is about 250 kilometers per second. This value corresponds to a tilt of the orbit plane of 30° to the line of sight.

Assuming, then, that the primary star of HD 47129 is moving in a circular orbit at 250 kilometers per second, what can we deduce concerning the masses in this system? We shall begin by applying Newton's first and second laws of motion. The first law is that a moving body not subjected to any external force will continue to move in the same direction and with unchanged velocity. Newton's second law states that a body moving with changing velocity or direction is being subjected to a force that is equal to the product of the body's mass and its acceleration (the change in amount and direction of velocity). This law is expressed in the well-known formula $f = ma$.

Suppose, in Figure 116, that the primary star is in position A. Its orbital velocity of 250 kilometers per second is tangential to the circular orbit, as shown by the arrow. If no force were acting on the star, it would arrive at D, the end of the arrow, after a lapse of one second. In reality, the star arrives at position B. Its speed is still 250 kilometers per second, but the direction of the next velocity arrow, starting from B, is not the same as that of the initial velocity at A. The star has experienced a central force that has caused it to "fall," in the course of one second, from D to B.

This distance of fall in one second is numerically just half of the acceleration. It is like the case of a stone falling from rest to the surface of the earth. Its acceleration or increase in velocity is 32 feet per second each second; and it falls 16 feet in the first second. If the stone has an initial horizontal velocity, the result is still the same, its fall toward the earth in the first second is still 16 feet, or half the acceleration.

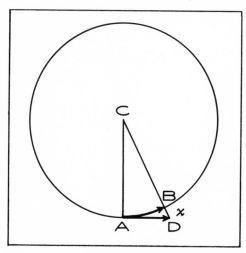

FIG. 116. In this diagram, where the circle represents the orbit of the primary star about the center of gravity, x indicates the distance of fall in one second.

In Figure 116, one leg of the triangle CAD is the radius of the orbit, the distance between the center of gravity and the star. The circumference of the orbit is the orbital velocity (250 kilometers per second) times the period (1.24×10^6 seconds), or 3.1×10^8 kilometers; the radius is thus about 5×10^7 kilometers. The other leg of the triangle, AD, is the star's motion in one second, or 250 kilometers. Finally, the hypotenuse is the orbital radius, 5×10^7 kilometers, plus the distance of the fall, which we shall call x.

From the Pythagorean theorem for a right-angle triangle,

$$(5 \times 10^7 + x)^2 = (250)^2 + (5 \times 10^7)^2.$$

Because x^2 is relatively very small we can neglect it, and a little arithmetic shows that $x = 6.25 \times 10^{-4}$ kilometers, or 62.5 centimeters. Doubling this distance of fall gives for the acceleration 125 centimeters per second each second. Newton's second law can therefore be written $f = 125m$, where f and m are in dynes and grams, respectively, the units in the centimeter-gram-second system.

In order to solve for the mass, however, we need Newton's law of universal gravitation. This states that the force in dynes between any two bodies is equal to 7×10^{-8} (the gravitational constant) times the product of their masses in grams, divided by the square of their distance apart in centimeters.

But we know only the primary star's distance from the center of gravity, which can be called d; for the other star the corresponding distance is d', and the stars' total separation is $d + d'$. From Figure 115 we may infer, despite the large scatter in the measurements, that the secondary's velocity curve has about the same range as that of the primary star. Therefore the radius of the secondary orbit should be about the same as the primary's, and d' should also be about 5×10^7 kilometers. The sum of these distances, $d + d'$, is thus twice this value, or 10^{13} centimeters.

Now we are ready to equate the force, which acts on the primary star according to the law of gravitation, with the force expressed by the second law of motion, making the assumption that gravitation alone holds the two stars in their orbits:

$$(7 \times 10^{-8})mm'/(d + d')^2 = 125m.$$

The factor m can be canceled from both sides of this equation, while $(d + d')^2$ is 10^{26}. The equation can be solved for m', the mass of the secondary star, which comes out 1.8×10^{35} grams.

Since the mass of the sun is 2×10^{33} grams, the secondary component of Plaskett's binary is about 90 times as great. The primary star should also be about 90 solar masses, because we believe that the center of gravity is about midway between the stars. The total mass of this double star is thus some 180 suns!

It is important to review our assumptions. We supposed that the force deduced from the observed acceleration is purely gravitational, but in principle it is the sum of physical forces of all possible types. Yet we know that in the solar system gravitation by itself suffices to explain the motions of the planets and satellites—magnetic, electrical, and other forces are negligible. If they were of consequence in a double-star system, they would be detectable from their spectroscopic effects.

Another assumption involved the tilt of the orbital plane to the line of sight. It is pretty certain that we have not underestimated the true orbital velocity of the primary component. As has been mentioned, if the orbital plane were close to the line of sight, Plaskett's star would be an eclipsing binary, but no eclipses have been observed. If the orbital plane is tilted to the line of sight by more than the 30° we selected, then the true orbital velocity would be even greater than 250 kilometers per second, and the resulting masses would be larger. Therefore, this assumption yields minimum values for the masses.

Our third assumption was that the two components have equal masses. This rests upon the rough estimate from Figure 115 that the range in radial velocity is the same for both components. If, as seems likely, the range of the secondary is somewhat smaller than the primary's, then the secondary is the more massive star.

These stellar masses, of the order of 90 times the sun's, are the largest definitely known at the present time. We may therefore conjecture that the upper limit of possible star masses is about 100 times the sun, or 2×10^{35} grams. It was suggested many years ago by Sir Arthur Eddington that the radiation pressure inside a star of this mass is high enough to offset the internal gravitation that holds the star together—if there were any star of larger mass, radiation pressure would blow it apart.

It is therefore of interest that Plaskett's star appears highly unstable. One or both components are shedding gas into interstellar space, and in many respects behave like a slowly exploding star of the P Cygni or Wolf-Rayet type.

Figure 117 shows a portion of the spectrum of Plaskett's star at two

FIG. 117. In spectra of HD 47129, the diffuse dark lines of the primary star are shifted by the Doppler effect. Sharp dark lines are of interstellar origin, hence are undisplaced by orbital motion.

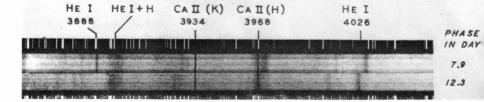

HE I 3888	HE I+H	CA II (K) 3934	CA II (H) 3968	HE I 4026	PHASE IN DAY
					7.9
					12.3

phases, 7.9 and 12.3 days. The large Doppler shift of the primary component can easily be seen for the helium line at 4026 angstroms. Features arising from the secondary star can hardly be discerned in this spectral region, the ultraviolet, but are easily seen in the red. The very sharp dark lines marked K and H are of interstellar origin; they result from the absorption of light by ionized calcium atoms situated between us and the star.

Of special importance is the strong line of helium at 3888 angstroms, discovered by J. Sahade. This absorption line is present only at phases close to 7.9 days, and then gives a velocity of approach of about 700 kilometers per second. At that time there is something resembling a rapidly approaching jet of helium gas which passes between us and the primary star. It is believed that this jet originates from the secondary component and diffuses toward all sides to form ultimately a vast expanding shell of tenuous nebulous matter. The primary component also ejects gas, especially hydrogen, but fairly uniformly in all directions.

Other evidence of the instability of Plaskett's star is provided by some of the absorption and emission lines, which suffer irregular changes from cycle to cycle. It is almost certain that similar variations will be found in the brightness of this system. Because of its instability, the star should be observed photoelectrically. In many respects, Plaskett's star is among the most remarkable known, and it promises us a rewarding insight into the problems of very massive stars.

The possible instability of very massive stars (M about 90) again raises the question of even larger masses that may have a brief life before exploding, possibly as supernovae or extremely luminous QSO's (see p. 158).

It has been emphasized throughout this chapter that masses of stars are determined essentially by the gravitational effect on another mass (planet or star) nearby—that is, on observations of double stars. The Einstein red shift has served so far only to confirm extreme cases of high density. The statistical study of motions of stars in a cluster serves only to determine average masses, possibly including invisible interstellar material.

One possibility involves the effects of stellar structure on the spectrum. — T L P

....

Masses of Single Stars

(Sky and Telescope, June 1961)

Practically all our information about masses of stars has been gained from observations of binary systems, the amount of material in a star being indicated by the orbital motion of its neighbor. Now the Washburn Observatory astronomer R. C. Bless has demonstrated a practical method for finding the masses of isolated stars of spectral class A.

His observations consist of photoelectric measurements of brightness at different wavelengths in the continuous spectrum. This was done for eighteen A stars of known distance, with the aid of the University of Michigan's 24-inch Schmidt telescope. The intensity distribution in a star's continuum depends upon its effective temperature, surface gravity, and chemical composition (which may be regarded as known). Bless, by comparing the observed distributions with those for model atmospheres calculated by K. Hunger and K. Osawa, was able to evaluate the first two properties.

From the temperature of the star he could calculate what its radius must be to provide the observed luminosity. And from the radius and surface gravity he could compute the star's mass. For example, Vega has an effective temperature of $9400°$ Kelvin, a radius 3.2 times the sun's, and 3.0 times the sun's mass.

Good observations should furnish stellar masses to within about 50 per cent by this method, Bless points out in *The Astrophysical Journal*.

8

Star Counts and Distribution of the Stars

How many stars are there? "Billions and billions" is a conservative answer, if the question refers to compact masses between 1/20 and 90 suns. But there may be many more nonluminous bodies between the stars we can see. And what about nebulae? Other galaxies?

The question is similar to, "How many buildings are there in New York?" Does the term "building" include tool sheds, dog kennels, and open-air stadiums? Where is the edge of New York's "metropolitan area"? One answer, similar to the astronomer's, could be reached by counting the number of large buildings on each of several city blocks, taking the average, and multiplying it by the number of blocks in Manhattan. Of course, some blocks have far more than the average, and some far less. By "distribution" we mean the change in numbers of buildings per block, or of stars per cubic parsec, between one part of town and another, or between one part of the Milky Way Galaxy and another. Of course, the whole idea of the galaxy came from just this type of study. —TLP

••

Counting the Stars

BART J. BOK

(*The Telescope,* June 1934)

The public has a right to insist that astronomers should at least *count* the stars carefully, and I feel quite embarrassed when I have to confess that that job has not by any means been finished.

The total number of stars which can be seen with the naked eye does not, as some poets wish us to believe, run into millions, but will for a person with keen eyesight not exceed 6000. If, however, we proceed to use a telescope, we find that this number increases very rapidly and that a total of 300,000 stars is within the reach of a 3-inch visual telescope. Photography enables us, however, to penetrate into the great depths of our Milky Way, or galactic, system. We shall obtain, for example, a record of approximately five million stars from a series of photographs, each with an exposure time of one hour, covering the entire sky, if we make use of one of the perfect 3-inch photographic lenses designed by F. E. Ross of the Yerkes Observatory. But this is again only a minor fraction of the total number of stars which can be reached with our giant telescopes and which may be estimated as numbering fairly close to one billion. The total number of stars which can be recorded depends therefore very much upon the optical and photographic means at one's disposal, or as the astronomer puts it, upon the "magnitude limit" to which his counts are reasonably complete.

FIG. 118. The Big Dipper—a short-exposure photograph showing only the bright stars. Many more stars show on a longer exposure photograph. (Yerkes Observatory photograph)

The valuation of the total number of stars is only one of the data which can be obtained from star counts. Those who are studying the structure of our galactic system are much more interested in the detailed distribution of these stars over the sky. The accompanying photograph [Fig. 119] of a region of the Southern Milky Way shows at a glance why this must be so. The distribution of the stars is by no means uniform over the area of the sky covered by this one photograph. We notice first of all the starry band of the Milky Way stretching across the plate, and it is evident upon a most cursory examination of the photograph that the number of stars on the print decreases rapidly as we proceed from the Milky Way to the upper or lower edge of the picture. A second outstanding feature is the presence near the center of the plate of a region in the Milky Way which impressed the early navigators by its extreme blackness and to which they gave the name "the Coalsack." It is, as our photograph shows, an area of abnormally low star density. And thirdly we notice many striking irregularities in the distribution of the stars in the Milky Way, irregularities which may not be so outstanding as the Coalsack, but which are of importance because of their persistence throughout the band of the Milky Way.

Much of our present knowledge concerning the distribution of the stars has been acquired during the past forty years, and it is largely due to the efforts of the famous Dutch astronomer Kapteyn, who developed most of the methods which are now in constant use among workers studying the structure of the stellar system, or galaxy, within which we dwell, that we already know a great deal about the distribution of the stars of various brightnesses or magnitudes over the sky. Kapteyn realized that it would be necessary, at least in the first attack upon the problem of galactic structure, to neglect the small-scale irregularities in the distribution of stars and to concentrate upon a study of the variations in

FIG. 119. The region of the Coalsack. (Harvard College Observatory photograph)

the numbers of stars with the angular distance from the Milky Way, or as we call it technically, upon a study of the galactic concentration of stars of various magnitudes. Kapteyn and his co-workers, Van Rhyn and Seares, found from a study of stellar distribution in about two hundred selected areas evenly distributed over the sky that the number of stars brighter than the tenth magnitude for an average field in the Milky Way was about four times as large as the corresponding number for a field with the same area but 90° away from the Milky Way. This ratio increases rapidly if we include fainter stars; it is equal to ten for the stars of the fifteenth magnitude and equal to forty for the stars of the twenty-first magnitude, which are about the faintest stars which can be photographed at present.

It was on the basis of this material that Kapteyn proposed in 1922 the picture of our galactic system which is now generally known among astronomers as the "Kapteyn universe." Kapteyn pictured our Milky Way system as shaped like a thin disk, the sun having a position close to the center of the disk. We might compare it with a watch, or perhaps even better with a pancake, in order to emphasize its extreme thinness.

It soon became apparent, however, that Kapteyn's picture did not tell the whole story. Kapteyn had paid little attention to the variations in star density occurring along the band of the Milky Way. . . . Certain portions of the Milky Way are much more brilliant, much more densely strewn with stars, than others. It was this important feature of galactic structure which had not been considered by Kapteyn. Harlow Shapley showed conclusively from a study of the distribution of globular clusters (closely packed spherical clusterings of many hundreds of thousands of galactic system and that, rather, this center lay some distance from the sun in the direction of the constellation Sagittarius—at a distance we now know to be some 200 quadrillion miles, a distance such that light traveling at the rate of 186,000 miles a second would require 30,000 years to reach us from a star located there. One of the main reasons why Kapteyn was led to assign to our sun a central, rather than an ex-centric, position in our galaxy lay in the fact that the astronomers of ten years ago were not aware of the presence of a cloud of absorbing material which screened off the light of the more distant stars of the Milky Way. We have now definite proof of the existence of such an absorbing cloud, and Kapteyn's ignorance of the presence of this "galactic fog" was responsible for the misinterpretation of the star counts at his disposal.

The variations in the numbers of stars along the Milky Way are therefore now of great importance in studies of galactic structure, and there is now a need for extensive star counts all along the Milky Way rather than for counts in only a few selected regions. Such counts have been made during the past three years at the Harvard Observatory by Lindsay and others, and we expect that it will be possible to study from these counts the regular features of galactic structure, freed from the irregularities arising from the presence of small star-clouds and isolated patches of absorbing material.

It is at once evident how important it is to cover as large an area of the sky as possible on a single photograph, to avoid the difficulties which arise from attempting to compare photographs taken at different times with various durations of exposure and varying clearness of the sky. It is for this reason that cameras capable of photographing large areas of the sky have been used so widely for star-counting purposes. . . .

Realizing that a cloud of absorbing material does exist in space, we have as yet only fragmentary information as to its extent and absorbing power. But one thing is known with certainty—namely, that at the very best, we can only hope to explore one half of our galactic system with existing instruments and photographic plates, the "galactic fog" being so dense that with the reduced visibility we shall probably never be able to see the other half. We can, however, in spite of this, make a fairly reliable estimate of the total number of stars in our system. The Swedish astronomer Bertil Lindblad and the Dutch astronomer J. H. Oort showed in 1926 that our whole galaxy is in rapid rotation. We might have suspected the existence of such a rotation offhand from the mere fact that our galaxy appears to be so highly flattened, but it is to the credit of Lindblad and Oort that they showed from [spectroscopic] observations that such a rotation did exist, and that they gave us at the same time a reliable estimate of the total amount of material in our galaxy. The total number of stars in our galaxy is probably of the order of 200 billion. . . .

But we should not forget that the telescope has revealed several million stellar systems outside our own galaxy and probably similar to it in many respects. As far as we know today, we have only explored a very minor part of the whole physical universe.

....

The Magical Schmidt

CHARLES H. SMILEY

(*The Sky*, July 1940)

To understand the importance of the Schmidt camera, consider its outstanding advantages. This peculiar hybrid telescope, half reflector, half refractor, will cover a region of the sky 20° in diameter, the stars appearing in all parts of the photograph as nice round dots. An ordinary reflecting telescope will photograph satisfactorily a region less than one degree in diameter, an area only 1/500 as great as that covered by the Schmidt camera. This limitation of the field of the ordinary reflector is due to coma, an aberration (fault) of lenses and mirrors which causes stars to photograph as fan-shaped images. This fault is a serious one in astronomical work where positions must be noted with great precision.

Of almost as great importance is the potential speed of the Schmidt camera. In photographing celestial objects, such as nebulae and comets, which cover an appreciable area in the sky, the focal ratio of a camera (the diameter of the lens in terms of the focal length) is most important. Schmidt cameras have already been constructed which are faster for this purpose than any reflector or refractor yet made. With a focal ratio f/1 (*i.e.*, the diameter of the lens equal to the focal length of the camera), nebulae can be photographed in about 1/10 the time required by the fastest astronomical lenses and mirrors previously available. . . .

This remarkable camera was invented in 1931 by a German, Bernhard Schmidt, of the Hamburg-Bergedorf Observatory. He made one himself with lens 14 inches in diameter, and focal length of the completed camera 25 inches. . . .

Essentially, the camera consists of a spherical mirror with a thin lens at the center of curvature and a filmholder about halfway between the mirror and the lens. The main purpose of the lens (correcting plate) is to eliminate the spherical aberration which would be present if the spherical mirror were used alone. . . .

There is a disadvantage of the Schmidt camera which should be mentioned. The focal surface is curved; it is, in fact, a convex spherical surface of radius equal to the focal length of the camera, so that ordinary plates cannot be used. The films must be bent to shape by a properly constructed filmholder. . . .

To date, about twenty Schmidt cameras have been completed, two thirds of them in the United States. For the most part, they have been made by courageous, patient amateur telescope makers. The first American amateur to construct a Schmidt camera was H. Page Bailey, of Riverside, California.

What kind of work is being done with Schmidt cameras? Fritz Zwicky, of the California Institute of Technology, has used the 18-inch Schmidt on Mount Palomar with notable success to discover supernovae, stars which suddenly increase tremendously in brightness. Otto Struve, director of the Yerkes and McDonald Observatories, has used a Schmidt camera to discover new red nebulae, and designed a new type of spectrograph

FIG. 120. Palomar's 48-inch Schmidt camera, with Edwin Hubble at the guiding telescope. (Mount Wilson and Palomar Observatories photograph)

employing a Schmidt camera. Theodore Dunham, of Mount Wilson Observatory, also incorporated Schmidt cameras in spectrographs for use with the 100-inch telescope. H. A. and C. A. Lower, of San Diego, California, have taken excellent photographs of comets with their Schmidt. The author used a Schmidt camera to photograph the outer corona of the sun and the zodiacal light in the neighborhood of the sun at the total solar eclipse of June 8, 1937. A number of the instruments are being used to photograph meteor trails and meteor spectra. . . .

The value of the Schmidt camera was quickly recognized, and the earlier instruments were dwarfed by the huge camera shown in Figure 120. Because the thin lens, or correcting plate, at the upper end is of 48-inch aperture, the camera is called "the 48-inch Schmidt," but the spherical mirror at the lower end is 72 inches in diameter. After it was completed in 1949, the Mount Wilson–Palomar–Cal Tech group of astronomers started one of the most effective and most important projects yet undertaken. It took seven years. — T L P

....

Sky Survey by 48-inch Schmidt Camera Completed

(*Sky and Telescope*, January 1957)

For seven years, practically the entire observing time of the 48-inch Schmidt camera has been occupied with the sky survey financed by the National Geographic Society. Beginning in July 1949 the whole sky accessible from Palomar Mountain (north of declination —27°) has been photographed in red and blue light, requiring 879 plates in each color. The plates are each 14 by 14 inches square. The blue photographs have a limiting magnitude of 21.1, the red plates reach 20.0.

In his annual report, published in *The Astronomical Journal* for October 1956, Ira S. Bowen, director of Mount Wilson and Palomar Observatories, notes that this survey penetrates roughly three times farther into space than any previous coverage of the whole sky; the volume of space is over twenty-five times larger than in any previous atlas.

The plates were taken by Albert G. Wilson, George O. Abell, and R. G. Harrington. Since prints had to meet high standards to be included in the atlas, many fields were rephotographed to replace plates rejected because of poor seeing conditions, errors in guiding, poor focus, or emulsion defects. For some fields more than one pair of acceptable plates were obtained. By July 1, 1953, the pairs of plates taken for the survey totaled 755, of which 338 were acceptable; at the completion of the observations in 1956 a total of 1606 pairs had been exposed, and 894 were graded as acceptable.

The graphic arts department of California Institute of Technology is busy printing copies of the atlas to fill orders from institutions here and abroad.

Bowen points out the enormous mass of research material embodied in the atlas plates: "Many decades will be required fully to exploit them. Already a rapid qualitative survey of the plates has noted many new objects, including four unusual asteroids, whose orbits pass close to that of the earth, eleven comets, thirteen globular clusters, and eighty-two planetary nebulae. Four new dwarf members of our local group of galaxies have also been discovered . . . . In a special search of the plates, Abell has found and listed the positions of about 2700 very rich clusters of galaxies, thereby increasing manyfold the number of known objects of this type. The statistics of the size and distribution of these clusters is of great importance since they are the largest known structures in the universe . . . ."

Even before the completion of the Palomar Sky Survey, progress had been made on interpreting star counts. This involved interstellar dust or "smoke" which obscures the stars, making them seem farther away. Fortunately, the dust can be recognized by its reddening effect, so that the formula giving distance from brightness and luminosity (p. 90) can be corrected. The evidence of interstellar reddening first came from the measures of color index and spectral type (p. 96). Nearby A stars have color 0.00, but fainter (more distant) ones are somewhat redder on the average. Other distance indicators were used, and "color-excess," or difference between measured color and the "normal" color for a star's spectral class, was found to increase with distance. The increase is most rapid in directions along the plane of the Milky Way; that is, toward points in the sky near the center of the Milky Way all around the sky. It is least rapid in directions 90° to that plane; that is, toward the two poles of the galaxy.

The amount of reddening was also measured in spectra, and the interstellar "smoke" was found to absorb starlight in proportion to $1/\lambda$; that is, twice as much ultraviolet light of wavelength $\lambda = 3250$ A was absorbed as red light of $\lambda = 6500$ A. This can be used to calculate how much the brightness is changed for a measured color excess, and it helps to identify the material causing both reddening and obscuration. This "smoke" could not be an ordinary gas, but it could be fine dust, the particle size being about the same as one wavelength of light (10^{-4} cm, or 1 micron).

Another effect was discovered by Hiltner and Hall at the McDonald Observatory in Texas: the polarization of light from distant stars, presumably caused by scattering as it passed through the "smoke." This linear polarization, very small, is lined up with the plane of the galaxy, which means that the dust particles causing it also tend to be lined up, and theories were developed to explain this in terms of magnetic fields between the stars. Very small magnetic fields had been proposed earlier to account for the generation of cosmic rays. Note how widely differing observations are linked together in the following article. —T L P

••

Cosmic Dust

OTTO STRUVE

(*Sky and Telescope*, October 1954)

About 150 astronomers attended the sixth international astrophysical symposium on July 15–17, 1954, organized by Professor P. Swings and the Institut d'Astrophysique of Liége University, Belgium. "Solid Particles in Astronomical Objects" was the theme of the sixty-three papers on the program; two thirds of these were by American, British, and German astronomers; the others came from Belgium, Czechoslovakia, France, Holland, Japan, Poland, Sweden, and the U.S.S.R.

. . . The largest section was devoted to "Smoke in Interstellar Space and in Nebulae." H. van de Hulst reviewed the evidence on the chemical

FIG. 121. This long-exposure photograph of the Milky Way in Ophiuchus, by E. E. Barnard, shows extensive dust clouds silhouetted against the stellar background. (Yerkes Observatory photograph)

composition of the grains, their temperatures, distribution of sizes and shapes, and their densities in different regions of the Milky Way.

The observed degree of obscuration amounts, on the average, to two magnitudes per kiloparsec, and could be achieved only by negative hydrogen ions, or by small ice grains about one micron in diameter, or by iron particles about 1/10 as large. All other types of particles would require such heavy concentrations in space as to make the total mass of the interstellar medium unreasonably large. Negative hydrogen ions do not form often enough in hydrogen gas clouds to play an important role.

This leaves only ice crystals and iron particles. Both could produce the observed relation of absorption and wavelength. But van de Hulst prefers the ice crystals because they have larger albedos [the fraction of incident sunlight that is reflected] and they scatter light in a predominantly forward direction. From the prior work of L. G. Henyey and J. L. Greenstein, it appears certain that the obscuring clouds in the Milky Way do in fact possess these properties.

The existence of interstellar polarization shows that the particles are not spherical in shape, but rather elongated needles or ellipsoids that show a predominantly parallel orientation. There are three competing theories to explain this orientation. Two, by L. Davis and Greenstein on the one hand, and by L. Spitzer, Jr., and J. Tukey on the other, attribute it to interstellar magnetic fields. But the former make use of a phenomenon known as paramagnetic relaxation, which operates upon ice needles rotating haphazardly in all directions as a result of mutual collisions. These rotations are modified by magnetic forces in such a manner as to produce a predominant orientation along the lines of magnetic force. The Spitzer-Tukey mechanism operates upon iron needles. Since most astronomers believe that the interstellar particles are dielectric rather than metallic in composition, the Davis-Greenstein mechanism is usually regarded as the more probable of the two. It has also the advantage of requiring a smaller interstellar magnetic field—of the order of 10^{-5} gauss—which fits well with the theory of interstellar magnetism developed during the past year by E. Fermi and S. Chandrasekhar.

The third theory, by T. Gold, attributes the orientation of the particles to what might be called "interstellar winds." If the motions of the interstellar gas tend to be directed predominantly at right angles to the plane of the Milky Way, then the elongated particles would indeed orient themselves in a preferential manner and would produce the observed kind of polarization in a transmitted beam of starlight.

One can agree with Gold that the winds, if they exist, must influence the distribution of the major axes of the particles in space, and it is therefore important to explore how far we can go without invoking the action of magnetic fields. Perhaps both mechanisms play a role. After all, van de Hulst showed that even with a perfect alignment of all particles it is not easy to account simultaneously for the observed amounts of obscuration and polarization. Neither theory, by itself, predicts such a perfect alignment. If several forces were operating to orient the particles in the same way, the alignment would be more nearly perfect, and the difficulty would be less severe.

A very important result of the observations, stressed especially in a paper contributed by Lucienne Divan, of Paris, is the fact that the curve that relates the amount of interstellar absorption and the wavelength is the same in all regions of the Milky Way thus far investigated—even in the Orion nebula, where previous investigators had found a marked anomaly. Oort and van de Hulst have suggested that interstellar grains grow quite rapidly around nuclei of condensation, which may, to begin with, be nothing more substantial than polyatomic molecules. They find that in 10^8 years an average particle reaches a diameter of about one micron. This is what the observations indicate for the particles in all dark nebulosities. Since the Milky Way Galaxy is certainly much older than 108 years, we arrive at one of several conclusions:

1. There must be a mechanism whereby the particles are prevented from growing beyond one micron. This may be due to collisions of dark clouds and the consequent evaporation of colliding grains.

2. It is surprising that all clouds show the same average size of particle. If some clouds are very young while others are old, the observed absorption curves would not all give the same relation with wavelength. The fact that the curves are the same suggests that in the vicinity of the sun —in our own spiral arm of the galaxy—all clouds are old enough to have reached equilibrium conditions.

3. The mechanism of particle production may not be at all the one considered by Oort and van de Hulst. In his introductory paper, Oort recommended further study of the mechanism of pulverization of meteoric particles, recently advanced by H. Zirin at Harvard, which has many advocates for zodiacal-light formation but had seemed rather improbable for interstellar dust.

Oort stressed the great predominance of gas in all interstellar clouds. According to the Leiden radio observations, and also according to the Harvard work by B. J. Bok and his associates, the average density of the gas is at least one hundred times that of the solid particles. The gas, and not the dust, is the primary factor connected with the formation of spiral arms. A galaxy deprived of its gaseous constituent, perhaps as the result of a collision with another galaxy, can become greatly flattened, but it is incapable of forming spiral arms or knots.

Can solid grains condense in all gaseous regions of the Milky Way? Oort's answer is No. He said, "It must be expected that at densities less than 1/10 that near the sun practically no solid particles can exist. We may conclude that wherever absorption effects are observed the average gas density must exceed 0.1 hydrogen atom per cubic centimeter." . . .

A good deal more was reported at the 1954 Liége conference, some of it concerning the formation of stars from the intergalactic material and changes of stars passing through it. The subject of star formation and stellar evolution is reserved for another volume in this series, but it is the basis for much of the interest in the distribution of stars and interstellar material. Where the density of "smoke" was high in the past there are probably many stars today. The association of hot blue B-type stars (which must be young stars) with clouds of interstellar gas and dust (from which stars are formed) is evidence of star formation going on now.

The B-stars are worthy of special study also because of their high luminosity; they can be seen to great distances. —T L P

The B Stars and
Galactic Exploration

R. M. PETRIE

(*Sky and Telescope*, December 1963)

Galactic research by means of spectroscopic observations of early-type stars has been an important part of the work of the Dominion Astrophysical Observatory ever since our 72-inch reflector was erected in 1918 at Victoria, British Columbia. . . .

J. S. Plaskett's results on O stars were most stimulating. He demonstrated the large masses and high luminosities of these objects, the very great distances to which they could be observed, and their relation to the interstellar clouds of ionized calcium. Therefore it was decided to extend the studies to the much more numerous, slightly cooler, but still very luminous B stars, and a large program for observing five hundred of them was begun in 1923. Plaskett was joined in this project by J. A. Pearce.

Their work on B stars proceeded with great vigor, some 2700 spectrograms being obtained in six years. These photographs were measured for radial velocity, the spectra were classified, and the intensities of the interstellar H and K lines of ionized calcium were estimated. The observational data were complete and ready for study by 1930.

Meanwhile, many galactic studies were going on at other observatories. Astronomers analyzed the proper motions and radial velocities of stars (Fig. 122) leading in the middle 1920s to models of the galaxy proposed by B. Lindblad in Sweden and by J. H. Oort in Holland. The latter advocated a model in which the sun and other stars move around the galactic center in circular orbits, much as planets move around the sun. Stars nearer the center would travel faster than the sun, those farther out at lower speeds.

This type of galactic rotation is detectable because it produces differential effects in the observed proper motions and radial velocities of stars. For example, it was shown that the radial velocities (after correction for the sun's motion relative to the local standard of rest) should follow a sine wave if the velocities are plotted completely around the circle of the Milky Way. This curve repeats itself in the complete 360°, hence astronomers often speak of it as the *Oort double wave* (Fig. 124). The

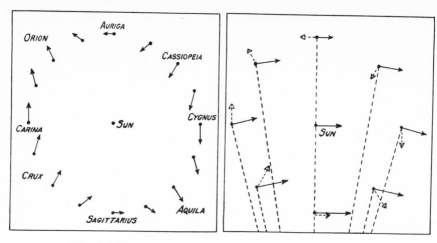

FIG. 122. The left-hand diagram shows the observed motions of stars with respect to the sun. In the diagram to the right, these motions (dashed arrows) are interpreted as a rotation of the galaxy around a distant center in Sagittarius, movement relative to this center being shown by solid arrows.

FIG. 123. The spiral galaxy M33 in Triangulum, photographed by J. S. Plaskett with the 72-inch reflector of the Dominion Astrophysical Observatory on November 5, 1918. This picture shows clearly M33's central condensation and its spiral arms outlined by stars and gaseous nebulae. Our galaxy probably looks something like this when viewed from M33's distance of about 2.3 million light years.

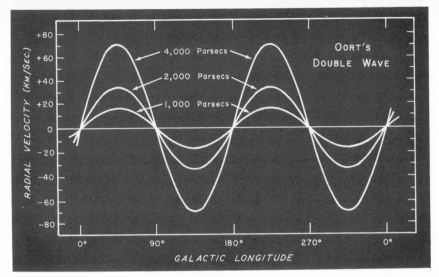

FIG. 124. Galactic rotation causes a systematic effect upon the observed line-of-sight motions of stars, its size varying with galactic longitude and increasing with distance from the sun. (Adapted from *The Astronomical Universe*, by W. S. Krogdahl, The Macmillan Company, New York, 1962)

amplitude of this wave increases with the average distance of the stars under consideration.

In practice, we must measure remote stars when we investigate galactic rotation by radial-velocity observations. Even at 1000 light years from the sun, the maximum differential effect is only about 5.5 kilometers per second. Very distant stars are needed if our conclusions are not to be too strongly influenced by observational errors and the stars' rather large random motions. In 1927 Oort had only very meager observational material to test his theory and to derive the galactic-rotation parameters. The Victoria observations of the line-of-sight velocities of about five hundred distant stars thus appeared just at the time such data were needed.

The work of Plaskett and Pearce gave a spectacular verification of Oort's predictions, confirming his basic idea that the mass of our galaxy is strongly concentrated toward the center, around which the stars pursue circular orbits. The Victoria radial velocities showed the now familiar double-wave effect, and agreed with star counts in placing the galactic center behind the great Sagittarius star clouds. It further showed the differential radial velocity effect to be 5 kilometers per second at 1000 light years—a numerical value very little changed by three decades of additional work.

Plaskett and Pearce's observations of the velocities of the interstellar calcium lines were very important. These astronomers demonstrated that the interstellar gas shares in the galactic rotation, but the amplitude of the effect is almost exactly half that given by the B stars. Two important conclusions follow: The galactic rotation as observed is a consequence of the gravitational field of our galaxy, not a phenomenon peculiar to stars. The ionized calcium gas is distributed uniformly throughout the volume of space covered by the Victoria observations.

Confirmation of these results soon came from studies of a quite different kind of star. A. H. Joy at Mount Wilson Observatory obtained radial velocities of many faint, distant Cepheid variables, and found the galactic-rotation effects very clearly demonstrated. This work showed pointedly the importance of the interstellar dimming in studies of distant stars—a matter that has troubled investigators of galactic structure ever since. Other observations of stars and clusters were soon made and analyzed, so that by 1940 galactic-rotation researches had made great progress, providing numerical values for the size and mass of our galaxy. They emphasized the role played by the absorption of light by the interstellar dust.

Much remained to be done however. The observations (except for some Cepheids and a few galactic clusters) had not been extended much beyond the immediate vicinity of the sun, so we were ignorant of the rotation effects in other parts of the galaxy. Stellar distances were not well known, thus limiting the accuracy of the numerical values characterizing the rotation. Furthermore, it will be recalled that Oort's simple model postulated circular motion of stars around the galactic center; existing observations were too scanty to test whether this was in fact true, or whether the stars moved in elliptical orbits.

This need for more observations of early-type stars led to the decision in 1940 to undertake at Victoria an extension of the earlier work to include more distant B stars. . . .

Why the emphasis upon B stars in our spectroscopic studies? Although relatively scarce—composing much less than 1 per cent of the stellar population—they are intrinsically so bright that we may photograph them with a slit spectrograph even when they are several thousand light years distant. Also, they are located close to the central plane of our galaxy, and therefore share fully in the galactic rotation. Their spectra are relatively simple, so absorption lines produced in the intervening interstellar gas can be distinguished, permitting the measurement of "interstellar velocities" as well as star motions. By comparison with other kinds of high-luminosity stars, such as the Cepheids, B stars are less scarce and at their best are more brilliant. All in all, they are excellent objects for the investigation of galactic structure.

The current program attempted to improve on the earlier work in two ways. First, we sought a reliable method of ascertaining the distance to each star. Second, we tried to adopt correct spectral-line wavelengths, so

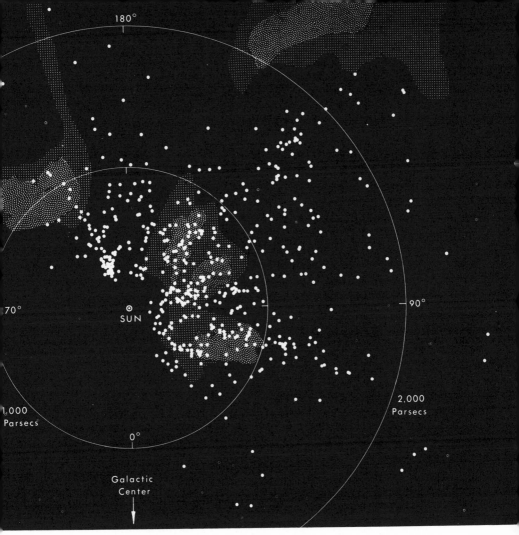

FIG. 125. In this diagram, the distribution of the O to B6 stars in the Victoria program is plotted on the central plane of the Milky Way. Shaded areas indicate the densest concentrations of interstellar neutral hydrogen gas, and the circles are approximately 3250 light years apart.

that our radial velocities would be free from spurious motions introduced by inexact values. It was easy enough to select these goals, but their fulfillment required much observing and the detailed measurement of nearly 1000 additional spectrograms. Furthermore, the dimming of starlight by interstellar dust had to be determined, since this factor affects our distance measurements. At present, the data are complete for 400 stars.

The distribution of these 400 stars on the galactic plane is seen in Figure 125. The two circles centered on the sun have radii of 1000 and 2000 parsecs (about 3250 and 6500 light years). Shaded areas indicate the two highest densities of neutral-hydrogen clouds, according to F. J. Kerr's recent analysis of the radioastronomy results. Our observations cover about half of the Milky Way: from Aquila through Cygnus, Lacerta, Cepheus, Cassiopeia, Perseus, Taurus, and into Orion.

Note the lack of any clear-cut spiral structure in the distribution. Our program included most known B stars to as faint as apparent magnitude 8.6, so our data are reasonably complete out to the first circle. . . .

It is interesting to compare the arrangement of the B stars with that of the hydrogen clouds, remembering that, on the scale of the chart, these stars have scarcely moved from their birthplaces. They seem neither to avoid the hydrogen clouds nor to congregate in them. This conclusion is subject to change after a more detailed analysis, which should contribute information about star formation.

When our mean radial velocities were corrected for local solar motion and plotted against galactic longitude, then the variation of radial velocity with galactic longitude, as predicted by Oort and shown by the curves, was very well confirmed. The amplitudes, reduced to a distance of 1000 light years, average 5.7 kilometers per second for the stars and 3.2 for the interstellar calcium. These numbers have a ratio of nearly one half, which means that the interstellar calcium is mostly uniformly distributed between the sun and the stars. The curves pass through zero velocity close to longitudes 90° and 180°, as they must if the simple rotational model of Oort is true. Evidently it is a good approximation in the case of B stars!

The curves are not quite centered on zero velocity, as they should be were the galactic orbits strictly circular, but give on the average 3 kilometers per second velocity of approach. We cannot tell yet whether this indicates an expansion of our galaxy at a rate diminishing outward, or a contraction motion increasing outward, but there is some hope of distinguishing between the two cases when our data are complete. Meanwhile, we may note that Kerr concludes that the hydrogen clouds exhibit an outwardly decreasing expansion, while Vera Rubin and her collaborators recently found the B stars to show galactic contraction when analyzed for both radial velocities and proper motions. . . .

Despite this program being one of the larger contributions to galactic studies, by itself it does not give all the information we need, since only half of the Milky Way is covered. When the Victoria results are combined with the work of other observatories, including those in the southern hemisphere, it will probably give us enough observations to investigate adequately the distributions and motions of B stars within 3000 light years.

But many questions will remain unanswered until we can study the regions beyond. The relation of the B stars to the neutral hydrogen clouds remains obscure, as does the relation between the B stars generally and the tracers of spiral arms (these tracers include star clusters and H II regions). Interstellar dimming of starlight has undoubtedly produced artificial gaps in our coverage, which we should endeavor to fill. Today we have radial velocities and approximate distances of about 2000 B stars, but much more data must be accumulated to complete the exploration of the galaxy to even such small distances as 6000 light years from the sun!

The lack of a clear association of B stars with clouds of hydrogen is surprising, since B stars were thought to be forming from interstellar clouds. In fact, many of them cause the hydrogen gas to shine by fluorescence. These "H II regions" are similar to the planetary nebulae discussed in Chapter 4. — T L P

....

Glowing Hydrogen in the Milky Way

OTTO STRUVE

(*Sky and Telescope*, January 1951)

The existence of large fields of nebular emission, far exceeding that of the catalogued nebulae, was first demonstrated with the nebular spectrograph of the McDonald Observatory, in 1938. Since that time B. Strömgren and several other astronomers have made various attempts to photograph or otherwise record even fainter emissions.

Figures 126 and 127 were recently obtained by Strömgren and C. Fehrenbach at the Haute Provence Observatory, near St. Michel, in southern France. The exposures were made simultaneously, through twin cameras of 50 millimeters aperture and 70 millimeters focal length. In front of each camera the observers had mounted an interference filter: that for Figure 126 was centered on the hydrogen line Hα, while that for Figure 127 was centered at wavelength 6200 A. Both filters transmitted about a 150-A range of wavelengths. The exposures were two hours, and the emulsion was Eastman 103a-E.

Since the background of the night sky, of the unresolved stars, and of the starlight diffusely scattered by the interstellar dust particles is nearly the

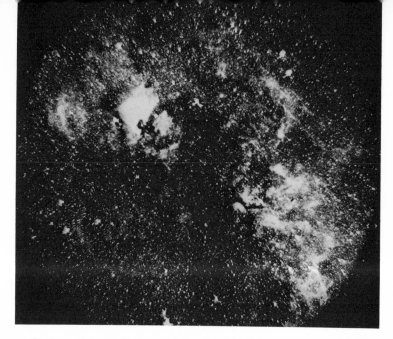

FIG. 126. A region of Cygnus photographed through an interference filter transmitting the hydrogen-alpha line and adjoining wavelengths. Note that the entire field is more luminous than that in Figure 127, indicating the presence of very diffuse hydrogen in this part of the Milky Way. (Photograph from Observatoire de Haute Provence du Centre National de la Recherche Scientifique)

FIG. 127. The same region of Cygnus as that shown in Figure 126 appears devoid of nebulosity through a filter transmitting wavelengths centered at 6200 angstroms. The field is also relatively faint. (Photograph from Observatoire de Haute Provence du Centre National de la Recherche Scientifique)

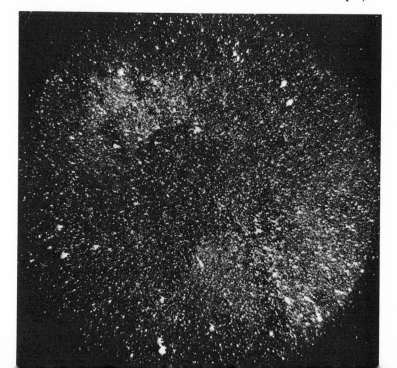

same for both pictures, the difference between them is due to the hydrogen emission in the Milky Way. And, indeed, this difference is enormous. We see in both photographs Alpha, Gamma, and Epsilon Cygni (also some defects caused by reflections in the optical parts). But while Figure 126 is more-or-less covered with irregular nebulosity, Figure 127 shows none at all.

Of particular interest in connection with these observations is the use of interference filters. In astronomical language, a filter is any optical device which transmits a limited range of wavelengths and absorbs light of all other colors. A piece of red glass is a filter; and many previous workers have helped to extend our knowledge of the emission nebulae by means of red-glass filters, transparent to Hα, mounted in front of photographic plates whose wide range of sensitivity included Hα. But as a rule these filters transmit a large range of wavelengths on both sides of the hydrogen wavelength. Hence, the contrast between the Hα-emitting regions and the normal background of the sky is less than it would be if the filter could be made to isolate a smaller portion of the spectrum. . . .

Until recently, interference filters also were too small in aperture to be useful for direct photography. They were first used for astronomical purposes by W. Baade and R. Minkowski, who isolated, with the help of such a filter, a narrow emission line in the Orion nebula. More recently, J. G. Baker has successfully experimented with interference filters at Harvard Observatory. By 1946 their manufacture had been greatly simplified, principally at the Zeiss works in Jena. . . .

In a Fabry-Perot interferometer, two transparent glass plates are separated by a parallel layer of some properly chosen transparent substance. The inner surfaces of the glass plates are lightly silvered, so that they reflect a portion of the incident light, which we assume to be white. Its rays penetrate partly into the space between the glasses and are there reflected back and forth with diminishing intensity between silvered surfaces. At every reflection some light passes through to the outside, and the resulting transmitted beam is the composite of many individual beams, some having traversed only once or twice between the glass plates, while others may have been reflected back and forth many times.

If the effective light path between the glasses is properly chosen, so that it is an exact multiple of the wavelength of light we wish to transmit, only those light beams that have that particular wavelength, or color, will reinforce one another, and will pass with considerable intensity. Light of other colors will experience more and more destructive interference: the crest of one wave will combine with the trough of another, and this will impede their passage through the filter. . . .

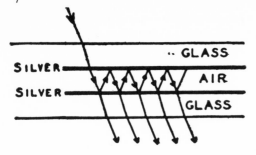

FIG. 128. The principle of the Fabry-Perot interferometer. Interference filters have a layer of transparent dielectric material instead of an air space between the mirrors.

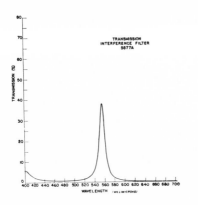

FIG. 129. The efficiency curve of an interference filter that is peaked at 5577 angstroms, with nearly 40 per cent transmission.

There are vast spaces in the Milky Way that are filled with hydrogen (and other atoms) having densities between one and about twenty hydrogen atoms per cubic centimeter. Only in exceptionally dense regions— which occupy an exceedingly small fraction of interstellar space—is the density as great as in the Orion nebula—about 1000 or even 10,000 atoms per cubic centimeter. (Contrast this with the number of atoms in one cubic centimeter of air at the surface of the earth, 3×10^{19}.)

The emission of light by hydrogen is caused by the ionizing action of the extreme ultraviolet radiation of the O and B stars. In those regions where such stars abound the interstellar hydrogen is mostly ionized, and we call these regions, following Strömgren, the H II regions. The emission of radiation occurs every time an ionized hydrogen atom (a proton) recombines with a free electron.

In regions which are devoid of O and B stars the hydrogen atoms are neutral. There is no glow from these unexcited atoms but we can observe in these "H I" regions, as well as in the H II regions, the effect of absorption produced upon starlight penetrating through them, by interstellar atoms of sodium, calcium, and so on. These interstellar absorption lines were known even before the hydrogen emission regions were discovered. But their interpretation became possible only when we understood that in interstellar space, as in the sun and the stars, hydrogen is by far the most abundant constituent.

··

Experiences with Cooled Color Emulsions

ARTHUR A. HOAG

(*Sky and Telescope*, December 1964)

In the past few years many of us amateur astronomers have experimented with fast new color films. . . . Most of us have noted that relatively short exposures with fast cameras show star colors well. We can even pick out the more spectacular emission nebulae in guided exposures made with ordinary lenses of 50-mm focal length. Some of us have noticed that photographs taken on cold winter nights reached fainter limits with better color balance than those exposed in warmer weather.

Since I am also a professional astronomer, I have had easy access to technical literature and equipment for further investigation of this temperature dependence. This is not a recently discovered effect. Early tests seemed to indicate a reduction in sensitivity when the temperature was lowered, but this result was valid only for high-intensity exposures. During the early 1900s, E. S. King, of Harvard Observatory, showed that the opposite effect occurred for the low-intensity exposures frequently encountered in astronomy.

King found that he could gain half a magnitude with plates cooled to winter temperatures, as compared with plates warmed over a heat register in the observatory laboratory. If this discovery had been followed up, we might have used emulsions more effectively during the past half century.

Several series of laboratory experiments—notably by J. H. Webb of Eastman Kodak Company and by A. N. Argue of Cambridge Observatory —have led to a better understanding of how temperature affects low-intensity exposures. If the incoming light is very weak, thermal activity tends to break up the sensitivity centers on the surfaces of emulsion grains before they can become stable enough to permit subsequent development. This has been referred to as *thermal regression* of the latent image. Reducing the temperature inhibits this regression. . . .

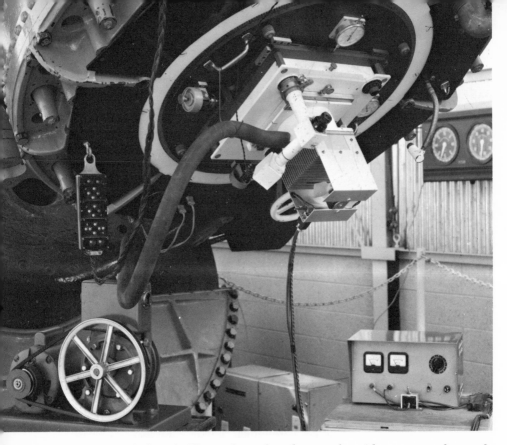

FIG. 130. Arthur A. Hoag takes color photographs with a camera that cools the film to increase speed and improve color balance. Here the device is seen mounted on the tailpiece of the 40-inch Ritchey-Chrétien reflector at the Naval Observatory's station in Arizona. A thermoelectric element cools the film or plate inside a low-pressure chamber, which is evacuated by the pump at the lower left. The vacuum prevents moisture from condensing on the emulsion, and it insulates the thermoelectric element. The power supply and temperature control are at lower right. (U.S. Naval Observatory photograph)

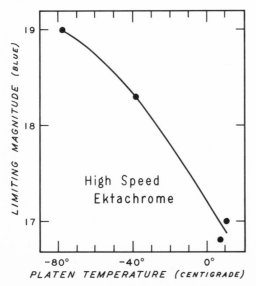

FIG. 131. Although all Hoag's exposure times were 20 minutes, stars about two magnitudes fainter were recorded when the temperature of High Speed Ektachrome was reduced from about +10°C to −78°C. A vacuum camera cooled by dry ice and a mixture of frozen and liquid mercury were used.

Ordinary photographic emulsions are designed for short-exposure use; they are most efficient for snapshots. For long exposures, they exhibit *reciprocity failure*. That is, the photographic result for a long exposure to weak light is not the same as for a short exposure to strong light, even though the total incident energy is the same.

A photographic emulsion may be likened to a leaky bucket—if you wish to fill the bucket, you must pour in water at a high rate. If you pour it in slowly, it leaks away before you can raise the water level. If you want to fill the leaky bucket while adding water slowly, lower the temperature so that the water freezes, and you will fill it in spite of the leaks!

In 1960 I tried a refrigerated camera to see how effectively the laboratory results could be applied to astronomical photography. Our instrument maker, Joseph Egan, built a camera that cooled the emulsion by heat conduction through a metal plate to dry ice. The photographic surface was kept frost free by a flow of dry gas that had been cooled in a copper tube inside the dry-ice container.

My first experiment was with High Speed Ektachrome, as this film had shown a very great reciprocity failure in previous work with my 35-mm camera. The refrigerated camera was used with the 40-inch *f*/6.8 Ritchey-Chrétien reflector, and the first tests gave spectacular results. A one-hour exposure on the Whirlpool galaxy (NGC 5194-5) at air temperature registered only the brightest parts, and near-threshold images appeared blue. But a similar exposure with the emulsion at about −35° centigrade showed faint detail almost down to the sky-fog limit, with good color discrimination. Cooling not only increased the effective speed for low intensities but maintained the color balance. In effect, the properties of the film designed for short exposures were transferred to longer exposures by cooling. . . .

FIG. 132. A cross-section drawing of a simple low-temperature camera. The platen and dry-ice reservoir should have high thermal conductivity, while the vacuum-chamber material should have poor conductivity. The film or plate can be held against the platen with springs.

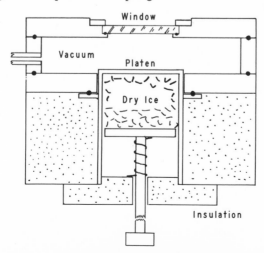

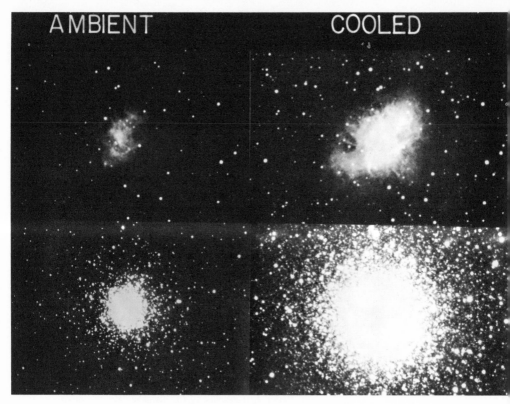

FIG. 133. A dramatic illustration of the gain in limiting magnitude of cooled color emulsions over those at normal temperatures is portrayed in these positive reproductions of the Crab nebula (top) and the globular cluster Messier 3. (U.S. Naval Observatory photographs)

We are now using a different camera, in which a two-stage thermoelectric device does the cooling. A vacuum chamber protects the emulsion from moisture during exposure, the vacuum acting as a good insulator which allows the thermoelectric element to work efficiently. Exposures are made through a coated window in the chamber. A variable-current power supply regulates the temperature of the cooling platen to as low as about —65°C.

All four test photographs with the thermoelectric camera in Figure 133 are one-hour exposures. Those on the left were taken at ordinary temperatures, those on the right at —65°C. . . .

Most emulsions gain in effective speed when cooled to low temperatures during astronomical exposures. Another interesting result is that the same technique increases the latitude of emulsions, as anticipated by E. S. King and others. This means, for example, that we can photograph the faint detail in galaxies without burning out the bright nuclear regions. . . .

Clusters of Stars and the Galaxy

Near the sun, the general distribution of stars and interstellar material forms a flat pancake—the Milky Way Galaxy. However, the stars are not uniformly distributed in this flat slab; many occur in pairs (see Chapter 7) and others in small groups and clusters. Study of the clusters has proved enormously profitable in the measurement of large distances and in understanding stellar evolution. Their main value in the study of stellar evolution depends on the assumption that all stars in one cluster were formed at one time and are of the same age. This gives a hint as to how the clusters were formed, but leaves the problem of their wide variety in structure and appearance. The globular clusters are spherical in form and appear closely packed (Fig. 134), whereas galactic clusters are irregular and more loosely packed, and stellar associations are scarcely packed at all. —TLP

FIG. 134. One of the finest globular clusters is 47 Tucanae in the far southern sky. To the naked eye it looks like a hazy fourth-magnitude star, but this one-hour exposure with the 60-inch Boyden Observatory reflector shows a dense ball of thirteenth-magnitude stars and fainter ones covering about twice the area of the full moon. The stellar swarm is about 22,000 light years distant from us. (Harvard College Observatory photograph)

∎∎

Stellar Associations

OTTO STRUVE

(*Sky and Telescope*, July 1949)

One of the most remarkable properties of the stars is their tendency to form closely connected groups, or clusters. The Pleiades, Praesepe, and the cluster in Coma Berenices are visible to the naked eye and have been known since ancient times. The Double Cluster in Perseus was recorded by Hipparchus, but was not resolved by him into separate stars. Similarly, Praesepe was known only as a diffuse luminous spot in the night sky, and it remained for Galileo in 1610 to announce that with his telescope he could see "the nebula called Praesepe, not as one star only, but as a mass of more than forty small stars."

In the past three centuries several hundred star clusters have been discovered. These fall into two large groups. The globular clusters, which are distinct groups associated with our galactic system, present a more-or-less spherical arrangement concentric with the flattened stellar system of the Milky Way. The other group consists of approximately two hundred galactic clusters, ranging from inconspicuous groupings of a few stars to closely knit clusters consisting of several hundred stars. The galactic clusters are strongly concentrated toward the central plane of the Milky Way. . . . A few of them are close to the solar system—their diameters are about thirty light years.

Several years ago an interesting feature was found in the Double Cluster of Perseus. This famous object is easily seen with the naked eye between the stars Eta Persei and Delta Cassiopeiae. With a telescope of short focal ratio its appearance is similar to that in Figure 135, which was obtained by E. E. Barnard with the 10-inch Bruce telescope of the Yerkes Observatory. There are two fairly compact groups of stars, each occupying an area of approximately ¼ square degree. From the spectral types of the brighter stars and from their radial velocities we estimate that the distance of the Double Cluster is approximately 5000 light years. The apparent radius of each cluster is ½°, corresponding to approximately 40 light years. . . .

The most interesting feature of the Double Cluster is that it appears to be surrounded by a much more widely scattered grouping of early-type stars and a few red supergiants. Figure 136 shows the same field as Figure

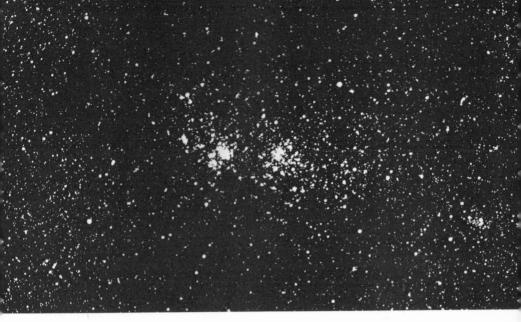

FIG. 135. The field of the Double Cluster in Perseus, photographed by E. E. Barnard. (Yerkes Observatory photograph)

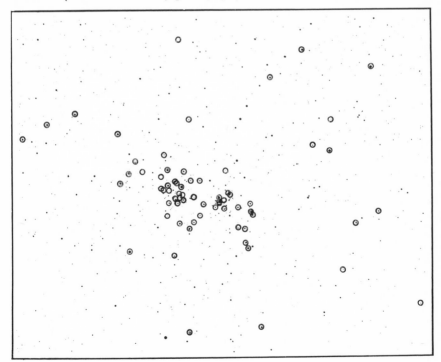

FIG. 136. The brighter stars in the Double Cluster field include giants and supergiants that are members of the cluster.

135, with circles marking those stars which, according to W. P. Bidelman, belong to the cluster. These stars are all supergiants and giants of spectral classes B, A, and M with a general tendency to be concentrated toward the clusters. This spherical distribution of supergiant stars bears little resemblance to an ordinary galactic cluster. . . . Bidelman has reached the conclusion that this group of high-luminosity stars associated with the Double Cluster in Perseus extends over approximately 450 light years. . . .

The extraordinary size of this outer cluster and its remarkably low star density raise the problem of the stability of such groupings of stars. Many years ago B. J. Bok investigated the manner in which a star cluster is gradually disrupted by the effect of galactic rotation. . . . An average cluster may be disrupted in about 30 million years. . . . The vast stellar associations which surround some of the more compact groups are especially vulnerable to the effect of tidal forces of the galaxy and to the disturbing action of other stars nearby.

In a remarkable paper which has just appeared in the *Astronomical Journal* of the Soviet Union, V. A. Ambarzumian has again called attention to these large stellar associations. He has found a number of new groupings, most of them consisting of stars of early spectral type. . . . A striking presentation of the separate clouds of B-type stars in the Milky Way, published in 1929 by A. Pannekoek, is reproduced in Figure 137. Since the work of Pannekoek some of the distances have been changed, but the general tendency of the hotter stars to appear in what Ambarzumian calls stellar associations is conspicuous.

As a rule these associations of early-type stars have radii of the order of 500 light years. . . . One very interesting conclusion is that from a distant spiral nebula the association would appear as a distinct cluster easily seen on the background of our Milky Way. (On our own photographs, taken from within the Milky Way, the intrinsically faint stars that are close to us appear projected upon the field of the stellar association, thereby producing the appearance of a uniform field of stars. But from a distant extragalactic system the intrinsically faint stars of our neighborhood would be completely invisible, and only the intrinsically luminous stars would stand out.) Thus, the cluster of Perseus, as observed from the Andromeda nebula, M31, would appear to have a diameter of about 450 light years. . . .

Associations of early-type stars and some late-type supergiants are unquestionably real and present an interesting problem of cosmogony. Ambarzumian has shown that the effect of galactic rotation will be to distend a group along the Milky Way in such a manner that it will become elongated to about twice its original radius in an interval of 40 million years. This is a short interval of time compared to the age of the galaxy, and we must

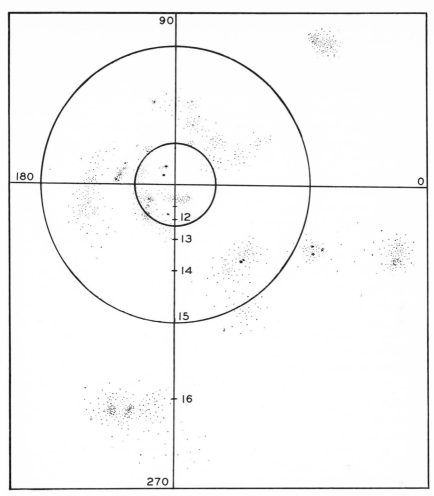

FIG. 137. Groups of B stars projected on the plane of the galaxy by A. Pannekoek from the *Henry Draper Catalogue*. The counterclockwise coordinate is galactic longitude; the radial coordinate is distance modulus (apparent minus absolute magnitude); the circles indicate distances of 300 and 1000 parsecs from the sun, as estimated in 1929. (From *Publications* of the Astronomical Institute of the University of Amsterdam)

therefore conclude that if the stellar groups are older than 40 million years, they would all show a general tendency to be elongated in the plane of the Milky Way. In reality no such elongation is observed.

This is rather surprising, because the gravitation of the cluster itself cannot keep it from dispersing. The only remaining possibility is that the associations expand so rapidly in all directions that the flattened shapes produced by galactic rotation cannot be recognized. On this basis, Ambarzumian estimates that the velocity of expansion of the stellar associations cannot be less than one kilometer per second. . . . On the other hand, the expansion cannot exceed ten kilometers per second, because otherwise the stars would show this effect in their radial velocities. He adopts an expansion of five kilometers per second as the most reasonable compromise and concludes that associations of stars which are now visible should become completely dispersed within the general mass of the stars in the galaxy in intervals of 10 or 20 million years.

If this rather revolutionary view should be substantiated, it would mean that the stellar associations like the one surrounding the Double Cluster in Perseus are only about 20 million years old. This would represent at the same time the age of the stars contained within the association, because it is clear that the stars could not have been formed before the expansion began. . . .

Ambarzumian estimates that the number of stellar associations containing early-type stars in the Milky Way is several thousand. Since each association can last only a few million years before becoming dissolved in the Milky Way, we must assume that on the average one association of stars is created every 1000 years.

Each association contains about 100 stars. During the [10-billion-year] lifetime of the Milky Way about 10 million stellar associations must have passed through their evolutionary cycles, each of them ending in complete disintegration. Hence, it is reasonable to suppose that billions of stars which we now observe throughout the galaxy have been, at some time in the past, members of these associations. Perhaps all stars have been formed in this manner.

But what precedes the formation of a stellar association? Apparently, Ambarzumian thinks of some kind of explosive process. He has advocated the unconventional idea that the stars may have been produced not from the dust and gas which we now observe in the Milky Way, but from dark objects of unknown constitution, whose masses may have been several hundred times the mass of the sun. No such objects can now be observed within our galactic system. . . . Nevertheless, there is probably no good reason to deny the possibility of their existence. . . . Ambarzumian believes that the surface brightnesses of some extragalactic systems give additional cause for believing that they contain masses of an unknown kind, in addition to the stars and diffuse clouds. . . .

....

Dynamics and Evolution of Star Clusters[1]

BART J. BOK

(*Sky and Telescope*, July and August 1951)

The presence in our Milky Way system of one hundred observable globular clusters and at least four times as many galactic (or open) clusters offers a constant challenge to the galactic investigator who interests himself in the problems of the dynamics and evolution of the system and its constituent parts. Star clusters can hardly be permanent and unchanging objects. What holds them together and what prevents them either from collapsing or from disintegrating? They must be undergoing gradual changes of a predictable sort. From a study of their likely future developments, one may at least endeavor to guess at their probable pasts. What are the rates at which they will develop? Are they gradually disappearing from the galactic scene, or can we count on having the supply replenished by new star clusters as the old ones disappear? These are questions of a fundamental nature. By attempting to answer them, we should not only learn much about star clusters and their evolution, but we may incidentally throw some light on the larger problem of the evolution of the Milky Way system.

The various gravitational forces influencing the motions of the individual stars in a cluster may be grouped as follows:

1. Forces exerted by the attraction of the star cluster as a whole upon each component member.

2. Forces exerted by the Milky Way system as a whole upon the cluster and its member stars; what concerns us especially are the *differences* between the galactic force of attraction upon individual stars and the average for the entire cluster.

3. Fluctuating forces produced by the attraction between two member stars of the cluster that happen to pass close by each other.

4. Fluctuating forces produced by the passage of galactic field stars through or close to the cluster. . . .

The attraction of a cluster as a whole upon each member can be calculated if we know the dimensions of the cluster, its total star population,

---

[1] The present article is based on the Rubbi lecture delivered at the University of Stellenbosch, in South Africa, on July 28, 1950.

and the distribution of the member stars inside the cluster. Here we must differentiate sharply between galactic and globular clusters. . . .

A globular star cluster is in all likelihood a rather permanent configuration of stars. The motion of the cluster as a unit through our Milky Way system is, of course, controlled by the attraction of the whole of the galaxy, especially the forces produced by the central parts of the galaxy. But when one studies the motions of the stars in a globular cluster relative to each other, he finds that the internal attractive forces are far more important than the differences among the general galactic forces for different points in the cluster.

On the other hand, a thinly populated and very extended galactic cluster will exert relatively small attractive forces upon its own members, and the disruptive tidal forces of the galaxy may often be considerably larger than the attraction produced by the cluster itself. . . . Where is the dividing line between stable and unstable star clusters?

Problems of stability of star clusters can be dealt with on a purely mathematical basis . . . and the mathematician will find an excellent summary in the volume *Principles of Stellar Dynamics* by S. Chandrasekhar (University of Chicago Press, 1942). But, fortunately, we can present the nature of the problem by a simple diagram. . . .

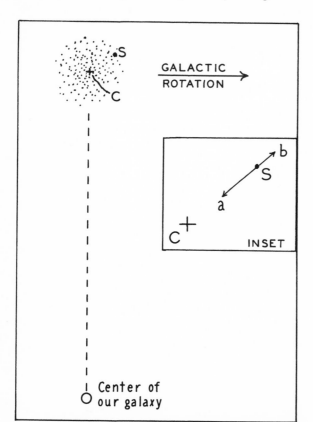

FIG. 138. A schematic representation of the simplified problem of the forces acting on a cluster in the galaxy.

In Figure 138, S represents a star in the cluster, and the cross at C marks the center of the cluster. The principal forces that control the motion of star S are the attraction of the cluster as a whole upon the star, represented by the force vector *a* in the enlarged inset diagram, and the *difference* in the attractive force exerted by our galaxy on the cluster at C and the attraction actually exerted at S. A little consideration shows that this second force vector, *b*, will point approximately *away from* C, that is, opposite to the direction of force vector *a*. It is clear from the diagram that *a* tends to hold the cluster together, whereas *b* is a tidal force and tends to disrupt the cluster. Who will win in this tug of war? If *a* is the larger of the two, stability may occur, but if *b* wins out over *a*, disruption will almost surely follow.

The principal controlling factor is going to be the average mass density in the cluster. . . . For a given star density the mass of the cluster will be proportional to R^3, if R is the radius of the cluster. But since the cluster attracts star S with a force that is *directly proportional* to the mass of the cluster and *inversely proportional* to the square of the distance of S from the center, C, the attractive force will be proportional to R^3 divided by R^2, that is, to R. Force *b*, on the other hand, depends wholly on the mass distribution and dimensions of our galactic system and is . . . directly proportioinal to the distance SC, that is, to R. In other words, the ratio of *a* to *b* depends only on the mass within distance R of the cluster center.

More precise calculations confirm this approximate reasoning. A spherical star cluster with an average star density equivalent to one solar mass per 300 cubic light years should have enough internal gravitational pull to hold out against the disruptive tidal forces of our rotating galaxy. . . .

It is of interest to apply these results to some of the known clusters. The globular clusters have average star densities well in excess of the above critical density, and they are well protected against galactic tidal disruption. . . .

It is relatively simple to compute the rates at which very loosely bound star clusters will in all probability disintegrate. We carry out the computations for the most favorable case, one in which at the start the motions of the group members are so attuned that under the influence of the smoothed force field of our rotating galaxy the stars in the group would retain indefinitely the same average distances apart. But this condition cannot be a permanent one, for the galactic field is subject to fluctuations, caused principally by encounters between cluster stars and distant field stars. Something very much milder than a collision or a dramatic close passage is all that is needed to divert a cluster star from its original path.

At this moment the Ursa Major group, with a total mass about one hundred times that of our sun, is spread over a volume of space with a diameter of the order of 150 light years. Computations show that this cluster should double its radius in about 200 million years, and that in about 500 million years the cluster will be so broken up as to have lost its identity.

I can almost hear some readers say, "Well, that is a comfortably long time." But, believe me, cosmically speaking it is a rapid process. Our sun completes one revolution around the distant galactic center in about 200 million years. . . . The Ursa Major cluster will double its radius in one such revolution, and in two and one half of them it will have vanished as a group. The age of our earth (two to three billion years) is only ten or fifteen revolutions of the sun; this is the most probable time required for complete disintegration of the most stable of the loose star clusters. Marked changes are apparently taking place in our Milky Way system in time intervals comparable in length to the age of our earth.

Let us now turn our attention to clusters that are relatively immune to the tidal effects of the galactic field of force. . . . If a tight globular cluster of stars is to keep approximately the same overall diameter, the member stars must have some motions of their own. (Otherwise the mutual gravitational attraction of the member stars would draw all of them gradually toward the center.) The velocities of the individual stars must not, however, be too great, for then large-scale escape of stars from the cluster would occur, with consequent disintegration of the cluster. Apparently, if a star cluster is to be a fairly permanent affair, there must exist a rather neat division between the total energy of motion (the *kinetic energy*, T, which is positive) and the total energy of position (the *potential energy*, W, which is negative) of all the cluster stars together. This equilibrium condition is expressed by the so-called *virial theorem*:

$$2T + W = 0.$$

. . . In the simplest case, the kinetic energy is given by

$$2T = MV^2,$$

where M is the total mass of the cluster and V^2 is the mean value of the squares of the random velocities of the member stars; and the potential energy is

$$W = -3GM^2/5R,$$

where G is Newton's universal constant of gravitation, M is again the total mass, and R is the radius of the cluster. Combining these three equations, we obtain the relation:

$$V^2 = 3GM/5R.$$

This formula is of the greatest importance in the study of dense galactic clusters and globular clusters. It states mathematically the sensible condition that, for a cluster of given total mass to attain a certain radius, the star members must be endowed with definite mean square velocities. In practice we can use this formula in reverse: if we measure the radius of a cluster, and if we have some information regarding the random velocities of the stars in the cluster (generally from proper motions), then we can obtain from our relation a value for the probable mass of the cluster. In the case of the Pleiades, for instance, using the approximate observed value of the average velocity of 0.6 kilometer per second and a radius of about 8 light years, we find that the total mass of the cluster should be about 400 times that of the sun, a value that agrees well with the estimated masses of the known member stars. For an average globular cluster, radial-velocity measurements indicate velocity spreads of the order of 15 kilometers per second. For a radius of approximately 50 light years, the deduced total mass of the average globular cluster appears to be somewhere between 100,000 and 1,000,000 times that of our sun.

At one time we thought that dense clusters would gradually "loosen up" because of passing field stars. . . . This has proved not to be the case. Ambarzumian in the Soviet Union and (independently) Spitzer in the United States showed that there is a second process, which leads to eventual collapse of dense clusters rather than to disintegration.

The Ambarzumian-Spitzer process depends on close passages of stars that are members of the system. When such an encounter between two cluster members results in one of them gaining high velocity and escaping from the cluster, then the escaping star takes with it more than its average share of energy, and the average amount of energy per star for the remaining stars will be less than before the encounter. The cluster will therefore contract slightly as a result of the encounter. The problem is to calculate the rate at which this process takes place. . . .

How fast does the escape process make the cluster contract? The estimates of Ambarzumian and Spitzer, later refined by Chandrasekhar, show that the . . . Pleiades are definitely headed for collapse. In about five billion years, they will have shrunk to an inconspicuous small group of perhaps not more than forty stars. For a cluster with half the radius of the Pleiades and one eighth the mass, a similar collapse will occur in only one billion years. Globular clusters will be "safe" from collapse for twenty billion years or more; the physical evolution of their individual stars will probably be far quicker than the collapse of the globular cluster as a whole.

It is difficult to say what will be the future development of the remnant nucleus of a collapsed cluster. The stars will be relatively close together, but there will still be enough room to prevent frequent star collisions. Probably, the remaining stars will form some sort of a super-multiple system in which the group stars move in complex periodic orbits.

TABLE 10.   SUMMARY OF THE DYNAMICAL EVOLUTION OF STAR CLUSTERS

Cluster	Mass (sun = 1)	Ra-dius (lt. yrs.)	Ve-locity disper-sion (km/ sec)	Time of relax-ation (yrs.)	Effect of galactic tidal forces	FUTURE?
Globular cluster	10^6	50	12-15	10^{10}	None	Not much change during next 10^{10} years
Pleiades	400	8	0.6	3×10^7	Probably slight	In 2×10^9 years, mass of 200 suns and radius of 3 light years
Small, dense galactic cluster	50	4	0.3	8×10^6	Probably slight	Multiple star system; periodic orbits within 10^9 years
Nucleus of Hyades	150	16	0.2	10^8	Disintegration in 3×10^9 years	Disintegration in 3×10^9 years
Nucleus of Ursa Major cluster	100	75	0.1??	Irrelevant	Disintegration in 5×10^8 years	Disintegration in 5×10^8 years

In Table 10 we have tried to summarize our knowledge to date regarding the dynamical evolution of various kinds of star clusters. All estimated total masses are in terms of the sun's mass (2×10^{33} grams). The table shows again that, dynamically speaking, the globular clusters are very stable, but that the galactic clusters, especially those smaller than or more open than the Pleiades, are subject to fairly rapid changes on the cosmic scale. . . .

···

Rotation of the Globular Cluster Omega Centauri

(*Sky and Telescope*, November 1964)

Many of the globular star clusters show slightly elliptical outlines, and this flattening has long been interpreted by astronomers as due to rotation. Now a direct demonstration of the rotation of the southern cluster Omega Centauri has been announced by the Astronomer Royal, R. v. d. R. Woolley, in the August 29 [1964] issue of *Nature*. This achievement is part of the continuing study of Omega Centauri under way at Greenwich and Cape observatories.

Omega Centauri as a whole is receding from the earth at about 230 kilometers per second. If this cluster is rotating around an axis that is more or less perpendicular to our line of sight, then all its member stars on one side of the axis should have radial velocities greater than 230, on the other side less than 230 kilometers per second. Furthermore, the farther a star is from the axis, the more its radial velocity should differ from 230.

That this is indeed the case for Omega Centauri was demonstrated from observations by G. A. Harding with the 74-inch reflector of Radcliffe Observatory. He was able to obtain three radial-velocity determinations of each of thirteen stars known to be cluster members. This was a difficult task because the brightest stars in the cluster are as faint as magnitude 13. From these observations, it turned out that the rotational velocity is 0.72 kilometer per second for each parsec of distance from the cluster axis, assuming that the axis of rotation is normal to the line of sight.

Woolley does not express this result in terms of the rotation period, but calculation shows that a complete rotation of this globular cluster takes a little less than ten million years. He comments, ". . . the elliptical shape of the cluster is a consequence of a rotation considerably faster than galactic rotation. This result disposes of the view that the elliptical shape is a consequence of galactic tidal forces."

....

Inside a Globular
Star Cluster

ANATOLE BOYKO

(*Sky and Telescope*, November 1964)

Authors of several recent popular books on astronomy have discussed the appearance of the sky as seen from a hypothetical planet near the center of a globular star cluster. The theme is all the more interesting as its subject is unattainable and is bound to remain so. No man born on earth seems destined ever to reach a globular cluster, nor even to come near one, for even the closest are almost 10,000 light years away.

And at smaller distances from us, there is no stretch of space as generously filled with stars as the center of a globular cluster, which may be many hundreds of times as dense as the neighborhood of our solar system.

In his *Guide to the Stars* (1960), Patrick Moore writes, "Instead of a few brilliant stars there will be many thousands; probably at least thirty will shine more brilliantly than Venus does to us, and . . . one or two will rival our moon, so that instead of appearing as twinkling points, they will show real disks. . . . The glare of the stars will provide much more light than our full moon. . . ."

Contrast this with Arthur C. Clarke's depiction in *The Challenge of the Spaceship* (1959) of "a sky that is a solid shield of stars, so that there is no darkness between them. . . ."

How real is this oft-repeated picture of a sky solid with stars? As seen in a telescope, the center of a concentrated globular cluster appears to have no dark space between the star images. Nevertheless, the cluster's surface is not blindingly bright, but shines with a soft light. Why? The image of the center does not consist of overlapping *star disks*, but of overlapping *diffraction patterns*. True star disks are far beyond the resolving power of telescopes. What appears to us as a continuous glow in the cluster center is, in fact, many star images diffused by diffraction. The result is a spot of light of intermediate brightness. Thus the low surface brightness we see proves that stars are not tightly packed in a globular cluster. In fact, the starry sky seen from the center of a globular cluster would look exactly half as dense as does the central region viewed from outside. It makes this difference that the line of sight is a radius rather than a diameter. . . .

Patrick Moore also points out that, although the average distance between individual stars near the middle of a globular cluster is much less than in our part of the galaxy, "The actual distances are still very great, and collisions must be excessively rare, but any one star is almost bound to have several more within a couple of light years of it." . . .

A simple calculation will help us get a truer feeling of these relations. If we assume that in the solar neighborhood there is roughly one star per 10 cubic parsecs, we find the average interstellar distance there to be $10^{1/3} = 2.15$ parsecs, or 7 light years. Similarly, a density 1500 times that, or one star per 0.0067 cubic parsec, corresponds to an average distance of 0.6 light year. . . .

What, then, must be the true view of the sky from a planet inside an actual concentrated globular cluster? Whether there is an earth under those skies or not, the question challenges man's inquiring mind.

Stars as viewed from anywhere in the cluster would still show no apparent diameters. They would still be the luminous points familiar to us, except for one or two very nearby ones, or for supergiants 1000 times larger in diameter than the sun. At a distance of 0.6 light year, even such a supergiant would present an angular diameter of less than one minute of arc—below the normal resolving power of the unaided eye.

The striking apparent brightness of these stars is not easy to imagine, since our skies have no point sources of comparable brilliance. For instance, at 0.6 light year a giant of 100 times the sun's intrinsic luminosity would be a dazzling star of magnitude -9, which is almost 100 times the brightness of Venus at its best. . . .

There are some 2500 naked-eye stars in a hemisphere of our own sky. In the view from the center of a rich globular cluster there may be of the order of 100 times as many, or 250,000. If we divide into this the number of square degrees in a hemisphere (about 20,600), we find 12 naked-eye stars per square degree in the cluster sky. This means that the average angular distance between neighboring stars is about 0.3 degree.

From this, we again see how uncrowded the cluster sky actually is, when we recall that with rare exceptions the stars will appear as mere luminous points. . . .

■■

Star Chains

OTTO STRUVE

(Sky and Telescope, April 1954)

On the photograph of the Milky Way in Figure 139 the North America nebula is a conspicuous feature in the lower right. Of more immediate concern to us now are certain lines of stars above it, easily located with the aid of a ruler.

Measure to a point about 2 inches from the bottom and 1½ inches from the right edge of the picture; then find a second point 3 inches from the bottom and 1 inch from the right edge. Place your eye near the middle of the lower edge of the photograph and sight along the straight line between the two points you have just measured.

You will notice that the stars along this line form a remarkably conspicuous chain in which a few relatively bright stars are followed by groups of three or four fainter ones, all of approximately the same brightness and at about equal distances from one another.

Next, shift your attention about ⅞ of an inch to the left and you will find another string of stars roughly parallel to the first, but less conspicuous. Then, about ½ inch to the right of the first line, there is still another string of stars parallel to these, but consisting mostly of very faint objects. . . .

Our attention was directed to these star chains by a reader of this magazine, Sidney O. Kastner, of the physics department of Syracuse University. As he states, "It is obvious that this lining-up could not have occurred by chance alone." He believes that these star chains might indicate that stars condense out of gaseous filaments in the spiral arms of the Milky Way.

The problem of star chains is not a new one. . . . In a recent study by J. Meurer at the Bonn Observatory, an effort was made to determine from a statistical point of view whether the tendency of an observer to recognize a chain of stars can be explained in terms of purely accidental groupings. . . .

Meurer concluded that in the Milky Way, on the whole, the stellar distribution does not noticeably differ from a random distribution . . . But it is still entirely possible that relatively *young* stars might have originated in filamentary nebulae and might for a comparatively short time retain the aspect of star chains.

On the theoretical side, K. E. Edgeworth, in 1946, published a series of papers in the *Monthly Notices* of the Royal Astronomical Society. He attempted to outline what might happen to a gaseous galaxy, consisting almost entirely of hydrogen, beginning with a density of approximately 10^{-24} gram per cubic centimeter. If this gaseous galaxy were rotating around its center in the manner in which the Milky Way is now rotating, its shape would be a thin disk with a thickness of approximately

FIG. 139. This region of the Milky Way includes the North America nebula, in the lower left, and parts of the constellations of Cygnus and Cepheus. Note the parallel lines of stars which are discussed in the accompanying article. (Yerkes Observatory photograph)

one eighth its diameter. If the internal mass distribution were similar to that of the Milky Way, a tube with 1 square centimeter cross-section between the top and bottom surfaces of the disk would contain about 1/20 of a gram of material, at a distance of 10,000 parsecs from the center. This is the actual situation at the sun's distance from the galactic center today; in other words, if all the material in the Milky Way were flattened out on the galactic plane, in our vicinity it would weigh about as much per unit area as a piece of cardboard, despite the fact that the total mass of the galaxy is more than 10^{11} solar masses!

With the lapse of time, the rotating nebula would contract at right angles to the plane of the disk [and become thinner, although its rotation kept it spread out to the same disk radius]. . . . Edgeworth presented the idea that a rotating disk of gas, when it had become unstable as a result of the inequalities in density bound to form in a thin sheet, would break up into a "number of long parallel filaments." . . . He concluded that condensations in a primordial galaxy do not shrink to individual stars, but that the gas and dust break up into filaments and fragments of filaments, from which stars are formed. Double and multiple stars might also be expected, but the main structure of a filament would disintegrate during two or three revolutions of the galaxy.

Apparently, the work of Edgeworth went unnoticed by most astronomers until . . . V. G. Fessenkov attempted to show that various filamentary nebulosities in the Milky Way are associated with star chains. At the high-altitude observatory in Alma Ata, in central Asia, he used a meniscus-type reflector . . . with equivalent focal length of 120 centimeters and effective focal ratio of 2.4. Plates of 10 by 10 centimeters cover approximately 25 square degrees. . . .

With the help of red-sensitive plates, some of which were said to be Eastman 103-E emulsion, Fessenkov and his associate, D. A. Rojkovsky, have obtained a large number of photographs of different regions of the sky. They have devoted most of their attention to the Network or Veil nebula in Cygnus, NGC 6960, 6992, and 6995, shown in Figure 140. One region in which they have found groupings of stars that they regard as typical star chains is shown in Figure 141. This is a photograph by N. U. Mayall taken with the 36-inch Crossley reflector at the Lick Observatory. . . . Careful examination of this and other photographs of the same region shows beyond doubt that many of Fessenkov's star chains, indicated by arrows on Figure 141, cannot be seen.

There are, however, a few cases in which the chains of starlike objects indicated by Fessenkov appear to be in the nature of gaseous condensations within the filaments. . . . On the whole, the evidence does not

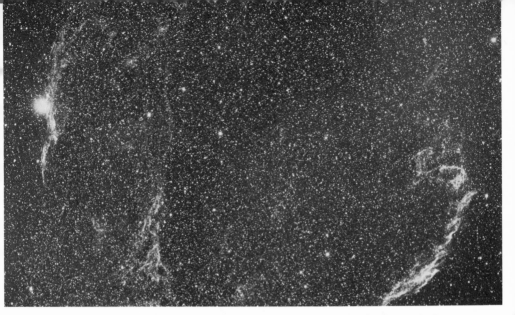

FIG. 140. The Veil nebula in Cygnus, photographed with the 24-33-inch Schmidt telescope of Harvard College Observatory. South is at the top. The nebulosity attached to the very bright star at the left is NGC 6960; the bright, elongated nebula in the lower right corner is NGC 6992, and the smaller detached mass just above it is NGC 6995.

FIG. 141. This negative of a photograph by N. U. Mayall, taken with the 36-inch Crossley reflector at the Lick Observatory, is of a region on the lower left of Figure 140. Arrows mark the locations of Fessenkov's star chains, which do not appear on this photograph.

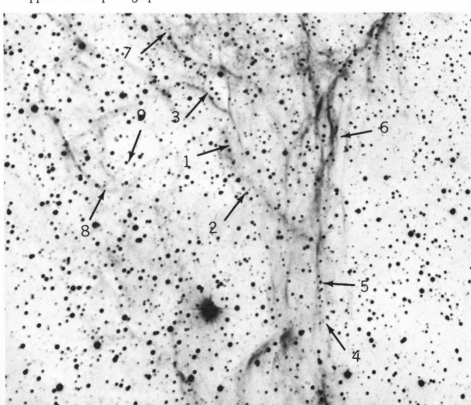

support the hypothesis that stars are being formed within *these* filaments of the nebulosity.

Fessenkov and Rojkovsky have also developed a theoretical basis for the formation of star chains. The tides of the Milky Way set a lower limit to the density a cloud must have before it can condense into a star. This density is of the order of 10^{-22} gram per cubic centimeter. But if a star has somehow been formed out of a suitable cosmic cloud of gas and dust . . . the newly formed star sets a new and greater limit for the density of the remaining cloud before it can produce a second star. In fact, the density must be 1000 times that required for the formation of the first star, because in the hypothetical star chains of Fessenkov the linear separations between neighboring stars are of the order of 0.1 parsec. This amounts to 100,000 hydrogen atoms per cubic centimeter and seems excessive to me. My own data led me to believe that the number of hydrogen atoms within a typical filament of the Veil nebula might be of the order of 1000 per cubic centimeter. In a recent article in *The Astrophysical Journal*, J. W. Chamberlain presented several different hypotheses concerning the structure of the Veil nebula, corresponding to densities between 171 and 46,000 hydrogen atoms per cubic centimeter, and expressed preference for about 500 hydrogen atoms per cubic centimeter.

Unless the distance of the Cygnus filamentary nebula is very much greater than 1000 parsecs—the value used by Fessenkov—the lower densities estimated by Chamberlain would allow only a mass of the order of 1/100 that of the sun to be contained within the volume allotted to the formation of a single star within a chain. . . . Even allowing for the uncertainty of the distance, it does not now appear probable that we can adjust the criterion of tidal instability to give the correct value of star mass from a reasonable value of the nebular density.

The conclusion of all of this is not too comforting. We are tempted to accept as real some such star chains as the one north of the North America nebula and perhaps one or two among those announced by Fessenkov. Few astronomers will deny that there are real chainlike groups of stars. . . . On the theoretical side the ideas of Edgeworth and some of the ideas of Fessenkov are undoubtedly sound, but the details of both the observational data and the theoretical interpretation remain indistinct. . . .

···

The Milky Way

PERCY W. WITHERELL

(*Sky and Telescope*, July 1942)

Only those who have been privileged to observe the Milky Way on a midsummer, moonless night from a free-from-light and clear-of-haze location in the country have any conception of its beauty.

In July, during the early evening in northern latitudes, may be seen one of the most beautiful portions of the Milky Way, extending from Cassiopeia (the W) in the northeastern sky, through Cepheus and Cygnus (the Northern Cross) in the zenith. Here it divides into two parts and continues through Aquila and Scutum to Sagittarius in the west.

Later in the night or the season, the regions in Perseus, Auriga, and Taurus may be seen. In the southern hemisphere of the sky are star-packed areas in Centaurus and Crux (the Southern Cross), extending through Carina, the brightest portion of the southern heavens. There, close to the Cross, is the peculiar Coalsack, which is darker and with fewer visible stars than the great dark rift in Cygnus and Aquila. However, to see all these southern sights to best advantage (at least 20° above the horizon), the observer must be as far south as the earth's equator.

As the use of any optical aid brings into view the fainter and more distant stars, the ratio of those seen in the Milky Way to those in a direction perpendicular to it increases from three to one with binoculars to more than ten to one with a 15-inch telescope.

The cooperative studies of the Milky Way carried on at many observatories have increased manyfold our knowledge of the structure and dynamics of the galaxy since the first really comprehensive observations made by Sir William Herschel. The Milky Way Galaxy is now believed to be an ill-defined circular disk about 100,000 light years in diameter, with a globular nucleus in its center. This is in the direction of Sagittarius, where the greatest width and brightness of the Milky Way is seen. The sun is located about 30,000 light years from this center, and about 50 light years above (north of) the central plane of the system.

The entire galaxy is rotating about the center, its outer portions revolving in longer periods, after the manner of the more distant planets around the sun. At the sun's distance from the center, the *cosmic year* is equal to about 200 million of our ordinary solar years. The sun's speed around the galactic center is about 150 miles per second.

It has been suggested that our galaxy resembles the somewhat smaller Andromeda nebula or possibly the spiral nebula Messier 33. The sun may be in one of the thinner spiral arms, and there is some evidence that it may be in one of the dark pockets.

There are several billions of stars in our galaxy, with more than 400 faint galactic clusters lying along its edge within a few degrees of the galactic plane, and 100 very distant globular clusters, over one third of which are in Sagittarius in an area that occupies only 2 per cent of the entire sky as seen from the earth.

The Pleiades, the Hyades, Praesepe (the Beehive), and the Double Cluster in Perseus are examples of easily seen galactic clusters. In most of these, the members are observed to be moving as a group in the same direction. The Hercules cluster (M13) is a globular cluster, as are also 47 Tucanae [Fig. 134] and Omega Centauri, of the southern sky. The typical galactic cluster has from 20 to 1000 stars; the globular clusters average 100,000 members.

FIG. 142. Our galaxy's nearest neighbor is the Great Spiral in the constellation Andromeda. The naked eye sees it as an elongated patch of light near the Great Square of Pegasus. (Harvard College Observatory photograph)

There are numerous faint gaseous nebulae along the galactic plane. The bright gaseous nebulae are illuminated and excited to shine by adjacent hot stars; they are very beautiful objects—the Orion nebula, the Trifid, and the Eta Carinae nebula are well-known examples. There are also many "dark" nebulae, such as the Horsehead, the Coalsack, the "Gulf of Mexico" in the North America nebula, which are masses of dust and gas that are not illuminated. These dark masses obscure many distant stars which undoubtedly are located behind them.

Hydrogen, sodium, calcium, and other elements, and cosmic dust are shown by the spectroscope to exist between the stars, and they complicate the study of the system at the same time that they contribute a powerful means of measuring large distances. Interstellar gases and dust in the galactic plane cut off our view of many extragalactic nebulae, which we may consider distant cousins, and of whom we hope to learn more in coming years. These other galaxies bear great resemblance to our own.

....

The Meaning of
Stellar Evolution

OTTO STRUVE

(*Sky and Telescope*, June 1951)

Twenty years ago it was fashionable for astronomers to engage in one of the spirited discussions that enlivened scientific meetings concerning the ages of the sun, the stars, and the galaxy. There was the "old guard," trained upon the classical concepts of celestial mechanics of the solar system, with its "invariable plane" and highly stable planetary orbits, who favored a very long time-scale, of the order of hundreds or even thousands of billions of years. And there were the "young Turks," impressed by such recent discoveries as the rotation of the galaxy, with its disrupting effect upon loosely bound, open galactic clusters, who insisted that the entire age of the galaxy could not be more than about three billion years.

Subsequent advances have favored the shorter time-scale. Not only would the open clusters be disrupted, and their members spread along the Milky Way in the longer time interval, but the geological determinations of the ages of terrestrial rocks and of meteorites, the processes of energy production in stars, and the phenomenon of the recession of the galaxies, all agree in their evidence—something very drastic must have happened in the universe about three billion years ago.[1]

We do not attempt to define exactly what we mean by the "age of the galaxy" or by the "astronomical time-scale." Those primarily interested in the dynamical effects are thinking of a time interval during which stellar motions would be greatly altered by the gravitational action of other stars, with an appreciable tendency of the members of an open star cluster to diffuse among the star clouds and spiral arms of the Milky Way. A theoretical astrophysicist would think of the time required to convert into helium a large fraction of the available hydrogen content of a star's interior. And a geologist would be content if he could specify how long basic rock has existed as a separate piece of solid material, without worrying much about what went before.

Thus, when we now say that the age of our galaxy is about three billion years, we mean that three billion years ago the galaxy was, as a whole, not very different from what it is now, but that its individual building blocks, the stars, planets, clusters, nebulae, and so on, have undergone large evolutionary changes since that time. We do not know enough even to speculate constructively about what the universe was like 100 or 1000 billion years ago. For all we know, it may have assumed its present aspect as the result of some tremendous catastrophe. Or it may have evolved gradually from some other condition, the nature of which is shrouded in darkness, and which probably will remain unknown to us for a long time to come.

Thus, our present aim is not to discuss the entire age of the galaxy, but only that part of its life during which the sun and the rest of the stars have undergone appreciable changes in their physical properties, primarily in their luminosities, masses, and radii. Three billion years is a long interval when we realize that very accurate astronomical observations have been conducted only in the past century or two, and that the rise of astrophysics took place very largely during the last thirty years. We can hardly expect that within this minute fraction of the entire lifetime of a star we would be able to detect any real changes of an evolutionary character.

But perhaps the nova outbursts and some of the strange phenomena among the variable stars are in reality evolutionary steps—something like the shedding of the skin of a rattlesnake, which can happen a limited number of times during the life of the snake, each time leaving it older, and perhaps equipped with an extra rattle! All we can say at present is that

---

[1] By 1966, fifteen years after Struve wrote this, the age is considered to be five to ten billion years.—TLP

these observed phenomena in novae and variable stars do not appreciably change the permanent mass, luminosity, and radius of such a star.

Presumably, then, it is futile to search for evolutionary changes among individual stars. All we can hope for is to try to infer what the unobserved evolutionary processes must have been during the past three billion years in order to have produced a universe having certain definite physical properties at the present time. Naturally, this is a difficult task. Suppose we observe 1000 stars in the vicinity of the sun, in order to make certain that we have chosen a fair sample. We find that there are many small stars, the dwarfs; quite a number of very small stars, the white dwarfs; and a few very large stars, the giants and supergiants. Does that necessarily mean that the giants contract until they become dwarfs, and the latter finally end up as white dwarfs? Not at all! It is quite possible that at the beginning of our era, three billion years ago, there were already substantially the same numbers of giants, dwarfs, and white dwarfs as now. The present distribution of the observed properties, or parameters, depends upon their original distribution as well as upon their subsequent evolution. . . .

In order to clarify our ideas, let us discuss an "earthy" analogy to the astronomical problem. Suppose that an imaginary scientist on Venus succeeded in observing the earth through a small hole in the thick layer of clouds which envelops his planet almost continuously, and that with a super-telescope he recorded during an interval of half a minute of our time a large number of strange living creatures running hither and thither on two legs and all obviously belonging to the same species. If our observer were inclined to study the evolution of these beings, he would quickly realize that their lifetimes greatly exceed the thirty seconds during which his observations were made. He might reason that though some of the "humans" do change in thirty seconds, in their relative positions, for example, these changes are not of evolutionary significance. He must rely upon a study of the statistical distribution of significant properties, or parameters, to infer what the evolution has been.

He might, perhaps, decide to measure the masses, the sizes, and the energies, mental or physical, of a sample of the human population. In doing so, he would discover that there is a large range of possible values in each of these parameters: from about five to 500 pounds in mass, from a foot or so in height to eight feet, and from a small fraction of a kilowatt to an amount of energy not much less than that of a small horse. He would also detect that not all combinations of these values are actually realized; a small human never has a large mass, nor does he have much strength. But a large specimen, though usually of considerable mass, may or may not have much energy (especially mental!).

Perhaps the astronomer on Venus would attempt to construct two diagrams. In one he might plot each individual as a dot, with its mass as the abscissa and energy as the ordinate. This would give a multitude of dots, scattering slightly on both sides of a curved line, with a trend such that larger masses would usually correspond to larger energies. The line would not be exactly straight; with the ordinate representing physical energy, the curve would even show a tendency to bend over at the upper end, because very heavy persons are notably sluggish in a physical sense. This diagram would be a "mass-energy relation," corresponding to the mass-luminosity relation of the stars. The analogy is a fairly good one. Most of the humans measured by the observer on Venus would conform to the relation, but some "peculiar" individuals, though massive, would have little energy, and would form a distinct sequence, like the white dwarfs in astronomy.

Another diagram could be constructed by plotting the sizes of the human individuals against their energies. Again there would be a main sequence along which most of the points would be located. But if the observations included the Pygmies of central Africa, there might well be a separate branch. This diagram would be analogous to the Hertzsprung-Russell diagram of astronomy, or more appropriately, to the stellar luminosity-radius diagram.

In attempting to interpret his diagrams, the astronomer on Venus would probably notice that the dots are distributed with varying frequency along his principal sequences. He would find there are a great many massive, large, and powerful individuals, and only relatively few, within a specified range, of small masses. He would not be certain how this peculiar distribution has come about, but he might venture a guess. Perhaps the human beings evolve along the main sequence, growing in size, mass, and strength, until they reach maturity. The evolutionary processes then become slower, and there is an accumulation of individuals having approximately the same parameters. . . .

The Venus observer would be puzzled by the fact that there are not more fully grown people on earth. Possibly, his theoretical colleagues had propounded a theory of the growth of living tissue through accretion by the intake of food and its subsequent chemical assimilation. The observations might have even shown a few instances of the process of accretion in action—through the feeding of a person—and while the interpretation would be difficult and would leave the observer only partly satisfied, he might be willing to try it as a working hypothesis. In astronomy the analogy would be the accretion of interstellar material, or the reverse process, the loss of a star's substance through eruptions, rotational instability and, on a very small scale, through the radiation of light and heat.

At any rate, the observer might conclude from his working hypothesis that humans grow rapidly. He would favor a short time-scale, and if the constants of the feeding process determined by his friend the theoretician were correct, he would conclude that it takes only some fifteen or twenty years to produce a mature man. But undoubtedly he would know that the human race must have existed much longer. A Charles Darwin on Venus would have told him that millions of years were required to produce, by natural selection, so strange an organism as man on earth. There were perhaps 10^8 small, growing creatures in the observed sample. Every twenty years or so they turn into mature men. This process has been going on for perhaps 10^7 years. Hence, there should now be on earth between 10^{13} and 10^{14} mature persons instead of the actual number, a billion or two. The diagrams give no indication of any other form into which mature men may turn—unless the observer is misled, and concludes that men ultimately become insects, of which there are plenty, or elephants, of which there are not enough.

But let us suppose that through luck, or sharp reasoning, he has avoided these pitfalls. What would he then think? Mature men continue to accumulate. They are not there in sufficient numbers. Somehow, they must disappear, disappear completely from the diagram; they must undergo some sort of a sudden process—death! Thus, even without necessarily observing death or noticing its significance, the observer on Venus might nevertheless conclude that there is a sudden termination to the life spans of the creatures on earth.

It would be possible to carry our analogy still further and find interesting parallels between what the astronomer really does when he tries to study the evolution of a star and what a distant observer might do if he could see us for a fraction of one minute.

The principal sources of our information are the H-R diagram [see Fig. 59] and the mass-luminosity diagram [discussed on p. 136]. They give us the principal sequences, with the main sequence, or dwarfs, running diagonally across both drawings. Until we knew something about the possible processes of evolution, we could only guess about the manner in which the representative point of a star might move in each diagram during three billion years.

We now know several possible evolutionary processes: nuclear transformation of the elements, loss of mass through prominence formation or through excessive rotation, gain of mass by the picking up of interstellar dust and gas. But we do not know which is the most important, or even whether they are the only processes that operate in the galaxy. We could, however, try each in succession and see what would happen to a star in three billion years. Taking the two diagrams as they are at the present time, we could then infer what they would be like that far in the future. Since, presumably, the changes in the past would be similar to those in the future, we could next modify the present diagrams by applying the computed changes with the opposite signs. This would give us an admittedly crude idea of what the galaxy was like three billion years ago. We would then ask, Is this distribution reasonable? Could we intelligently believe that the stars in the beginning of our era were distributed with regard to mass, size, and luminosity as shown by our hypothetical diagrams computed for three billion years ago?

The multiplicity of possible evolutionary processes makes it unprofitable to discuss this question seriously at the present time. There are leads, but nothing even approaching a final answer. For example, the nuclear mechanism that goes under the name of the carbon cycle has the remarkable property that, while the radius and luminosity of a star would change greatly in three billion years, its mass would change less than 1 per cent. Yet the observed stellar masses range from small values, probably less than one tenth the mass of the sun, to about fifty times the mass of the sun. Hence, if the carbon cycle alone were at work, we would conclude that the stars were "born" essentially with their present masses, and that the main sequence of the H-R diagram, as well as of the mass-luminosity diagram, does not constitute an evolutionary arrangement of young stars at one end and old stars at the other.

On the other hand, we might ask, Where on these diagrams are those luminous stars that spend their energies at a prodigious rate and convert all of their hydrogen into helium in much less than three billion years? Their masses remain nearly constant, but their luminosities increase with time; for any given mass there should be stars of vastly different luminosities.

But wait a minute! We just assumed that stars are born even now, just as children are born, so that we now observe young stars having lots of hydrogen and little helium, and old stars having little hydrogen and a great deal of helium. Can we justify this assumption? Perhaps we can, for the hottest supergiant stars, such as Rigel, exhaust their hydrogen so rapidly that we would not see them at all unless they were "born" only a short 10^7 years ago.

We come back to our question, Where in the diagrams are those older stars that 10^7 or 10^8 or 10^9 years ago were similar to Rigel now? We do not know. Perhaps they are still near the main sequence, producing a scatter of values at the upper ends of both diagrams. Such a scatter is not at present indicated, but our observations of the parameters of the most luminous stars may be inadequate.

It is also possible that processes other than nuclear ones play an important role. Hoyle and Lyttleton have developed the hypothesis of mass *accretion* through the capture of interstellar material. Undoubtedly, this process does exist. But heretofore most astronomers were inclined to believe that the present density of the cosmic clouds of dust and gas is insufficient to produce large increases in mass. Others, notably Fessenkov and Miss Massevich in Russia, and the present writer in this country, have explored the consequences of corpuscular radiations from the sun and stars, or loss of mass through the formation of gaseous rings in rapidly rotating objects. But still others have pointed out that there is no certainty that normal stars (that is, stars that are not novae or supernovae) lose much matter in these processes.

We must admit that there is no fully satisfactory theory of stellar evolution, and presumably many years will elapse before we have one. In the meantime we must go along the road of "multiple hypotheses," exploring each in detail, accumulating experience, as well as many interesting ideas and their consequences. After all, every advance in science merely pushes the boundaries of knowledge a little farther, and every question that is answered raises a new question awaiting an answer.

• • •

Starlight has a great deal to tell us. The most obvious thing is the direction toward each star. Small changes in these directions, or positions of stars on a map of the sky, can be used to determine distances (by parallax) and part of the motions of stars. The other part, the radial velocity, or speed of approach or recession, is told by the Doppler shift in the spectrum. Spectra also show what the stars are made of, and how hot they are—3000° to 50,000° or more—some with glowing gas clouds around them.

The orbital motion of double stars—changing direction or changing radial velocity—measures their masses and shows that some are fifty times as massive as the sun, some only one or two per cent of the sun's mass. Apparent brightness, together with distance, shows that some are 10,000 times more luminous than the sun, and some 1/10,000 as luminous. A few vary in luminosity, some of them periodically.

The order in this wide variety shows up on the Hertzsprung-Russell diagram and in the mass-luminosity relation. That is, most of the massive stars are blue-hot and highly luminous; most low-luminosity stars have small mass and low temperature. The characteristics of most of the stars lie between these two extremes along the main sequence on the H-R diagram.

Other stellar statistics collected during the past fifty or sixty years show the value of observing many different stars and looking for correlations between their separate "stories." Differences between H-R diagrams for different clusters of stars, for instance, led to the present theory of star formation and stellar evolution. When the periods and luminosities were measured for many periodic variable stars, the period-luminosity relation was recognized. These Cepheid variables were used to measure larger and larger distances, mapping out the distribution of stars in all directions from the sun. Combined with Doppler shifts measured from the spectra of many stars, these led to our present picture of the Milky Way Galaxy—hundreds of billions of stars spread out in a wheel-like disk with spiral "spokes." Statistical studies of colors and brightnesses of stars revealed the interstellar cosmic dust that reddens and dims stars far from the sun in the plane of the Milky Way.

Of course, the light from an individual star can provide important information—and has started statistical studies in many cases, as shown in Chapters 5, 6, and 7. The white dwarfs, novae, supernovae, flare stars, magnetic stars, radio sources, spectroscopic binaries, and stars of variable proper motion are classes or categories recognized from the initial study of one or two peculiar objects.

The guiding principle in astronomy, or any other science, is to fit together all these categories of observations in a consistent pattern or theory. Over the past thirty years covered by articles in this volume, the theory of stellar evolution has developed to link most of the characteristics of stars, their chemical compositions, ages, locations in the galaxy, and their relation to interstellar clouds of dust and gas. There are many gaps, of course —in the full explanation of magnetic stars, novae, and irregular variables. A large part of the theory is based upon laboratory physics: experiments that show how gases behave at high temperatures, how atoms and ions absorb and emit light, how nuclear reactions go, and the behavior of ionized gases in magnetic fields.

In the same way, larger scale astronomical studies are based on our understanding of the nearby objects; studies of stellar structure are based on our understanding of the sun, for instance. Studies of the Milky Way Galaxy, covered in a later volume of this series, are based on our knowledge of the stars summarized here. — T L P

Appendix I
The Origin of
Sky and Telescope

In March 1931 publication of a small quarterly magazine, *The Telescope*, began at Perkins Observatory of Ohio Wesleyan University in Delaware, Ohio, with the director of the observatory, Harlan T. Stetson, as editor. By July 1933 the magazine had become a larger, bimonthly periodical. After Stetson moved to the Massachusetts Institute of Technology, the Bond Astronomical Club, a society of Cambridge amateur astronomers, and Harvard College Observatory assumed sponsorship of the magazine. Loring B. Andrews became editor, and in 1937 Donald H. Menzel succeeded him. *The Telescope* carried stories of important astronomical discoveries, reviews of current astronomical work, and articles on the history of the science.

In the meantime, the first issue of the small *Monthly Bulletin of the Hayden Planetarium* (New York City) appeared, in November 1935, edited by Hans Christian Adamson. In addition to a review of the current show at the planetarium, it contained other astronomical notes and articles. The interest and encouragement of its readers led, in October 1936, to the enlargement of its size and scope. Its name was changed to *The Sky*, and while retaining its planetarium ties, it became the official organ of the Amateur Astronomers' Association in New York City, replacing the magazine *Amateur Astronomer*, which had been published from April 1929 to the spring of 1936.

The Sky grew in reputation and circulation. In February 1938 Clyde Fisher, curator-in-chief of the planetarium, became editor. On November 1, 1939, the Sky Publishing Corporation was formed, owned by Charles A. Federer, Jr., who for four years had been a planetarium lecturer. He and his wife, Helen Spence Federer, edited and published *The Sky* through its fifth volume.

Then, encouraged by Harlow Shapley, director of the Harvard College Observatory, Sky Publishing Corporation moved to Cambridge, Massachusetts, and combined *The Telescope* and *The Sky*, into *Sky and Telescope*, born with the November 1941 issue. The ties with Harvard have been strong. Until the middle 1950s the magazine's offices were in the observatory—now they are located less than a mile away.

The present editorial staff includes Mr. Federer as editor-in-chief, Joseph Ashbrook as editor, and William Shawcross as managing editor. Observer's material is handled by Leif J. Robinson, books and art by Mollie Boring. Unsigned material in the magazine is prepared by this group.

During its twenty-five years, *Sky and Telescope* has been a distinguished and increasingly well-received publication, with two overlapping purposes. It has served as a forum where amateur astronomers can exchange views and experiences, and where they are furnished with observing data. It has brought to an ever-widening circle of scientists and educated laymen detailed and reliable information on new astronomical developments, and through its pages, has introduced them to the important figures of modern astronomy.

....

Appendix II
Astronomy through the
Ages: A Brief Chronology

ca. 3000 B.C.:	Earliest recorded Babylonian observations of eclipses, planets, and stars.
ca. 2500 B.C.:	Egyptian pyramids constructed, oriented north-south by the stars.
ca. 2000 B.C.:	Babylonian story of creation: *Enuma Elish.*
	Stonehenge built in southern England with stones lined up by the stars.
ca. 1000 B.C.:	Beginnings of Chinese and Hindu astronomical observations.
700–400 B.C.:	Greek story of creation: Hesiod's *Theogony.*
	Hebrew story of creation: *Genesis.*
	Greek philosophers Thales, Pythagoras, and Meton note regularity of celestial motions.
400–300 B.C.:	Greek philosophers Plato, Eudoxus, and Calippus develop the concept of celestial motions on spheres.
	Aristotle develops the idea of four elements and the concept that heavy things fall, light ones rise.
300–100 B.C.:	Aristarchus proposes that the earth moves.
	Eratosthenes measures the size of the earth.
	Hipparchus makes accurate observations of star positions.

ca. A.D. 150:   Ptolemy's *Almagest* summarizes the geocentric theory; the planets' motions are explained by epicycles and other motions in circles.

ca. 1400:   Ulugh-Beg, in Samarkand, reobserves star positions.

1530:   Copernicus, in Poland, postulates that the earth and planets move around the sun because this involves fewer circular motions. This revolutionary idea later rouses strong opposition.

ca. 1600:   Tycho Brahe measures the motions of the planets accurately; Kepler uses these measurements to show that the orbits of planets are ellipses rather than combinations of circles.

Galileo uses the first telescope to observe the moons of Jupiter and the crescent shape of Venus, supplying strong support for the Copernican idea. Galileo also establishes that falling weights would all be accelerated in the same way if there were no air to hold the lighter ones back.

1680:   Newton combines Kepler's and Galileo's findings, together with observations of moon and comets, into the fundamental laws of mechanics and gravitation. He also studies light, its colors, and spectrum. By this time, accurate pendulum clocks are in use.

1690:   Halley notes the periodic reports of a large comet every seventy years and concludes they refer to one object moving in a long, thin ellipse around the sun.

1755:   Kant postulates that the sun and planets were formed by the coagulation of a cloud of gas like the spiral nebulae.

1780:   William Herschel builds large telescopes, discovers the planet Uranus, and explains the Milky Way as a flat disk of stars around the sun.

1700–1800:   Mathematical astronomy flourishes, involving many Europeans—Cassini, Bradley, d'Alembert, Laplace, Lagrange, and others—who apply Newton's mechanics to celestial motions with remarkable precision.

1840:   The first astronomical photograph (of the moon) obtained by J. W. Draper. By 1905 photography is well established for accurate observations with telescopes ranging up to 40 inches in aperture, photographing stars 100,000 times fainter than those visible to the naked eye.

1800–1900:   Navigation has become a precise and important practical application of astronomy. The accurate observations of star positions show that annual parallax is due to the earth's orbital motion around the sun, confirming the Copernican idea and providing a method of measuring distances to the stars. Other small motions show that the stars are moving.

1850–1900: The laboratory study of light together with physical theory shows that spectrum analysis can be used to determine temperature and chemical composition of a light source.

1843: Doppler explains the effect of motion on the spectrum of a light source.

1877: Schiaparelli observes "canals" on Mars.

1900: Chamberlin and Moulton speculate that the planets were formed after another star passed close to the sun.

1904–20: Einstein establishes the theory of relativity.

Large reflecting telescopes are built at the Mount Wilson Observatory in California.

1910–30: Russell and Eddington establish the theory of stellar structure.

1917–30: Shapley and Oort establish the size, shape, and rotation of the Milky Way Galaxy.

1930: Discovery of Pluto.

1910–40: Slipher and Hubble find that other galaxies are moving away from ours. De Sitter, Eddington, Lemaitre, and others explain this recession by application of relativity theory.

1930–60: Bethe, Gamow, and others in the U.S. apply the results of nuclear physics to explaining the source of stellar energy. This is followed by the work of many astrophysicists on evolution of the stars from large interstellar gas clouds.

Von Weizsäcker, Kuiper, Urey, and others develop a theory of the origin of the solar system from a large gas cloud.

1947–60: Instruments are shot above the atmosphere in the U.S. for astronomical observations.

Large radiotelescopes are built in the U.S., Australia, and England.

1957: Sputnik I, the first artificial satellite of the earth, is launched by Soviet scientists.

1959: First space probe to hit the moon is launched by Soviet scientists.

1961: First manned space flight around the earth by Soviet astronaut Yuri Gagarin.

1963–64: Radiotelescopes locate quasi-stellar sources ("quasars"), found to have large optical red shifts.

1964–65: First close-up photographs of the lunar surface obtained by U.S. space probes Ranger 7 and Ranger 8.

1965: Photographs of Mars, taken at about 11,000 miles distance by Mariner 4, show a cratered surface.

1966: First soft landing on the moon (by the Russian Luna 9). Photographs of the surface taken from a few feet show no loose dust.

···

Appendix III
Notes on the Contributors

AITKEN, ROBERT G. (1864–1951), astronomer at the Lick Observatory from 1895 to 1935 and its director from 1930 to 1935; awarded the Gold Medal of the Royal Astronomical Society in 1932 for his discovery of over 3000 double stars. ("Sirius and Its Companion")

BOK, BART J. (1906–), Dutch-born astronomer; director of Steward Observatory, University of Arizona; from 1957 to 1966, director of the Mount Stromlo Observatory, Canberra, Australia; on the faculty of Harvard University from 1930 to 1957; author of *The Astronomer's Universe* and *The Distribution of the Stars in Space*, coauthor of *The Milky Way*. ("Counting the Stars," "Dynamics and Evolution of Star Clusters")

BOYCE, PETER B. (1936–), resident astronomer at Lowell Observatory, Flagstaff, Arizona, specializing in interferometric spectroscopy. ("Infrared Spectroscopy with an Interferometer," with William M. Sinton)

BOYKO, ANATOLE (1905–), Russian-born American; a photographic darkroom worker with wide interests in astronomy. ("Inside a Globular Star Cluster")

BROWN, R. HANBURY (1916–), British radioastronomer; now professor of physics at the University of Sydney, Australia; formerly a radar expert at the Naval Research Laboratory in Washington; from 1949 to 1964 at Manchester University in England, working with the radiotelescope at Jodrell Bank; after 1960 professor of radioastronomy; coauthor of

The Exploration of Space by Radio. ("The Stellar Interferometer at Narrabri Observatory")

CANNON, ANNIE J. (1863–1941), astronomer at the Harvard College Observatory who compiled the *Henry Draper Catalogue* of stellar spectra; see "Miss Cannon and Stellar Spectroscopy" on page 117 of this volume. ("William Henry Pickering," "The Story of Starlight")

CHOU, KYONG CHOL (1929–), Korean-born astronomer at the U.S. Naval Observatory since 1962; member of the faculty of the University of Maryland since 1964; captain in the South Korean army, 1950–53. ("Algol—Still a Demon Star!")

COLES, ROBERT R. (1907–), lecturer and curator at the Hayden Planetarium in New York City from 1939 to 1951 and its chairman from 1951 to 1953. ("Atoms, Stars, and Cosmic Bombs")

FEDERER, C. A., JR. (1909–), editor-in-chief of *Sky and Telescope*; as a staff assistant at the Hayden Planetarium he lectured on its opening day in 1935; in 1939 he became editor and publisher of *The Sky*, which later moved from New York City to Harvard College Observatory and merged with *The Telescope*. ("Little Stars and Big Ones")

GAPOSCHKIN, CECILIA PAYNE, see PAYNE-GAPOSCHKIN, CECILIA H.

GAPOSCHKIN, SERGEI (1898–), Russian-born American astronomer at Harvard College Observatory since 1933; his greatest contributions have been in the study of variable and double stars, clusters, and stellar photometry. ("How Heavy Are the Stars?")

GINGERICH, OWEN (1930–), lecturer at Harvard University and astrophysicist working on the theory of stellar atmospheres at the Smithsonian Astrophysical Observatory; former director of the observatory at American University of Beirut. ("Laboratory Exercises in Astronomy— Spectral Classification")

GOLDBERG, LEO (1913–), director of the Harvard College Observatory; formerly professor and chairman of the astronomy department at the University of Michigan; expert on solar physics, spectroscopy, and atmospheric physics; editor of *Annual Review of Astronomy and Astrophysics*, coauthor of *Atoms, Stars and Nebulae*. ("The Atom in Astronomy")

HALE, GEORGE E. (1868–1938), founder (1897) of the Yerkes Observatory of the University of Chicago, equipped with the world's largest refracting telescope; founder of the Mount Wilson Observatory near Pasadena, California, equipped with 60-inch and 100-inch reflectors; he chose the site on Mount Palomar, about ninety-five miles southeast of Mount Wilson, for the 200-inch Hale telescope; author of *Beyond the Milky Way, The Depths of the Universe, The New Heavens, Signals From the Stars, The Study of Stellar Evolution.* ("The Magnetism of the Sun")

HIGGINS, C. S. (1915–), senior technical officer at the Commonwealth Scientific and Industrial Research Organisation (CSIRO) Sydney, Australia; a specialist in radioastronomy. ("Visual and Radio Observations of Flare Stars," with O. B. Slee and G. E. Patston)

HOAG, ARTHUR A. (1921–), formerly astronomer at the U.S. Naval Observatory; now at the Kitt Peak National Observatory in Arizona. ("Experiences with Cooled Color Emulsions")

IRIARTE, BRAULIO (1920–), research fellow of the National University of Mexico; a specialist in galactic structure. ("Five-color Photometry of Bright Stars," with Harold L. Johnson, Richard I. Mitchell, and Wieslaw Z. Wisniewski)

JOHNSON, HAROLD L. (1921–), astronomer at the Lunar and Planetary Laboratory of the University of Arizona; formerly at Lick Observatory, Lowell Observatory, Washburn Observatory (University of Wisconsin), Yerkes Observatory, and University of Texas; a specialist in accurate photoelectric photometry. ("The Fifty Brightest Stars"; "Five-color Photometry of Bright Stars," with Braulio Iriarte, Richard I. Mitchell, and Wieslaw Z. Wisniewski.

KAMP, PETER VAN DE (1901–), professor of astronomy at Swarthmore College in Pennsylvania since 1940 and director of Sproul Observatory there since 1937; widely known for measurements of proper motions and parallaxes of the stars. ("Stars Nearer than Five Parsecs," "Barnard's Star as an Astrometric Binary")

KOPAL, ZDENEK (1914–), American astronomer born in Czechoslovakia; since 1951 professor and head of the department of astronomy at the University of Manchester, England; formerly at Harvard University and Massachusetts Institute of Technology; author of *Advances in Astronomy and Astrophysics, Astronomical Optics and Related Subjects, Close Binary Systems, Physics and Astronomy of the Moon.* ("A New Atlas of the Heavens")

KUIPER, GERARD P. (1905–), Dutch-born astronomer; formerly director of the Yerkes and McDonald Observatories and now head of the Lunar and Planetary Laboratory of the University of Arizona; editor of *The Atmospheres of the Earth and Planets, The Solar System,* and *Stars and Stellar Systems.* ("The Story of Beta Lyrae")

LIPPINCOTT, SARAH LEE (1920–), research associate and lecturer at the Sproul Observatory, Swarthmore College, Pennsylvania, with which she has been associated since 1951; Fulbright scholar at the Paris Observatory, 1953–54; coauthor of *Point to the Stars* and *Philadelphia, the Unexpected*. ("The Star of Smallest Known Mass")

LOVI, GEORGE (1939–), draftsman and technical illustrator; assistant editor of *Review of Popular Astronomy*; member of the American Association of Variable Star Observers and of the astronomy department of the Brooklyn (New York) Children's Museum. ("Star Charts of Former Days")

McLAUGHLIN, DEAN B. (1901–65), for more than forty years an astronomer at the University of Michigan; he was an expert on novae and variable stars and well known as a geologist who made important contributions to Martian studies; author of *Introduction to Astronomy*, coeditor of *Stellar Structure*. ("What Becomes of the Novae?")

MITCHELL, RICHARD I. (1927–), astrophysicist at the Lunar and Planetary Laboratory of the University of Arizona; formerly a mathematician at Lawrence Radiation Laboratory, University of California. ("Five-color Photometry of Bright Stars," with Braulio Iriarte, Harold L. Johnson, and Wieslaw Z. Wisniewski)

MOFFET, ALAN T. (1936–), astronomer; research fellow at California Institute of Technology; especially interested in the physical properties of extragalactic radio sources; an editor of Dover's *Classics in Science* series. ("Argelander and the BD")

MUMFORD, GEORGE S. (1928–), astronomer on the faculty of Tufts University; since January 1965 he has conducted the "News Notes" department of *Sky and Telescope*. ("Distance Modulus")

PATSTON, G. E. (1927–), senior lecturer in aeronautical engineering in the Department of Technical Education of New South Wales, Australia; interested in photographic and photoelectric studies of flare stars and T Tauri stars; past president of the Astronomical Society of New South Wales. ("Visual and Radio Observations of Flare Stars," with O. B. Slee and C. S. Higgins)

PAYNE-GAPOSCHKIN, CECILIA H. (1900–), British-born American astronomer; now Phillips Professor of Astronomy at Harvard University, where she has been since 1923; chairman of the astronomy department there from 1956 to 1960; an authority on variable stars, stellar evolution, galactic structure, and novae; author of *Introduction to Astronomy*, *Stars in the Making*. ("Miss Cannon and Stellar Spectroscopy," "A New Star Has Its Day")

PETRIE, R. M. (1906–1966), Scottish-born director of the Dominion Astrophysical Observatory in Victoria, British Columbia, where he was since 1935; planned the 150-inch telescope to be built on Mount Kobau in

Victoria; well known for his work on radial velocities, galactic structure, and double stars. ("The B Stars and Galactic Exploration")

RENSE, WILLIAM A. (1914–), professor of physics at the University of Colorado since 1949; formerly at Louisiana State University, University of Miami (Florida), and Rutgers University; best known for his work in solar spectroscopy and upper-air physics. ("Rocket Ultraviolet Solar Spectroscopy")

SCHWARZSCHILD, MARTIN (1912–), German-born astrophysicist; Higgins Professor of Astronomy at Princeton University, where he has been since 1947; an authority on variable stars, stellar interiors, and astronomical observations from the stratosphere; author of *Structure and Evolution of the Stars*. ("What Determines the Color of a Star?")

SHAPLEY, HARLOW (1885–), professor of astronomy at Harvard University from 1921 to 1956; director of the Harvard College Observatory from 1921 to 1952; famed for his work on star clusters and galaxies; author of *Galaxies, Star Clusters, Source Book in Astronomy*. ("A Master of Stellar Spectra")

SINTON, WILLIAM M. (1925–), physicist at Lowell Observatory, Flagstaff, Arizona; formerly at The Johns Hopkins University and at Harvard, he is an expert on the infrared spectra of planets; coauthor of *Tools of the Astronomer*. ("Infrared Spectroscopy with an Interferometer," with Peter B. Boyce)

SLEE, O. B. (1924–), on the staff of the Division of Radiophysics, Commonwealth Scientific and Industrial Research Organisation (CSIRO), Sydney, Australia, where he has participated in radioastronomy studies of the sun, the planet Jupiter, stars, nebulae, and galaxies. ("Visual and Radio Observations of Flare Stars," with C. S. Higgins and G. E. Patston.

SLOCUM, FREDERICK (1873–1944), professor of astronomy at Wesleyan University, Middletown, Connecticut, from 1914, and director of its Van Vleck Observatory from 1920 until his death; an expert in nautical science, stellar parallaxes, and eclipses. ("Stellar Parallax")

SLOWEY, J. W. (1932–), astronomer in the satellite-tracking program of the Smithsonian Astrophysical Observatory since 1956; an expert on artificial earth-satellite orbits and the density of the upper atmosphere. ("A Model of the Solar Neighborhood," with A. E. Whitford)

SMILEY, CHARLES H. (1903–), chairman of the department of astronomy and director of Ladd Observatory at Brown University, Providence, Rhode Island, where he has been since 1930; well known for his mathematical work on orbits and solar eclipses, his work on optics, and his historical study of Mayan astronomy. ("The Magical Schmidt")

STRUVE, OTTO (1897–1963), director of the Yerkes Observatory of the University of Chicago from 1932 to 1949; the last of a family which produced four generations of renowned astronomers; one of the leading figures in American astronomy in this century, he was widely known for his research on stellar spectra, and the author of many research papers and books, his last book being *Astronomy of the 20th Century*. ("Solar Physics News," "Stellar Rotation," "The Hottest Star," "The Origin of Planetary Nebulae," "The Crab Nebula as a Supernova Remnant," "Stars as Magnets," "The Most Massive Stars Known," "Cosmic Dust," "Glowing Hydrogen in the Milky Way," "Stellar Associations," "Star Chains," "The Meaning of Stellar Evolution")

WALKER, MERLE F. (1926–), astronomer at Lick Observatory since 1957; formerly at Mount Wilson–Palomar, Yerkes, and the Warner and Swasey (Cleveland, Ohio) Observatories; specialist in photoelectric photometry of stars and stellar spectra. ("New Observations of AE Aquarii")

WHITFORD, A. E. (1905–), director of the Lick Observatory, Mount Hamilton, California, since 1958; formerly professor of astronomy and director of Washburn Observatory at the University of Wisconsin; well known for his photoelectric photometry of stars and nebulae, studies of atomic spectra, and instrument development. ("A Model of the Solar Neighborhood," with J. W. Slowey)

WISNIEWSKI, WIESLAW Z. (1931–), astronomer at Cracow Observatory, Poland, on leave since 1963 at the Lunar and Planetary Laboratory, University of Arizona; from 1957 to 1959 a member of the Polish polar expedition to Spitsbergen; his fields of interest are celestial mechanics, auroras, and photoelectric photometry. ("Five-color Photometry of Bright Stars," with Braulio Iriarte, Harold L. Johnson, and Richard I. Mitchell)

WITHERELL, PERCY W. (1877–), graduate of Massachusetts Institute of Technology; past president of the Bond Club at Harvard College Observatory; for many years the treasurer of the American Association of Variable Star Observers (AAVSO) and now its auditor. ("The Milky Way")

Glossary

absorption lines See **spectrum.**

acceleration Speeding up or slowing down; more precisely, a change in amount or direction of velocity.

angle Angular distance measured in degrees, minutes, and seconds of arc: all the way around the sky is $360°$; $1° = 60'$ (minutes of arc), $1' = 60''$ (seconds of arc).

angstrom Unit of length used to measure wavelengths of light, abbreviated A; 1 centimeter (about 0.4 inch) is 100 million A.

astronomical unit The distance from sun to earth (about 93 million miles), abbreviated *a.u.*, and used as a unit of distance in the solar system.

astrophysics Study of physical conditions in planets, stars, nebulae, galaxies, and regions between them.

atmosphere The outer, gaseous layers of a star (or planet), through which light can pass, and where the absorption or emission lines in the spectrum are formed.

atomic energy Energy released in nuclear reactions which change the total mass of material by packing nuclear particles in a different arrangement. See pp. 36-46.

BD (followed by a number) The *Bonner Durchmusterung* catalogue number, which serves to identify a star. See pp. 7-11.

binary A double star or pair of stars close together in the sky. *Visual* binaries can be seen as two separate stellar images in a telescope. An *eclipsing* binary looks like one star but varies periodically in brightness. A *spectroscopic* binary varies periodically in radial velocity (measured by Doppler shift in its spectrum).

CD (followed by a number) The *Cordoba Catalogue* number, similar to the BD number but referring to stars in the southern sky. See p. 30.

calorie A unit of energy; the amount of heat energy necessary to warm up 1 gram of water $1°C$; equal to 4.185×10^7 ergs. (Food analysts use the word for a larger unit, 1000 of these "small calories.")

carbon cycle A series of nuclear reactions involving carbon, nitrogen, and hydrogen at very high temperature. It results in four hydrogen atoms forming one helium atom and releasing energy. See pp. 40-43.

catalogue A list of stars or other celestial objects, giving their positions on the sky and some other characteristic, such as brightness (BD and CD Catalogues), spectral type (HD Catalogue), parallax, proper motion, or color.

chromosphere A layer of the sun's atmosphere just above the visible surface, or photosphere. See p. 46.

color index Difference between photographic and visual magnitude, ranging from $-0^m.5$ for blue stars to $+1^m.5$ and more for red stars.

comet A small body moving around the sun in an orbit generally of high eccentricity. Comets generate an atmosphere (coma) and a tail as they come close to the sun but are virtually invisible while they are 10 to 50 astronomical units from the sun.

constellation A group of bright stars in one region of the sky, or the area on the sky occupied by such a group, named, in most cases, for ancient Greek mythological figures. See p. 3.

coordinate A distance or angle characterizing the position or location of an object. Coordinates x and y are generally used on a plane surface, longitude and latitude on the earth's surface, right ascension and declination on the sky. Three coordinates are needed in space.

corona A faint haze and streamers around the sun, visible only during total solar eclipse. See p. 206.

coudé focus The place where a large telescope with extra mirrors forms an image that remains fixed when the telescope is moved.

declination Angle in the sky north or south of the celestial equator; a coordinate analogous to latitude on the earth's surface. See pp. 7, 18.

diffraction The bending of light around an obstruction of any size, such as the edge of the moon or the edges of small particles.

distance modulus Difference between apparent magnitude and absolute magnitude; a measure of the ratio of luminosity to brightness, or of the distance of an object (on the assumption that space is "clean," so that brightness is proportional to $1/distance^2$.) See p. 86.

diurnal motion Daily apparent motion of celestial objects westward due to the eastward rotation of the earth.

Doppler shift A slight shift in wavelength in the spectrum of a light source moving toward or away from the observer. The shift is toward shorter wavelength (more violet color) for an approaching source and toward longer wavelength (redder color) for a receding source.

dyne A very small unit of force, about 1/1000 the weight of a gram, the force necessary to speed up 1 gram by 1 cm/sec in 1 sec.

element A chemically pure substance consisting of only one type of atom.

ellipse an oval-shaped closed curve, precisely defined by the equation in rectangular coordinates $x^2/a^2 + y^2/b^2 = 1$.

emission line A sharp excess of one color (one wavelength of light or radio waves) in a spectrum; generally characteristic of low-density gas.

emulsion The light-sensitive coating on film or glass plate which is "developed" to show a negative image of the light falling on the film or plate.

energy Capacity for doing work—that is, exerting a force through some distance. In many processes energy is changed from one form to another (radiation, heat, chemical energy, potential energy) without being created or destroyed. In nuclear reactions mass can be converted into energy.

erg A unit of energy; the work done in pushing 1 gram so that it speeds up from rest to 1.414 cm/sec.

evolution of stars The formation of stars from clouds of gas and dust by initial collapse, increase in temperature, and subsequent nuclear reactions that convert a small fraction of the original mass to energy and produce new elements in the material. See pp. 303-309.

flux The amount of energy (usually in the form of radiation: light or radio waves) passing through 1 square meter per second. Flux on a telescope mirror from one celestial object is a measure of the brightness of that object.

focal ratio The "speed" of a lens or telescope mirror, expressed (inversely) as the ratio of focal length, f, to aperture (lens size). A telescope of focal ratio $f/4$ has an aperture equal to one quarter of its focal length and can photograph a nebula or other extended object in one ninth of the exposure time required with an $f/12$ telescope.

Fraunhofer spectrum See **spectrum**.

frequency Number of periodic changes (cycles) per second. The *period* is the reciprocal of the frequency. Radio waves have frequencies of thousands of cycles per second (kilocycles per second) to many millions (megacycles per second, or *Mc/sec*) and wavelengths of c/f, where c is the velocity of light and radio waves, 3×10^{10} cm/sec, and f is the frequency.

galaxy A vast disk-shaped assemblage of stars, gas, and dust. The sun is located in the Milky Way Galaxy.

gauss A unit of magnetic-field strength; the force on a unit magnetic pole is 1 dyne where the field is 1 gauss.

granulation The grainy appearance of the sun's surface on a sharp, high-magnification photograph. See p. 70.

grating A set of parallel narrow slits which deflect light passing through them by the process of diffraction. A coarse grating used in front of a telescope lens gives several images of each bright star. A fine diffraction grating produces the spectrum of colors in light passing through it or reflected from a reflection grating.

HD (followed by a number) The *Henry Draper Catalogue* number, referring to stars with spectral type determined at the Harvard College Observatory. See p. 117.

H-R diagram A plot of brightness versus color (or temperature, or spectral type), both on a logarithmic or magnitude scale, the brightness adjusted for distance. Each star appears as a point on the H-R diagram, and many of these points (for a group of stars) fall near a diagonal line called the *main sequence.*

helium A gas formed of single atoms each about four times the mass of the hydrogen atom.

inertia The tendency of massive bodies to remain at rest or continue moving in a straight line.

infrared The "color" of invisible light with longer wavelength than red light and shorter wavelength than radio waves.

intensity Energy received per second, usually in the form of light or radio waves, but also as sound waves or such particles as cosmic rays. The intensity of an absorption line measures the gap in energy near one wavelength, or frequency, in a spectrum.

interferometer An instrument that measures the small difference in direction of light arriving from two sources by the interference of the light waves. See pp. 77-85. It can also be used to measure the wavelength of light with high precision.

ion An atom or group of atoms with one or more electrons removed (positive ion) or added (negative ion).

ionization The process of forming ions, or the number of ions in a given region (usually the number per cubic centimeter).

isotopes Two atoms of the same type (element) with masses differing by one or more neutron masses. Unstable isotopes undergo *radioactive decay.* Atoms of stable isotopes normally remain unchanged.

kinetic energy Energy of motion, $\frac{1}{2}mv^2$, equal to the work done in pushing a mass m until it moves at speed v.

light year A large unit of distance, about 10^{13} kilometers or 6×10^{12} miles. It is the distance that light travels in one year (3.17×10^7 sec) at a speed of 3×10^5 km/sec. See p. 24.

lines Gaps in the spectrum of sunlight (colors missing) are called

Fraunhofer lines; gaps in the spectra of light from other stars are called *absorption lines*. The stronger ones are known by letters, such as H and K lines; all of them can be designated by wavelength. Nebulae and some stars have *emission lines*, brighter patches in their spectra. See **spectrum**.

luminosity The inherent brightness of a star in terms of the sun's brightness, if the two were at the same distance from us. See p. 73.

Lyman alpha A line in the far-ultraviolet part of the spectrum (1215 angstroms), strongly absorbed and easily emitted by hydrogen atoms. Lyman beta, Lyman gamma, and others, as well as Lyman continuum are similar but at shorter wavelengths.

magnetic field A region near a magnet where another magnet would be acted upon by a force; also a region near moving electric charges where a magnet is affected similarly. See p. 202.

magnifying power Magnification of an image by a telescope-eyepiece combination. "Power 50X" means that an object like the moon appears 50 times larger in the eyepiece than to the unaided eye.

magnitude An indication of the brightness of a celestial object. The brightest stars are "of the first magnitude" and the faintest stars visible to the naked eye are of the sixth magnitude (6 mag.). With telescopes the scale has been extended to over 20 mag. Every 5 magnitudes corresponds to 100 times fainter. See p. 30.

main sequence See **H-R diagram**.

megacycle One million cycles, a unit of radio frequency abbreviated Mc.

minute of arc An angle equal to 1/60 of a degree; therefore an angular distance in the sky which is 1/(60)(360) of a circle; written 1'.

NGC (followed by a number) The *New General Catalogue* number, which serves to identify clusters, nebulae, and galaxies.

nebula A vast cloud of gas between the stars.

neutrino A small particle with no electric charge and almost zero mass, produced in some of the nuclear reactions inside stars. See p. 42.

neutron A neutral particle with approximately the same mass as a proton; a component of atomic nuclei.

nova A star that suddenly increases its light output 10,000 times or more and then fades slowly. See p. 182.

nuclear processes Interactions between the nuclei of atoms that generally release vast quantities of energy as one kind of atom is changed into another.

parallax The very small change in direction of a star caused by the motion of the earth around the sun. It can be measured only for the nearer stars, on photographs taken six months apart, and is used to obtain the distance (1/parallax = distance in parsecs; 3.26/parallax = distance in light years). See pp. 18-29.

parsec A large unit of distance equal to 3.26 light years; the distance at which a star has a parallax of 1 second of arc (1″). See p. 24.

period The time interval of one complete circuit of an orbit or one complete rotation of a rotating body or the complete cycle of any periodic change.

photodiode and **photomultiplier** Photoelectric cells.

photometer An instrument designed to measure the brightness of light falling on it. It is described as visual, photographic, or photoelectric, depending on the detector used. See p. 92.

planet A nonluminous body moving around the sun or a star in a nearly circular orbit, shining by reflected light.

planetary nebula A shell of gas ejected from and expanding around an extremely hot star; many appear as a ring because we are viewing it through the thin dimension on the front and rear parts of the shell. See p. 151.

polarized light Light that consists of waves that vibrate across the beam of light in one direction. Ordinary light is generally unpolarized, and the vibrations are in all directions. The polarization may be partial or complete (100 per cent).

pole of the galaxy A point 90° from the center line of the Milky Way. There are two such poles at opposite points in the sky, analogous to the two poles of the earth, each 90° from the earth's equator.

position angle The direction of a line in the sky, measured from 0° (direction north) through 90° (direction east).

profile The plot of intensity versus wavelength of a line in the spectrum of the sun or of a star from which motions of the gas producing the line can be inferred (such as the rotation of a star).

prominence A flamelike cloud of luminous gas, usually photographed in the light of one emission line of that gas near the edge of the sun. See p. 54.

proper motion The very small change in direction of a star due to its velocity across the line of sight as seen from near the sun. It is expressed as a fraction of a second of arc per year, and can be measured on photographs of the star taken many years apart. See p. 27.

proton A hydrogen atom with its one electron removed.

quantum A discrete amount of energy; the smallest amount that can be radiated or absorbed by matter. The size depends upon the wavelength and is larger for the shorter wavelengths.

radial velocity The motion of a star or other light source along the line of sight, detected by *Doppler shift* of lines in the spectrum; red shift indicates recession (positive radial velocity). See pp. 27, 137.

radioastronomy The study of astronomical bodies by use of radiotelescopes.

radiometer A radio receiver designed to measure the radio energy received per second by the antenna.

refractor A telescope in which a large lens (rather than a concave mirror) forms images of sun, stars, moon, or planets.

resolving power The ability of a telescope to distinguish two stars very close together in the sky; the ability of a spectrograph to distinguish two lines very close together in a spectrum.

right ascension One coordinate of a star in the sky, measured eastward like longitude on earth, starting from a point called the vernal equinox. See pp. 7, 18.

satellite A small body moving in an orbit around a larger one. The satellites of planets are often called moons.

Schmidt camera A telescope or camera consisting of a spherical mirror with a "correcting plate" (thin lens) in front of it, generally with large focal ratio and able to take a wide-angle photograph. See p. 259.

seeing Changing fuzziness and a slight jumping of a star image in a telescope is caused by air currents in the earth's atmosphere and is called "poor seeing."

sidereal time Time that gains on normal time by 4 minutes each day or 24 hours in 1 year. "Sidereal" refers to stars, which appear to move 360° around the sky in 24 hours sidereal time (23 hours and 56 minutes of normal time), the true rotation period of the earth.

solar flare A short-lived bright patch on the sun's surface which causes extra ionization in gases such as the earth's upper atmosphere, due to ultraviolet light from the flare.

spectral type One of the designations O, B, A, F, G, K, M, based on the pattern of lines in a star's spectrum. Surface temperature is high in "early-type" O and B stars and lower in "late-type" K and M stars. See p. 119.

spectrogram Photograph of a spectrum.

spectrograph An instrument attached to a telescope to obtain photographs of stellar spectra. See p. 104.

spectrum The various colors of light from a source spread out in the sequence from red to violet (long wavelength to short wavelength), as in a rainbow. Invisible wavelengths extend from the red to infrared and radio waves, and from blue-violet to ultraviolet and X rays.

The spectrum of the sun is often called a Fraunhofer spectrum; this, like the spectra of most stars, lacks certain colors, in gaps called *Fraunhofer lines* or *absorption lines*. See p. 104.

sunspot   A region on the sun's surface about 1000° cooler than its surroundings. Spots usually occur in pairs, one with north-magnetic polarity, and the other with south-magnetic polarity.

tide   The bulge in liquid (water on the earth) or gas (atmosphere) produced by the gravitational attraction of another nearby mass (such as the moon). The rotation of the earth beneath this bulge causes the rising and falling of sea level on earth and similar atmospheric pressure changes.

transmutation   A change from one type of atom (element) into another by nuclear reactions or radioactive decay.

triangulation   Determining the distance to an inaccessible object by measuring its direction from the two ends of a base line of known length.

turbulence   Whirls or vortices in a fluid (liquid or gas).

ultraviolet   The "color" of invisible light with wavelengths shorter than those of visible light (less than about 4000 angstroms).

variable star   A star that changes in brightness due to pulsations of its surface, or flares, or eclipse by a companion star.

vernal equinox   The point in the sky where the sun crosses the celestial equator on about March 21 each year; used as the origin of the coordinates right ascension and declination. See pp. 7, 18.

wavelength   The distance between the crests (or troughs) of regular waves. Visible light of various colors has wavelengths ranging from about 1/10,000 inch to about twice that length. See **spectrum.**

white dwarf   A small hot star of high density and low luminosity; the remains of a large bright star that blew up. See pp. 234-237.

width of a spectral line   Neither absorption lines nor emission lines are at exactly one wavelength; many have a spread of several angstroms. See p. 141.

X rays   Light of too short a wavelength to be visible that can penetrate some distance into most materials. X rays from the sun are entirely absorbed in the earth's ionosphere.

zodiacal light   A glow seen on either side of the sun extending faintly around the sky near the ecliptic (apparent yearly path of the sun), caused by sunlight on dust and other particles between the planets.

Suggestions

for

Further Reading

GENERAL

Abell, G. O. *Exploring the Universe*. New York: Holt, Rinehart, Winston, 1964.

Baker, R. H. *Astronomy* (8th ed.). Princeton, N. J.: Van Nostrand, 1964.

Bok, B. J. *The Astronomer's Universe*. Cambridge, England: Cambridge University Press, 1959.

Goldberg, L., and L. H. Aller. *Atoms, Stars, and Nebulae*. New York: McGraw-Hill, 1943.

Inglis, S. J. *Planets, Stars, and Galaxies*. New York: Wiley, 1961.

Page, T., ed., *Stars and Galaxies*. Englewood Cliffs, N. J.: Prentice-Hall, 1962.

Payne-Gaposchkin, Cecilia. *Introduction to Astronomy*. Englewood Cliffs, N.J.: Prentice-Hall, 1954.

Rapport, S., and H. Wright. *Astronomy*. New York: New York University Press, 1965.

Struve, O., and V. Zebergs. *Astronomy of the 20th Century*. New York: Macmillan, 1962.

INTRODUCTION

Bečvář, A. *Skalnate Pleso Atlas of the Heavens*. Cambridge, Mass.: Sky Publishing.

Vehrenberg, H. *Photographic Star Atlas*. Cambridge, Mass.: Sky Publishing.

Atlas Borealis. Cambridge, Mass.: Sky Publishing.

Atlas Eclipticalis. Cambridge, Mass.: Sky Publishing.

CHAPTER 1

Abetti, G. *The Sun*. London: Faber and Faber, 1957.

Gamow, G. *A Star Called The Sun*. New York: Viking, 1964.

Menzel, D. H. *Our Sun* (rev. ed.). Cambridge, Mass.: Harvard University Press, 1960.

CHAPTERS 2, 3, AND 4

Aller, L. H. *Astrophysics: The Atmospheres of the Sun and the Stars*. New York: Ronald, 1953.

Clark, G. L. *Encyclopedia of Spectroscopy*. New York: Reinhold, 1962.

Schwarzschild, M. *Structure and Evolution of the Stars*. Princeton, N. J.: Princeton University Press, 1958.

Thackeray, A. D. *Astronomical Spectroscopy*. London: Eyre and Spottiswoode, 1962.

CHAPTERS 5 AND 6

Campbell, L., and L. Jacchia. *The Story of Variable Stars*. New York: McGraw-Hill, 1941.

Kopal, Z. *An Introduction to the Study of Eclipsing Variables*. Cambridge, Mass.: Harvard University Press, 1946.

Payne-Gaposchkin, Cecilia. *Galactic Novae*. New York: Dover, 1957.

CHAPTERS 7, 8, AND 9

Aitken, Robert G. *The Binary Stars*. New York: McGraw-Hill, 1935.

Binnendijk, L. *Properties of Double Stars*. Philadelphia: University of Pennsylvania Press, 1960.

Bok, B. J., and P. F. Bok. *The Milky Way*. Cambridge, Mass.: Harvard University Press, 1957.

Couderc, P. *The Wider Universe*. New York: Harper, 1960.

Index